The Air Pilot's **Man**

Volume 3

Air Navigation

'Recommended reading'
Civil Aviation Authority

POOLEY'S
Air Pilot Publishing

Nothing in this manual supersedes any EU legislation, rules or EASA regulations or procedures and any operational documents issued by The Stationery Office, the Civil Aviation Authority, National Aviation Authorities, the manufacturers of aircraft, engines and systems, or by the operators of aircraft throughout the world. Note that as maps and chart are changed regularly, those extracts reproduced in this book must not be used for flight planning or flight operations.

Jeppesen charts in this manual have been reproduced with permission and are copyrighted by Jeppesen & Co GmbH.

Aerad charts in this manual have been reproduced with permission and are copyrighted by Thales Avionics.

Copyright © 2017 Pooleys-Air Pilot Publishing

ISBN 978-1-84336-233-3

First edition published 1987
Second revised edition 1987
Third revised edition published 1997
Fourth edition 1999
Fifth revised edition 2003
Reprinted with amendments 2004
Reprinted with amendments 2005
Reprinted with revisions and colour illustrations 2007
Reprinted with amendments 2008
Sixth edition 2010
Reprinted with amendments 2011
Reprinted with revisions 2013
Seventh edition 2015
Reprint with amendments 2017

All rights reserved. No part of this book may be reproduced or transmitted in any form by any means, electronic or mechanical, including photocopying, recording or by any information storage and retrieval system, without permission from the publisher in writing.

Origination by Pooleys-Air Pilot Publishing Limited.

Printed in England by Portland Print, Kettering, N16 8UN.

Published by Pooleys-Air Pilot Publishing Ltd
Elstree Aerodrome, Elstree, Hertfordshire, WD6 3AW. UK.
Tel: +44(0)208 207 3749
Web: www.pooleys.com
Email: sales@pooleys.com

The Air Pilot's **Manual**

Volume 3

Contents

Section Four covers the en-route navigation requirements of the Part-FCL syllabus. Refer to the notes on page 278. Section Four will not apply to the UK National PPL training syllabus nor to the LAPL syllabus.

Section Four – En-Route Navigation with Radio Navigation Aids "Navaids"

Editorial Team

Dorothy Saul-Pooley LLB(Hons) FRAeS

Dorothy holds an ATPL (A) and a CPL (H), and is both an instructor and examiner on aeroplanes and an instructor on helicopters. She is Head of Training for a school dedicated to running Flight Instructor courses at Shoreham. She is also a CAA Flight Instructor Examiner. In addition, having qualified as a solicitor in 1982, Dorothy acted for many years as a consultant specialising in aviation and insurance liability issues, and has lectured widely on air law and aviation insurance. This highly unusual combination of qualifications led to her appointment as Honorary Solicitor to the Guild of Air Pilots and Navigators (GAPAN).

Dorothy is a Fellow of the Royal Aeronautical Society, Past Chairman of the GAPAN Instructor Committee of which she was a founding member and the prime instigator of the Guild's Joint Forum with Central Flying School at RAF Cranwell for Senior Flying Instructors. She is a Past Chairman of the Education & Training Committee. After serving as a Warden on the Court of GAPAN for three years, she was appointed Master for the year 2014–2015 of the newly renamed Honourable Company of Air Pilots. She is also Chairman of the Professional Flying Instructors Association.

In 2003 Dorothy was awarded the Jean Lennox Bird Trophy for her contribution to aviation and support of Women in Aviation and the BWPA (British Women Pilots Association). In 2013, Dorothy received the prestigious award of a Master Air Pilots Certificate from GAPAN. In 2015 she was awarded the Brabazon Cup by the BWPA for her outstanding achievement in aviation. A regular contributor to seminars and conferences, Dorothy is the author and editor of a large number of flying training books and has published articles in legal and insurance journals and many in aviation magazines.

Stephen Wicks PhD

Steve won an ATC Flying Scholarship and made his first solo flight at Ipswich Airport, moving on to join the Stapleford Flying Club as a PPL. He was a member of the Bristol University Air Squadron and trained on Bulldogs at Filton and RAF St Mawgan whilst at the University of Bath. Steve acted for many years both as a university lecturer and industrial scientist, publishing patents and articles in scientific journals. He is a regular contributor to scientific conferences, seminars and executive education workshops and is a visiting professor at the University of Bath and the University of Greenwich After retiring from an industrial career, he started flying with TG Aviation at Manston and obtained a CPL(A) from the London Metropolitan University and the Sussex Flight Centre at Shoreham.

He obtained a Flight Instructor Certificate from Pooley's Flying Instructor School and is now active in *ab initio* flight training and the ground school operation at TG Aviation, Lydd. He is an activist in the Save Manston Airport campaign.

Acknowledgements

The Civil Aviation Authority; ICAO; Cessna, Piper, and Gulf-stream American for technical material; Daljeet Gill, Peter Godwin, Capt. R.W. K. Snell, Lotti Skeen and Dan Robertson; and the many other instructors and students whose comments have helped to improve this manual.

A Condensed History of the Air Pilot Manuals

For over 25 years the Air Pilot Manuals have led the academic training of pilots in the United Kingdom and in many countries around the world.

I first met Trevor Thom, a professional pilot and natural teacher, in Melbourne during a visit to Australia in January 1985. He already had his series of PPL Manuals for the Australian market and I asked him to produce a series for the New Zealand market where we had a small aviation business. Having completed this task, Trevor immediately began writing the first of the Air Pilot Manuals for the United Kingdom market and this project began in earnest on 5th December 1985.

Both Trevor Thom and Robert Johnson commenced the task in my office at Feldon. By the end of the following year, all four volumes were complete and were published in February 1987. By the end of that year, we estimated that 95% of all the UK Flying Schools were using our manuals. Volumes 5, 6 and 7 followed, so completing the full series.

Unfortunately, Trevor Thom had a serious accident at home which prevented him from continuing with the editing of the manuals. His rights were eventually sold to David Robson, another experienced pilot and natural teacher, who progressively improved the drawings and brought colour into the manuals for the first time.

Over the years there have been many assistant editors, in particular Peter Godwin, whose help I first asked for in the very early days with Trevor Thom and which continued until quite recently. The rights in the Air Pilot Manuals are now vested with the Pooley family and they continue to be edited and published from our offices and the Flying Instructor School at Shoreham Airport.

The Air Pilot Manuals have an outstanding reputation for accuracy and are continuously updated. They are recommended CAA reading material and are referred to extensively in the CAA examination answer booklet.

Robert Pooley
CStJ FRIN FRAeS

Introduction

Volume 3 of *The Air Pilot's Manual – Air Navigation –* presents this important area of training for the Private Pilot's Licence in a logical sequence of theory, preparation and performance.

The Cockpit is a Difficult Environment in which to Learn

As with the other volumes of *The Air Pilot's Manual,* in *Air Navigation* we have avoided the presentation of 'facts only'. A thorough understanding of the principles will enable you to gain maximum benefit from your actual navigation exercise flights.

This approach will enable you to become a competent pilot/ navigator and will also help to minimise your flight training hours. (It does, however, mean that our book is a little longer than it could be if the aim was only to cram in facts without a reasonable understanding.)

In determining the order in which the information is presented, care has been taken to keep things as logical and practical as possible.

Understanding makes for remembering.

Operational Decisions

Navigation of an aeroplane consists mainly of making common sense operational decisions. These decisions are based on knowledge and experience. Very few are difficult to make – most being logical and simple – but occasionally there are difficult decisions (both on the ground and in flight) to be made. These are the ones for which we must prepare for.

We have adopted a professional approach right from the start, whether your ultimate aim is to be a private pilot or to go on and make aviation your career.

Operational decisions will often have to be taken well away from your home base, and to a large extent you will be on your own. They fall into two categories:
- **those made on the ground** during pre-flight planning; and
- **in-flight operational decisions.**

Many decisions are so simple and 'second nature' that you don't realise you are making them. Others require a calm, cool but quick assessment, followed by a decision and action. Proceeding into an area of poor visibility could fall into this category.

The aeroplane will not stand still while you decide what to do in difficult in-flight situations. You cannot just pull over to the side of the road and study your maps. Good pre-flight planning, with many operational decisions taken on the ground – and alternative courses of action considered in the event of in-flight problems occurring – takes a lot of pressure off the pilot/navigator.

The Navigation Computer

As a pilot/navigator you will become adept at estimating angles, distances, time intervals, fuel consumption, and so on. The art of estimating is an important skill to develop. It is also important that you can calculate these various quantities easily and accurately. To achieve this you will use a navigation computer. It is a simple device (looks complicated but isn't) that allows us to carry out almost every navigation calculation with speed and accuracy.

Electronic navigation computers are available, but we suggest you steer away from them, at least initially, because they do not encourage the pilot/navigator to visualise each situation – an important ability to develop. Once you are adept at the various computing problems involved in air navigation, you might decide to 'go electronic'. Beware of becoming over-reliant on electronic computers because you are not permitted to use them in the examination.

The basic concept of the slide navigation computer dates back to early navigation days. The modern version is an essential piece of equipment for a pilot/navigator.

The slide navigation computer has two sides:
- **a wind side,** which enables solution of *triangle of velocities* problems for flight-planning and en route navigation; and
- **a calculator side** (the main component of which is a circular slide-rule on the outer scales), used to perform the simple arithmetical calculations involved in flight operations, e.g. distance, speed and time; conversion of units; fuel quantities and consumption; true airspeed.

Two chapters in the first section describe using the navigation computer – one chapter for each side. Although it may appear a little complicated at first, working through the examples and illustrations we have set out will make using the computer logical and simple.

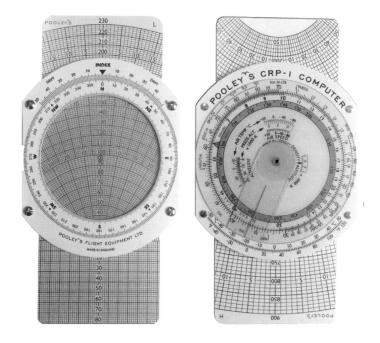

■ **The wind and calculator sides of a navigation computer**

The Theory Examination

Navigation is part of one of the theory examinations for the UK Private Pilot's Licence (PPL), which you will sit at your flying school. Prior to this you should be achieving considerable success in completing questions at the end of most of the chapters. In this volume some chapters have exercises interspersed through the text to give you practice on a particular aspect of the chapter before moving on.

The Exercises form an important part of the course and we recommend that you work through them carefully.

This manual is more than just a text to allow you to pass the examination, though this is one of its aims. It is designed to remain as a reference text on your shelf for as long as you fly.

The En route Navigation Section (PPL Skill Test)

This is the province of your flying instructor. The test is carried out at the completion of your flying training and is part of the PPL Skill Test (although with the agreement of your examiner it may be flown as a separate section.) It is designed to assess your ability as a pilot/navigator. This manual, and your navigation cross-country training, will prepare you fully for the Navigation element of the PPL Skill Test.

Private Pilot Licences

This edition covers the material contained in the NPPL training syllabus as well as that required by the European Part-FCL and Light Aircraft Pilot Licence (LAPL) syllabus. Students should follow <u>one</u> syllabus only. Section Four of this manual is only required for the Part-FCL Licence, not for the NPPL or LAPL, although the theoretical knowledge examination may include some of this material for any of the licences.

Operational Information

For safe flight operations it is essential that all pilots refer to current operational information. This basically involves using latest issues of aeronautical charts, and amended flight information publications, circulars and NOTAM (Notices to Airmen).

In the UK, the primary source of operational information is the UK Aeronautical Information Publication (AIP), a large, frequently amended manual produced to an international standard by the Civil Aviation Authority. Your flying school and Air Traffic Services (ATS) units should have amended copies of the UK AIP available for reference, although these days they are often available on a CD rom, or directly on the internet from the AIS website: www.ais.org.uk. As the AIP is a formidable and bulky set of documents for a PPL holder (because the majority covers airline-type instrument flight procedures), there is also available a conveniently sized publication known as *Pooley's Flight Guide,* which is revised regularly. You will find references to both *Pooley's Flight Guide* and the UK AIP throughout *The Air Pilot's Manual.* Note that these references are no substitute for referring to current, amended documents. If you are ever in any doubt about operational information, in *Pooley's Flight Guide* or the UK AIP, refer to an amended copy of the AIP and current air legislation documents; and **always** check the latest AIRACs (which detail AIP updates), AIP Supplements and Aeronautical Information Circulars (AICs) and NOTAM prior to flight.

NOTE There are many examples of extracts of tables from the AIP and other sources and excerpts from aeronautical charts and their legends in this manual. It is not always practical to replace these illustrations every time the source document becomes out of date, so please be aware that information contained in these table and charts is not necessarily current. The tables or charts illustrate a particular point in the text for which their insertion into this manual is relevant.

Section **One**

Basic Navigation Theory

The Earth

To navigate an aeroplane efficiently from one place to another over long distances or in poor visibility, we need to refer to some representation of the earth. This representation must be smaller in size than the earth; in other words, it must be a picture of a 'reduced earth'.

The simplest and most accurate reduced earth is a globe, which retains the spherical shape of the earth and displays the various oceans, continents, cities, and so on. The task of the cartographer (map-maker) is to project a picture of a reduced earth globe onto a flat surface and make a map or a chart from this.

Maps represent the earth's surface (or parts thereof) on a flat surface; **charts** show further information or special conditions, possibly using only an outline of geographical features such as the coastline. Since most maps that pilots use show specific aeronautical and navigation data, they are referred to as charts.

The Form or Shape of the Earth

The exact shape of the earth's surface is constantly changing. Volcanoes erupt and grow, new islands form and others disappear, landslides and earthquakes cause large land movements, the ocean surface continually changes in height with the tides and, on a very long-term basis, the continents gradually move.

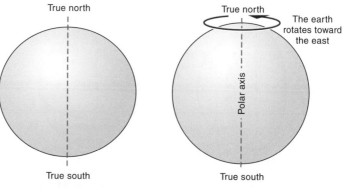

■ Figure 1-1 **The earth is a slightly flattened (oblate) sphere**

■ Figure 1-2 **The earth rotates about its axis**

The regular geometric shape which the earth resembles most is a sphere but, even when all the surface bumps are ironed out, the earth is still not a perfect sphere. It is slightly flat at the North and South Poles, forming a flattened (or oblate) spheroid, the polar diameter being approximately 23 nm less than the equatorial diameter (6,865 nm as against 6,888 nm). For the purposes of practical navigation, however, the earth can be treated as a sphere.

As well as moving in an orbit about the sun, the earth rotates on its own axis. The axis of rotation is called the geographic **polar axis,** and the two points where the axis meets the surface of the sphere are called:

- the **geographic North Pole** or **true north;** and
- the **geographic South Pole** or **true south.**

If you stand anywhere on earth and face towards the geographic North Pole, then you are facing true north.

Imaginary Lines on the Earth's Surface

A GREAT CIRCLE. drawn on the earth's surface is one whose plane passes through the centre of the sphere (earth). Significant properties of great circles are:

- **A great circle** is the largest circle that can be drawn on the surface of the earth or on any sphere.
- **The shortest distance** between any two points on the surface of a sphere is the arc of a great circle.
- **Only one great circle** can be drawn between two points on the surface of a sphere (unless the two points are diametrically opposed, as are the geographic poles).

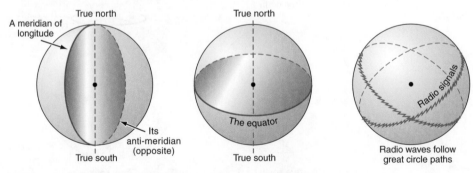

■ *Figure 1-3* **A great circle has the centre of the earth as its axis**

Some examples of great circles are:

- meridians of longitude;
- the equator;
- the paths that radio waves follow.

A SMALL CIRCLE is any circle on the surface of a sphere that is not a great circle, i.e. the centre of a small circle is not at the centre of the earth. Parallels of latitude (except for the equator) are small circles.

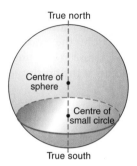

■ Figure 1-4 **The plane of a small circle does not pass through the centre of a sphere**

Latitude and Longitude

A convenient way of specifying the position of any point on earth is to relate it to the imaginary lines that form the latitude and longitude graticule (or grid) on the surface of the earth.

LATITUDE. The reference for latitude is the plane of the equator, the great circle whose plane is perpendicular (i.e. at right angles, or 90°) to the polar axis.

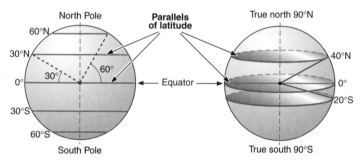

■ Figure 1-5 **Latitude**

- **The latitude of a place** is its angular distance in degrees from the equator, measured at the centre of the earth and designated either north or south. For instance, Nottingham is at 53°N latitude.
- **A parallel of latitude** joins all points of the same latitude and (except for the equator) is a small circle. Nottingham, Bremen in Germany, Torun in Poland, Yellowhead Pass in the Canadian Rockies, and Wicklow in Ireland are all about 53° north of the

equator, and therefore the line joining them is called the 53°N parallel of latitude.

- **Parallels of latitude** are parallel to the equator and to each other.
- **The longest parallel** of latitude is the equator (latitude 0°). The other parallels, as you move away from the equator towards the higher latitudes, progressively decrease in size, until the 90° parallels of latitude become just points at the north and south geographic poles.

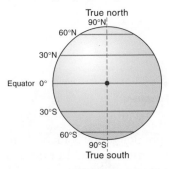

■ Figure 1-6 **The further from the equator, the smaller the parallel of latitude**

LONGITUDE. The basic reference for longitude is the **Greenwich meridian,** which is also known as the **prime meridian.** It is that half of the great circle which contains the polar axis (about which the earth rotates), and passes through the Greenwich Observatory near London, as well as the north and south geographic poles. The prime meridian is designated as 'longitude 0°'.

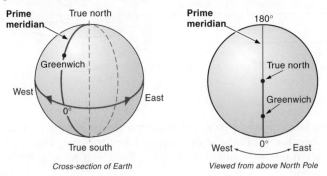

■ Figure 1-7 **The prime meridian**

The other half of the same great circle that contains the prime meridian runs from the north geographic pole to the south geographic pole, but on the other side of the earth to Greenwich. It passes down the western side of the Pacific Ocean and is known as 'longitude 180°'. It can be reached by travelling either east from the prime meridian or by travelling the same angular distance (180°) west from the prime meridian. Therefore it can be called either '180°E' or '180°W'. It is also called the **anti-meridian** of Greenwich.

- **All of the great circles** containing the polar axis (and therefore passing through the north and south geographic poles) are called meridians of longitude.
- **Meridians of longitude** are specified by their angular difference in degrees east or west from the prime meridian.

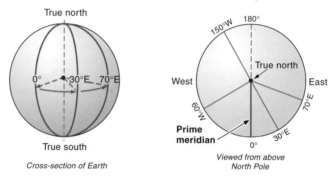

Cross-section of Earth | Viewed from above North Pole

■ *Figure 1-8* **The longitude of a place is the angle between its meridian of longitude and the prime (Greenwich) meridian, measured eastward or westward from the prime meridian**

Specifying Position

The parallels of latitude and meridians of longitude form an imaginary graticule or grid over the surface of the earth. The position of any point on the earth can be specified by its:

- **latitude** – angular position north or south of the plane of the equator; together with:
- **longitude** – angular position east or west of the prime meridian.

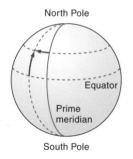
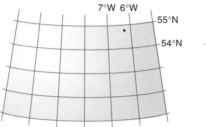
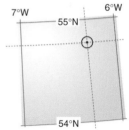

■ *Figure 1-9* **The position of Belfast (Aldergrove) in Northern Ireland is 54°39′N, 06°14′W**

It is usually sufficiently accurate to specify the latitude and longitude of a place in degrees and minutes (one minute equals ⅟₆₀ of one degree). For extreme accuracy, each minute can be divided into 60 seconds of arc. The symbols used are ° (degrees), ′ (minutes) and ″ (seconds).

For example, the position of Belfast (Aldergrove) in Northern Ireland is: 543927N 0061257W (54°39′27″N, 006°12′57″W). For our purposes 54°39′N, 006°13′W is sufficiently accurate.

NOTE With the advent of inertial navigation systems that use latitude/longitude reference, some documents, show the N or S and E or W *prior* to the coordinate, as this is the order in which latitude and longitude are entered on such equipment. Also, instead of seconds (mentioned above), the minutes of the coordinates are decimalised, i.e. N52°16.4′, W002°45.9′; or N5216.4, W00245.9. (The standard is that the N/S coordinate has four digits prior to the decimal point, while that for E/W has five; the reason being that latitude extends to 90° N or S, and longitude extends to 180° E or W.)

Specifying latitude and longitude is the normal method of indicating a particular position on earth, and is the one we most commonly use at the flight-planning stage when preparing maps and flight plans. Once in flight, however, there are other means of specifying the position of the aircraft, such as:

- **By position over or abeam** a landmark or radio beacon, for instance, "over Shrewsbury", "abeam Prestatyn", "over Lydd VOR".
- **By range (distance) and bearing** from a landmark or radio beacon, for instance, "10 nm on a bearing of 290°T from Ocean City" (see Figure 1-10).

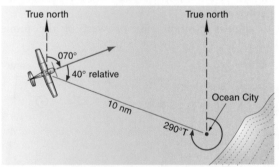

■ *Figure 1-10* **Specifying position by relative bearing**

NOTE The use of place names needs to be confined to places that are likely to be known to the recipient of the message, and that are shown on the commonly used aeronautical charts. In the UK, with its high density of population, place names are frequently duplicated and can be misleading.

Distances

The standard unit of distance in navigation is the **nautical mile (nm),** which is the length of 1 minute of arc of any great circle on earth (assuming the earth to be a perfect sphere).

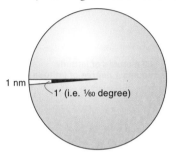

■ *Figure 1-11* **1 nm is the length of 1 minute of arc of a great circle on the earth**

There are 360 degrees in a circle and 60 minutes in a degree, making 60 × 360 = 21,600 minutes of arc in a circle. The circumference of the earth is therefore (60 × 360) = 21,600 minutes of arc, which is 21,600 nm.

LATITUDE (the angular distance north or south of the equator) is measured up and down a meridian of longitude (which is a great circle) and therefore:

1 minute of latitude at any point on earth = 1 nautical mile (nm).

This is useful for measuring distance on a chart.

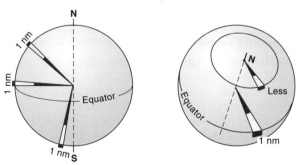

■ *Figure 1-12* **1 minute of latitude = 1 nm; 1 minute of longitude varies in length**

1 degree of latitude at any point on earth = 60 nm.

LONGITUDE is measured around the parallels of latitude (small circles except for the equator), and so 1 minute of longitude varies in length depending on where it is on the earth's surface.

The only place where 1 minute of longitude is equal to 1 nm is around the equator; the higher the latitude, the further away from the equator the place is, and the shorter the length in nm of 1 minute of longitude in that region.

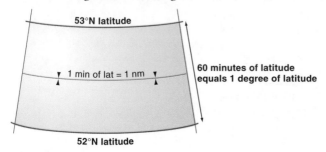

■ *Figure 1-13* **1 minute of latitude = 1 nautical mile**

When using charts, do not be confused by the fact that we measure 1 minute of latitude (always 1 nm) up or down the side of the chart along a meridian of longitude.

Angles

The most fundamental reference from which angles are measured is that of true north, from 000°T, through 090°T, 180°T, 270°T, to 360°T. Figure 1-14 shows that if an aeroplane follows a long-range great circle track, the track direction referred to true north will gradually change, i.e. the **great circle (GC) track** will cross successive meridians at a gradually changing angle.

Sometimes it is convenient to fly a track whose direction remains constant when referred to true north, i.e. so that the track crosses all meridians of longitude at the same angle. This is known as a **rhumb line (RL) track.**

The rhumb line track and great circle track between two places coincide only if the two places lie on either the same meridian of longitude (a great circle), the track between them being 180°T or 360°T, or on the equator (which is also a great circle), the track between them being 090°T or 270°T. In practical terms, the GC direction and the RL direction may be considered to be the same over short distances, such as those typically flown within the UK.

You must always be clear as to whether you are referring direction to true north or to magnetic north, the difference between the two being the magnetic variation, as discussed in Chapter 4. In this chapter, we are referring direction to true north.

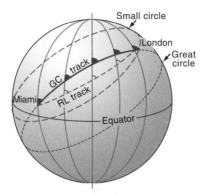

■ *Figure 1-14* **The great circle track and the rhumb line track**

Representing the Spherical Earth on Flat Charts

The latitude–longitude graticule is translated onto maps and charts by cartographers whose major problem is to represent the spherical surface of the earth on a flat sheet of paper. The process consists of:

- **scaling** the earth down to a 'reduced earth'; and then
- **projecting** the reduced earth's surface onto a sheet.

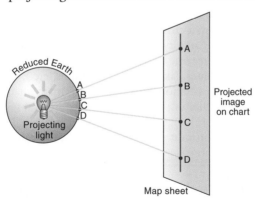

■ *Figure 1-15* **Making a chart**

This process always leads to some distortion, either of areas, distances, angles or shapes. By using certain mathematical techniques when projecting the spherical earth onto a flat chart, the cartographer can preserve some properties, but not all. Some property will always be distorted to a greater or lesser extent depending on how the points on the surface of the reduced spherical earth are transferred onto the flat chart.

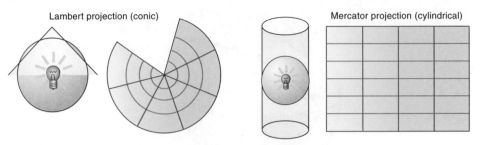

■ *Figure 1-16* **A conical projection and a cylindrical projection**

Unlike a sphere, certain other curved surfaces (such as a cylinder or a cone) can be cut and laid out flat; conversely, a cylinder or a cone can be made out of a flat sheet of paper. This is not possible with a spherical surface – try it with an orange peel! By projecting points on the surface of the reduced earth onto either a conical or cylindrical surface (which can then be flattened out to form a sheet), less distortion occurs and a better chart results, compared with a projection onto an already flat sheet as illustrated in Figure 1-15.

A simple view of map-making is to think of a light projecting the shadows of the latitude-longitude graticule of the reduced sphere onto a cone (Lambert's conical projection) or onto a cylinder (Mercator's cylindrical projection). The cone or cylinder is then laid out flat to form a chart.

Charts based on conic and cylindrical projections are widely used in aviation, mainly because they:
- **preserve shape** (of islands, lakes, towns, countries, etc.);
- **preserve angular relationships** – (in mathematical terminology, maps exhibiting this vital property are said to be conformal or orthomorphic); and
- **have a reasonably constant scale** over the whole chart (for ease of measuring distance).

Topographical Charts

When navigating by visual reference to the ground we refer to land features. A topographical chart showing the surface features of the area in detail is therefore of great value. There are various topographical charts available for visual navigation in the UK, and these include (in order of importance):
- **ICAO Aeronautical Charts,** scale 1:500,000 (half-million).
- **Topographical Air Charts** of the United Kingdom, scale 1:250,000 (quarter-million).
- **Operational Navigational Chart** series (ONC), scale 1:1,000,000 (one million).

The ICAO and ONC series charts are based on the Lambert's conformal *conic* projection. The chart sheet is formed from a secant cone that cuts the sphere representing the reduced earth at two standard parallels of latitude. Just which two parallels of latitude are chosen by the cartographer depends on which part of the earth, and how much of it, he wants to represent on that particular chart.

The standard parallels are usually mentioned at the bottom or on the side of the chart – for example, on the 'one to half-million Southern England and Wales' chart (Map Sheet Number 2171 CD), the standard parallels are 49°20′N and 54°40′N. There is no distortion along the standard parallels, and very little distortion north or south of them in the UK because of the short distance involved.

The projection for the 1:250,000 Topographical Air Charts of the UK is based on a *cylindrical* projection known as the transverse Mercator projection. Whereas the normal Mercator projection starts with a cylinder wrapped around the equator with its sides parallel to the polar axis, the transverse Mercator starts with a cylinder wrapped around a chosen meridian of longitude and its anti-meridian, with the sides of the cylinder at 90° to the polar axis.

The UK 1:250,000 transverse Mercator charts are based on the 2° west meridian of longitude, which passes north–south through the middle of the British Isles. When flattened out, this provides a chart with no distortion down the 2°W meridian and, in fact, very little distortion anywhere east or west of this meridian within the UK.

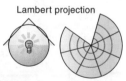

AERONAUTICAL CHART ICAO 1:500 000

Lambert Conformal Conic Projection Standard Parallels 49°20′ and 54°40′
Convergence factor 0·78829§

Lambert projection

■ *Figure 1-17* **Most 1:1,000,000 and 1:500,000 aeronautical charts are based on the Lambert conformal conic projection**

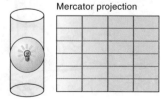

TOPOGRAPHICAL AIR CHART OF THE UNITED KINGDOM

SCALE 1:250 000
TRANSVERSE MERCATOR PROJECTION

Mercator projection

■ *Figure 1-18* **The UK 1:250,000 topographical air charts are based on the transverse mercator cylindrical projection**

Both chart types covering the relatively small area of the UK have the following properties:

- **conformal** – angles and bearings are accurate (absolutely vital);
- **constant scale** over the whole chart in practical terms (i.e. distances are accurate);
- **shapes are preserved** in practical terms;
- **the track between two places is a straight line** (there is no significant difference between the rhumb line and the great circle track between any two places within the UK).

Scale

Charts represent a scaled-down view of the earth, and there are various ways of describing just how much the earth is scaled down on a particular chart. **Scale** is defined as the ratio of the chart length compared to the earth distance that it represents.

$$Scale = \frac{chart\ length}{earth\ distance} \quad \textit{(with both items in the same unit)}$$

The greater the chart length for a given earth distance, the larger the scale and the more detail that can be shown. A large-scale chart covers a small area in detail. For example, a UK 1:250,000 Topographical Air Chart has a larger scale and can show more detail than an ICAO 1:500,000 Aeronautical Chart.

One centimetre on a 1:250,000 chart represents 250,000 cm on the earth, whereas, on a 1:500,000 chart, it represents double this earth distance, i.e. 500,000 cm, hence not as much detail can be shown.

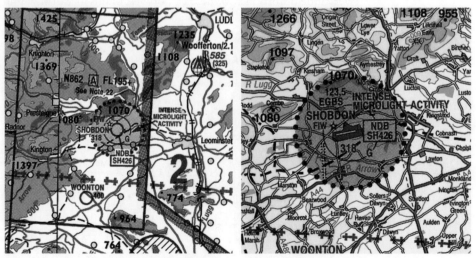

■ *Figure 1-19* **Excerpts from 1:500,000 (left) and 1:250,000 charts**

Scale can be expressed in various ways:

1. **As a representative fraction.** For instance, the WAC and the ONC series are 1: 1,000,000 charts (one to a million), where 1 centimetre on the chart will represent 1,000,000 cm or 10 kilometres on the earth, or where 1 nm on earth is represented by 1 millionth of a nautical mile on the chart. On the ICAO 1:500,000 Aeronautical Charts, an earth distance is represented by one half-millionth of its length; on the UK 1:250,000 Topographical Air Charts, an earth distance is represented by one quarter-millionth of its length.

2. **As a graduated scale line,** which is usually situated at the bottom of the chart. A graduated scale line allows you to measure the distance between two points on the chart and match it against the scale line. Make sure you use the correct scale line (usually nautical miles), since there may be several so that nautical miles, statute miles or kilometres can be measured.

3. **In words** – for instance '1 cm equals 5 nm', which obviously means that 5 nm on the earth's surface is represented by 1 cm on the chart.

SCALE 1:500 000

	KILOMETRES	10	5	0	10
NAUTICAL MILES	10		5	0	
STATUTE MILES	10		5	0	

■ Figure 1-20 **Typical scale lines**

Even if there is no scale line on the chart, you can always compare the distance between two places on the chart with the latitude scale which runs down the side of the chart, remembering that 1′ of latitude = 1 nm, and 1° of latitude = 60 nm.

On conic projections (ICAO 1:500,000), use the latitude scale about mid-way between the two places, because on some charts scale may vary slightly depending on proximity to the standard parallels. In practical terms, however, scale can be considered as constant over all of a 1:500,000 chart.

On the UK transverse Mercator 1:250,000 charts, the scale is exactly correct at the 2°W meridian, and can be considered as constant to about 300 nm either side of this. Since the UK does not have a large east–west spread, the slight variation in scale is not significant.

To all intents and purposes, therefore, scale may be considered constant at all points on both aeronautical chart series, quarter- and half-million.

Converting Chart Length to Earth Distance

While the following calculations are not normally done by pilots, they provide an insight into the making of charts.

EXAMPLE 1 What earth distance is represented by a chart length of 5.2 inches on a 1:250,000 chart?

$$1 \text{ inch on the chart} = 250,000 \text{ inches on the earth}$$

$$= \frac{250,000}{12} \text{ feet (1 ft = 12 inches)}$$

$$= \frac{250,000}{12 \times 6,076} \text{ nm (1 nm = 6,076 ft)}$$

$$= 3.43 \text{ nm}$$

$$5.2 \text{ inches on the chart} = 5.2 \times 3.43$$

$$= 17.8 \text{ nm on the earth}$$

ANSWER 17.8 nm

EXAMPLE 2 On a 1:500,000 chart, 9 inches represents approximately 62 nm. How many kilometres does 9 inches represent on a 1:250,000 chart?

9 inches = 62 nm on a 1:500,000 chart
therefore, on a 1:250,000 chart (i.e. double the scale):

9 inches = 62 ÷ 2 = 31 nm = 57.5 km (by computer).

ANSWER 57.5 km (your answer should be accurate to ±1 km)

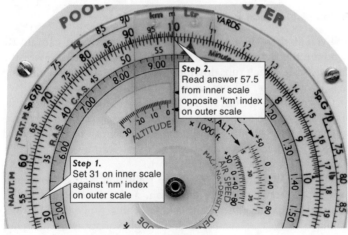

■ Figure 1-21 **Example 2: 31 nm = 57.5 km**

Now complete: **Practice Questions - The Earth**

1. Regarding meridians of longitude, which statement is correct?

(a) *Meridians of longitude are semi-circles joining the poles and are numbered 0° to 360°.*

(b) *Meridians of longitude are numbered 0° at the prime meridian and 001 - 179° west or east and 180°W/E.*

(c) *Meridians of longitude are semi-circles joining the poles. All have centres at the centre of the earth.*

(d) *Meridians of longitude are semi-circles which are numbered 0° at the equator and 90° at the poles.*

2. Parallels of latitude:

(a) *Are described as being either east or west of 0°.*

(b) *Are all small circles, except for the equator.*

(c) *Are all great circles.*

(d) *Are numbered from 0 to 180.*

3. What is the name given to a line which crosses all meridians at the same angle?

(a) *A parallel.*

(b) *A great circle.*

(c) *A rhumb line.*

(d) *A grid line.*

4. If an aircraft flies due north along a meridian from latitude 05° 30'S to 32° 30'N. In kilometres what distance is covered?

(a) *2,280 km*

(b) *1,620 km*

(c) *4,218 km*

(d) *4,280 km*

5. A "Lambert" projection is best used for covering:

(a) *Mid-latitudes.*

(b) *Polar regions.*

(c) *Areas within 10° north or south of the equator.*

(d) *Areas with a great north/south extent.*

6. If the scale of a chart is given as 1:500,000 then which of the following statements is true?

(a) *500,000 cm on the chart represents 1 nm on the earth's surface.*

(b) *1 cm on the chart represents 500,000 km on the earth's surface.*

(c) *1 cm on the chart represents 500,000 cm on the earth's surface.*

(d) *The scale is greater than a chart with a 1:250,000 scale.*

Answers: 1b, 2b, 3c, 4c, 5a, 6c.

Aeronautical Charts

VFR Charts

The two main charts used for visual navigation in the United Kingdom are:

- **1:500,000 ICAO Aeronautical Charts** (the most commonly used); and
- **The CAA 1:250,000 Topographical Air Charts** (which are suitable for visual navigation up to 5,000 ft amsl).

Amendments to current VFR charts are shown on the CAA's web site: www.ais.org.uk under VFR charts

Three ICAO 1:500,000 charts cover the whole of the UK and there are two more of the same scale for the Republic of Ireland. Because of the larger scale of the 1:250,000 charts, it takes a greater number to cover the same area (8 for the UK). The 1:250,000 charts can, however, show much greater detail than the 1:500,000 scale.

ICAO stands for International Civil Aviation Organization– an agency of the United Nations that suggests world aviation standards to ensure commonality of presentation between countries.

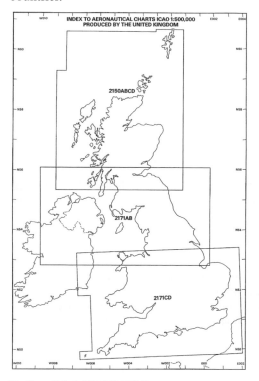

■ *Figure 2-1* **1:500,000 UK Coverage**

CAA 1:250,000 CHARTS. The vertical limit of the series is 5,000 ft altitude. To assist users, airspace with a base of Flight Level 55 (FL55) is shown, *except* where a minimum altitude in excess of 5,000 ft applies. If the QNH is below 1013 hPa, controlled airspace not shown on the charts may be below 5,000 ft altitude and you must refer to a 1:500,000 chart to ensure that adequate vertical separation is maintained.

In general, therefore, the 1:250,000 charts are used only for cross-country flying up to 5,000 ft amsl, or when operating at low level in a terminal area. Both series of charts provide:

- **topographical information** (mountains, lakes, rivers, coastlines);
- **cultural information** (cities, towns, motorways, railway lines);
- **aeronautical information** (controlled airspace, Airways, Aerodrome Traffic Zones, Prohibited, Restricted and Danger Areas, airfields, radio beacons). The aeronautical information is printed over the top of the topographical and cultural information, generally in blue and magenta (purple).

Use only the current issue of the chart. Reprints occur periodically (usually every one or two years) and the date of the current chart is specified in NOTAM (Notices to Airmen). Some items on a chart may change from time to time (for instance, a new radio mast or a new road may be built; airspace may be reorganised) and these changes will be notified to pilots by NOTAM. Your charts should be amended by hand if necessary.

It will help if you now refer to some typical charts; the two that we will use mainly are:

- **Aeronautical Chart ICAO 1:500,000** (half million), Sheet 2171AB, Northern England and Northern Ireland (see Note below); and
- **Topographical Air Chart** of the United Kingdom 1:250,000 (quarter million) – eight charts cover the UK.

The charts are self-explanatory. Study them thoroughly and become familiar with their legends. As a guide, we will consider the 1:500,000 chart now, with occasional reference to the 1:250,000 series, where applicable.

> Note that the chart excerpts and information in this chapter are for study purposes only. For actual flight operations ensure that you have the latest edition of charts, updated by NOTAM issued since the chart's validity date. Be aware that, once changes are incorporated in the AIP (normally after six months), relevant NOTAM are cancelled.

TOPOGRAPHICAL INFORMATION shown is that considered to be of most use to the pilot/navigator. It is obviously impossible to show everything on a chart, so there may be some details on the ground not shown. Features shown on the chart, however, will exist on the ground, e.g. an isolated rock may not be considered significant by the cartographer and therefore will not be shown on the chart. If, however, there is an isolated rock shown on the chart, it will certainly exist on the ground. The same thing may be said about cultural features depicted on UK charts, such as Stonehenge or white horses – if they are shown on the chart, then they exist on the ground and will be suitable as visual landmarks.

DRAINAGE AND WATER FEATURES (hydrographic features). These are generally depicted in blue. Hydrographic features include creeks, streams, rivers, canals, lakes, reservoirs, marshes, shore-lines, tidal flats, etc. Just how they are depicted on the chart is explained by the chart legend, but bear in mind that after heavy rain, for instance, what is shown as a small stream on the chart may in fact have flooded.

RELIEF. There are various ways of bringing ground contours into relief so that an impression of hills, mountains, valleys, etc., is obtained when you look at the chart. The UK 1:500,000 chart series uses contours – lines joining places of equal elevation above mean sea level – to depict relief. The closer the contour lines are to each other on the chart, the steeper the terrain. The spacing between contour lines is different on the various series of aeronautical charts.

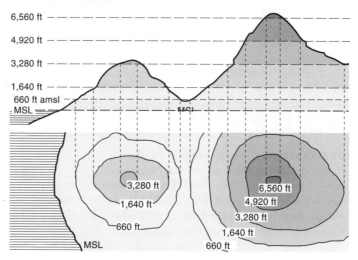

■ Figure 2-2 **Contour lines represent changes in height amsl**

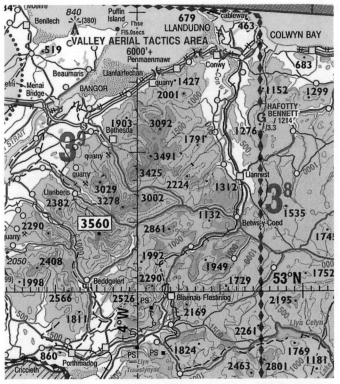

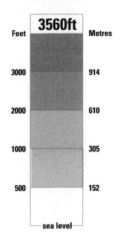

RELIEF PORTRAYAL

ELEVATIONS IN FEET

ELEVATION TINT LEGEND

HIGHEST ELEVATION KNOWN IS
530407N 0040432W

SPOT ELEVATION (AMSL) .... • 2270

■ Figure 2-3 *Hypsometric tints to portray relief on a 1:500,000 chart*

Colour or layer tinting is used in conjunction with the contour lines to give even more relief. The colours or tints used for the various ground elevations are shown on a hypsometric tint table at the bottom of the chart. (Hypsometric means establishment of vertical heights or elevations.) The shades of colour generally start with white for low land, then go through light brown and into brown, gradually darkening as the ground becomes higher. Remember that a particular colour may indicate ground elevation up to the level of the next contour above it.

SPOT ELEVATIONS (or spot heights) are shown using a black spot with an adjacent number to indicate the elevation (height amsl – above mean sea level) in feet. These elevations are generally accurate (unless amended by NOTAM). Spot elevations are normally used to show local peaks and other critical elevations that are significantly higher than the surrounding terrain. The highest point on each chart (in this case Mount Snowdon in North Wales) has its elevation printed slightly larger than the rest and is displayed in a white rectangle with a black edge. It also rates a mention on the relief portrayal table.

MAXIMUM ELEVATION FIGURES (MEF) are shown in quadrangles bounded by graticule lines for every half degree of latitude and longitude. The figure is based on the highest known feature in each quadrangle, including terrain and obstacles, and allowing for unknown features. **Note that the MEF is *not* a safety height.**

HACHURING OR HILL SHADING is used to give a three-dimensional effect on some aeronautical charts. Hachuring consists of short lines running downhill, and is commonly used to portray bluffs, cliffs and escarpments. Hill shading shows darkened areas on the low side of high ground where you would expect to see shadows with the light coming from the north-west (a graphic standard).

■ *Figure 2-4* **Hachuring**

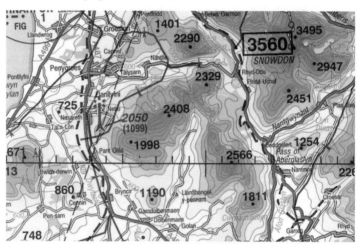

■ *Figure 2-5* **Contours and hill shading in Wales shown on a 1:250,000 chart (sample only)**

On the CAA 1:250,000 charts, hill shading and contours are used, but there is no hachuring. There is no hachuring or hill shading on the UK 1:500,000 series – just contours and layer tints.

Be aware that many continental European charts show contours, elevations and spot heights, not in feet but in metres amsl. When flying in France, for instance, you may need to convert feet to metres, or vice versa. This can be done with a navigation computer, or by using the conversion table that is printed on some charts. The aeronautical charts used in the UK display elevations and heights only in feet.

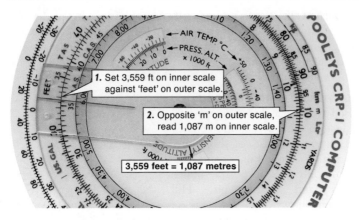

1. Set 3,559 ft on inner scale against 'feet' on outer scale.

2. Opposite 'm' on outer scale, read 1,087 m on inner scale.

3,559 feet = 1,087 metres

■ *Figure 2-6* **Converting feet to metres and vice versa.**

1:500,000 ICAO Aeronautical Charts

Cultural Features on the 1:500,000 Chart

Cultural features are of great help to the pilot/navigator. It is not possible to show every town on the chart, so a choice is made to show what is significant and of value for visual air navigation. A group of 100 houses is of little significance if it lies in the middle of a city the size of Manchester and so will not be specifically depicted on the chart, yet on the moors it may be extremely significant and will be shown.

NOTE Built-up areas are coloured yellow on the full 1:500,000 chart and grey on the equivalent low-level chart.

Roads and railways can be of great assistance to visual navigation. Those that will be most significant will be shown. Distinctive patterns such as curves, roads running parallel to railway lines and then crossing over, junctions, forks, overpasses and tunnels, are especially useful. Even the beds of disused railway lines can be useful, and are shown as broken black lines on charts.

Other useful cultural features, such as the white horses carved into the ground in various parts of England, may also be shown. Study the chart legend and become familiar with the symbols (which differ slightly between the various series of charts).

Figure 2-7 shows some 1:500,000 chart cultural symbols.

Aeronautical Information on the UK 1:500,000 Charts

Most people are familiar with topographical and cultural information, since these are surface features which are shown on a road map and in an atlas. Pilots, however, operate in a three-dimensional environment and therefore require information on the airspace above the surface of the earth as well.

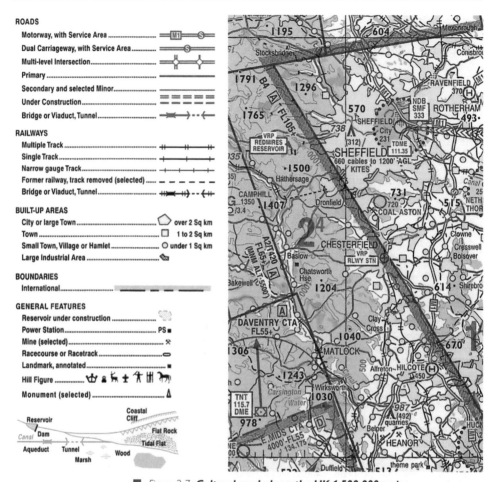

ROADS

Motorway, with Service Area	
Dual Carriageway, with Service Area	
Multi-level Intersection	
Primary	
Secondary and selected Minor	
Under Construction	
Bridge or Viaduct, Tunnel	

RAILWAYS

Multiple Track	
Single Track	
Narrow gauge Track	
Former railway, track removed (selected)	
Bridge or Viaduct, Tunnel	

BUILT-UP AREAS

City or large Town	over 2 Sq km
Town	1 to 2 Sq km
Small Town, Village or Hamlet	under 1 Sq km
Large Industrial Area	

BOUNDARIES

International

GENERAL FEATURES

Reservoir under construction	
Power Station	PS ■
Mine (selected)	☆
Racecourse or Racetrack	
Landmark, annotated	■
Hill Figure	
Monument (selected)	▲

Reservoir Coastal Cliff
Canal Dam Flat Rock
Aqueduct Tunnel Tidal Flat
Marsh Wood

■ *Figure 2-7* **Cultural symbols on the UK 1:500,000 series**

Aeronautical information is vital information for pilots, showing not only the position of aerodromes on the ground, but also the division of airspace through which aeroplanes fly, and other useful information. The chart legends explain this information. Memorise the most commonly used symbols, such as aerodromes, airspace, obstructions, etc.

Note that, in the case of the 1:250,000 chart (the low-level chart that shows surface features in great detail), only controlled airspace with a lower limit at or below 5,000 ft amsl or FL55 is shown. If flying above 5,000 ft amsl or FL55, a 1:500,000 chart must be used.

The chart will have all the changes that are effective on the 'Effective Date of Implementation', which is printed on the chart. Out-of-date charts can be dangerous, so always check that you have the latest edition. Check NOTAM, UK air information publications (such as the Aeronautical Information Circulars – AICs) and the Chart of UK Airspace Restrictions (AIP ENR) for any information affecting the chart after the published date. Note that, once an aeronautical change has been incorporated in the AIP (usually after about six months), the relevant NOTAM or AIC will be cancelled.

NOTE Aerodrome Traffic Zone (ATZs) are only shown on the chart where they lie outside controlled airspace. There is, however, a full list of ATZs on each chart, with the VHF-COM frequency of the responsible Air Traffic Service Unit (ATSU).

AERODROME - Civil..	⬡
AERODROME - Civil, limited or no facilities...	◯
HELIPORT - Civil...	Ⓗ
AERODROME - Government, available for Civil use. See UK AIP AD 1-1-1...............	◉
AERODROME - Government..	◎
HELIPORT - Government	⊛
MICROLIGHT FLYING SITES - Intensive Activity also takes place at certain Licensed and Unlicensed Aerodromes. See UK AIP ENR 1-1..........................	Ⓜ
DISUSED or ABANDONED Aerodrome. Shown for navigational landmark purposes only. See AIC 17/97 (Pink 135)	⊗
ELEVATIONS of Active Aeronautical Sites are shown adjacent to the symbol. Shown in feet above Mean Sea Level... 250	250
CUSTOMS AERODROMES are distinguished by a pecked line around the name of the aerodrome and elevation	⌐ MANCHESTER ¬ ⌊ 257 ⌋
AERODROME LIGHT BEACON ....✩ FIG ⋮⌐.⊤⋅ ✩ FlR ⋮⊤⊥⋅	

FOR CURRENT STATUS, AVAILABILITY, RESTRICTIONS AND WARNINGS APPLICABLE TO AERODROMES SHOWN ON THIS CHART CONSULT AIR INFORMATION PUBLICATIONS AND AERODROME OPERATORS OR OWNERS. PORTRAYAL DOES NOT IMPLY ANY RIGHT TO USE AN UNLICENSED AERODROME WITHOUT PERMISSION.

GLIDER LAUNCHING SITES. UK AIP ENR 1-1.

a. Primary activity at locations showing Maximum Altitude of winch launch. AMSL....... **ⓖ** /2.5

b. Additional activity at locations showing Maximum Altitude of winch launch. AMSL.. ◯ G/2.5

c. Additional activity without cables... ◯ G

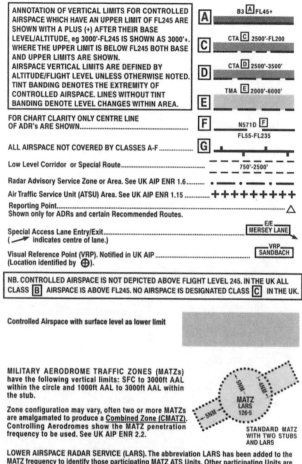

ANNOTATION OF VERTICAL LIMITS FOR CONTROLLED AIRSPACE WHICH HAVE AN UPPER LIMIT OF FL245 ARE SHOWN WITH A PLUS (+) AFTER THEIR BASE LEVEL/ALTITUDE, eg 3000'-FL245 IS SHOWN AS 3000'+. WHERE THE UPPER LIMIT IS BELOW FL245 BOTH BASE AND UPPER LIMITS ARE SHOWN.
AIRSPACE VERTICAL LIMITS ARE DEFINED BY ALTITUDE/FLIGHT LEVEL UNLESS OTHERWISE NOTED.
TINT BANDING DENOTES THE EXTREMITY OF CONTROLLED AIRSPACE. LINES WITHOUT TINT BANDING DENOTE LEVEL CHANGES WITHIN AREA.

A — B3 **A** FL45+

C — CTA **C** 2500'-FL200

D — CTA **D** 2500'-3500'

E — TMA **E** 2000'-6000'

FOR CHART CLARITY ONLY CENTRE LINE OF ADR's ARE SHOWN... **F** — N571D **F** FL55-FL235

ALL AIRSPACE NOT COVERED BY CLASSES A-F.................. **G**

Low Level Corridor or Special Route.. 750'-2500'

Radar Advisory Service Zone or Area. See UK AIP ENR 1.6.........

Air Traffic Service Unit (ATSU) Area. See UK AIP ENR 1.15 .... +++++++++

Reporting Point.. △
Shown only for ADRs and certain Recommended Routes.

Special Access Lane Entry/Exit... E/E
(➛ indicates centre of lane.)   MERSEY LANE

Visual Reference Point (VRP). Notified in UK AIP .... VRP
(Location identified by ⊕).   SANDBACH

NB. CONTROLLED AIRSPACE IS NOT DEPICTED ABOVE FLIGHT LEVEL 245. IN THE UK ALL CLASS **B** AIRSPACE IS ABOVE FL245. NO AIRSPACE IS DESIGNATED CLASS **C** IN THE UK.

Controlled Airspace with surface level as lower limit

MILITARY AERODROME TRAFFIC ZONES (MATZs) have the following vertical limits: SFC to 3000ft AAL within the circle and 1000ft AAL to 3000ft AAL within the stub.

Zone configuration may vary, often two or more MATZs are amalgamated to produce a **Combined Zone (CMATZ)**. Controlling Aerodromes show the MATZ penetration frequency to be used. See UK AIP ENR 2.2.

MATZ
LARS
126·5

STANDARD MATZ
WITH TWO STUBS
AND LARS

LOWER AIRSPACE RADAR SERVICE (LARS). The abbreviation LARS has been added to the MATZ frequency to identify those participating MATZ ATS Units. Other participating Units are identified by a LARS frequency annotation. The Service, Radar Advisory (RAS) or Radar Information (RIS), is available to all aircraft in unregulated airspace up to and including FL95 within approximately 30NM of each participating ATS Unit. See UK AIP ENR 1.6.

■ *Figure 2-8 (above & previous page) Sample 1:500,000 legend excerpts*

Figure 2-9, overleaf, illustrates how airspace information is depicted on a chart, showing a busy area of UK airspace – around Manchester and Liverpool. Figure 2-10 shows a section of the airspace around Prestwick and Glasgow.

■ *Figure 2-9 (overleaf) 1:500,000 chart excerpt*

- **Blackpool Aerodrome:** elevation 34 ft amsl
- **Airway A1 (Class A airspace) above FL65**
- **Manchester Terminal Control Area (TMA), Class A airspace (not available to VFR), above 3,500 ft amsl**
- **Warton Aerodrome Traffic Zone (ATZ)**
- **Warton MATZ:** Lower Airspace Radar Information Service freq. 129.525 MHz
- **Special Access Lane Entry/Exit into Liverpool CTR (blue arrow indicates centre of lane)**
- **Visual Reference Point: Aintree Racecourse**
- **Class A airspace above 3,500 ft amsl**
- **Liverpool Control Zone (CTR), Class D airspace, from surface to 1,500 ft altitude, operating on frequency 119.85 MHz**
- **Manchester Control Area, Class D, (available to VFR), 1,500 ft to 3,500 ft amsl**
- **Restricted Area 311:** from AMSL to 2,200 ft altitude
- **Low-level Route: max. altitude 1,250 ft on Manchester QNH**
- **Final instrument approach track to Hawarden runway**
- **Wrexham Aerodrome (disused or abandoned)**

Figure 2-10 **1:500,000 chart excerpt**

Further information is given in 'Legend Notes', which should be read carefully. Examples appear in Figure 2-11.

LEGEND NOTES

1. PROHIBITED AND RESTRICTED AREAS - NORTHERN IRELAND. Pilots are urgently warned against inadvertent entry into Prohibited or Restricted areas in Northern Ireland. Such entry could entail a danger that the flight might be judged to have a hostile or criminal intent and the aircraft could be liable to counter measures. See UK AIP ENR 5.1.

2. RESTRICTED AREAS R315, R318, R319, R320, R321, R432 and R504 apply only to Helicopters. See UK AIP ENR 5.1.

3. FYLINGDALES HIGH INTENSITY RADIO TRANSMISSION AREA. Up to 8000ft ALT aircraft should not remain for more than one minute within 1·5NM radius of position 542147N 0004012W. See UK AIP ENR 5.3.

Figure 2-11 **Legend notes from a 1:500,000 chart (sample only)**

HAZARDS TO AVIATION information is also depicted. These hazards include certain aerial activities such as parachuting or hang-gliding, as well as permanent obstructions such as radio masts or cables.

Obstructions that reach 300 ft or more above ground level (agl) are considered to be hazards to aeroplanes and are shown on charts. The numerals in brackets beside the symbol for the obstruction indicate the height of its top agl, and the numerals in italics without brackets indicate the elevation of the top of the obstruction amsl. Obstructions 299 ft agl and lower may not be shown.

Note that, since the first contour is at 500 ft amsl and obstructions less than 300 ft agl may not be shown, it is possible to have an obstruction that is just less than 800 ft amsl not indicated at all on the chart.

HANG/PARA GLIDING - Winch Launch Sites showing Maximum Altitude of
winch launch. AMSL. See UK AIP ENR 1-1.. /2.5

WINCH LAUNCHED ACTIVITIES. Maximum Altitude of cables is represented in thousands and
hundreds of feet above mean sea level calculated using a minimum cable height of 2000ft AGL
plus site elevation. At some sites the cable may extend above 2000ft AGL. Due to the
ground-based cable, aircraft should avoid over-flying these sites below the indicated altitude.

Symbols depicting Non Winch Launch Hang/Para Gliding sites have been removed as they
were not an accurate representation of the activity on any given day. Airspace users should
be aware that single or groups of soaring or motorised Hang/Para Gliders can be found flying
anywhere in the open FIR up to 15,000ft.

FREE-FALL PARACHUTING DROP ZONE. UK AIP ENR 1-1.
Parachutists may be expected within the airspace contained in a circle radius
1.5NM of the DZ up to FL150. Night parachuting may take place at any of
the sites shown on this chart.

AIR NAVIGATION OBSTACLES

Exceptionally High Obstacle (Lighted)   *1978*
1000ft or more AGL..   (1031)

                                                                       825
Single Obstacle (Unlighted) ....   (350)   *1614*
Multiple Obstacle (Lighted) ....   (505)
Cable joining Obstacles .... cables

Numerals in italics indicate elevation of top of obstacle above Mean Sea Level. Numerals
in brackets indicate height of top of obstacle above local Ground Level. Obstacles
annotated 'flarestack' burn off high pressure gas. The flame, which may not be visible in
bright sunlight, can extend up to 600ft above the installation.

KNOWN LAND SITED OBSTACLES ABOVE 300ft AGL ARE SHOWN ON THIS CHART.
A SMALL NUMBER OF OBSTACLES BELOW 300ft AGL ARE SHOWN FOR LANDMARK
PURPOSES. PERMANENT OFF-SHORE OBSTACLES ARE SHOWN REGARDLESS OF
HEIGHT CATEGORY. See UK AIP ENR 1-1.
WARNING : INFORMATION IS TAKEN FROM BEST AVAILABLE SOURCES BUT IS NOT
GUARANTEED COMPLETE.

Marine Light....................... ● Fl(3)30-0secs   Lightship FIWR12-0secs
(Normally shown if visibility range is not less than 15NM).

■ *Figure 2-12* **Hazard and other information on the**
1:500,000 series (sample only)

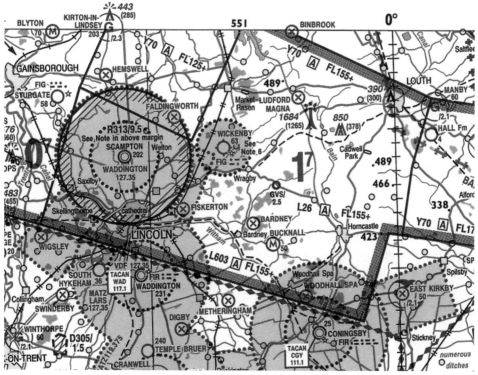

■ Figure 2-13 **1:500,000 Lincolnshire excerpt (sample only)**

In the chart extract in Figure 2-13, a number of hazards to aviation are shown, including:

- an exceptionally high obstruction (lighted), with a top 1,684 ft amsl, itself being 1,265 ft high (i.e. height agl);
- an unlit obstruction just beside it with a top 850 ft amsl and 378 ft agl;
- a further obstruction (single unlit) to the NE at Louth, with a top 390 ft amsl and 300 ft agl;
- a glider launching site with cables at Kirton-in-Lindsey.

Other items on the chart excerpt that could be hazardous to aviation, but which are listed elsewhere on the legend, are:

- the Wickenby ATZ vertical limit increases from 1,500 ft aal on weekdays to 2,000 ft aal at weekends;
- numerous disused or abandoned aerodromes, e.g. Bardney.

NOTE Much of the area portrayed lies within the Lincolnshire AIAA (Area of Intense Aerial Activity), which extends from 2,500 ft ALT (amsl) up to Flight Level 180. A Lower Airspace Radar Service (LARS) is available from Waddington, Cottesmore and Coningsby ATS units, on the frequencies shown. These are contact frequencies for flight within the Lincolnshire AIAA. Note also the combined MATZ (CMATZ) of Scampton and Waddington, using Waddington frequency 127.35 MHz.

Airspace Restrictions and other Hazard Information

These are also listed on the legend. If you refer back to Figure 2-9, some Airspace Restrictions were shown (R312 and P311).

A DANGER AREA (D) is airspace of defined dimensions within which activities dangerous to the flight of aircraft may exist at specified times, such as the flying of captive balloons, or weapons ranges, possibly with military aircraft towing targets on long cables. Pilots should avoid Danger Areas and, when flying in their vicinity, keep a sharp lookout for military aircraft.

Charts show only those Danger Areas that extend above 500 ft agl. Many rifle ranges have upper limits less than 500 ft agl, so pilots must ensure that they fly clear of such activities.

A PROHIBITED AREA (P) is an airspace of defined dimensions in which the flight of aircraft is prohibited.

A RESTRICTED AREA (R) is an airspace of defined dimensions within which the flight of aircraft is restricted in accordance with certain specified conditions (see AIP ENR or NOTAM).

AREAS ACTIVATED BY NOTAM are shown with a broken boundary line.

AIRSPACE RESTRICTIONS Prohibited 'P', Restricted 'R' and Danger Areas 'D' are shown with identification number/ effective altitude (in thousands of feet AMSL). Areas activated by Notam are shown with a broken boundary line.

For those Scheduled Danger Areas whose Upper Limit changes at specified times during its period of activity, only the higher of the Upper Limits is shown. Areas which may be active up to levels below the indicated Upper Limit are depicted by ↑ . Areas whose identification numbers are prefixed with an asterisk (⁑) contain airspace subject to byelaws which prohibit entry during the period of activity. See UK AIP ENR 1.1.

BRIEFING INFORMATION Pre-flight information on notifiable activities can be obtained H24 from AIS Heathrow via Tel: 020 8745 3451. Pre-flight information is also available for D508 (indicated on the chart by the prefix ⬆) Newcastle ATC 0191 2860966 Ext 3251.

MILITARY LOW FLYING SYSTEM.
Military low flying occurs in most parts of the UK at any height up to 2000ft above the surface. However, the greatest concentration is between 250 and 600ft and pilots should avoid flying in that height band whenever possible. Detailed information can be found on Chart of UK AIAA, ATA and Military Low Flying System, (UK AIP ENR 6-5-2-1).

AIAA AND ATA AREAS .... ◆◆◆◆◆◆◆◆◆◆
Areas are shown with name, vertical limits and where applicable contact frequency. Pilots of aircraft who transit these areas are strongly advised to make use of the Radar Service.

HIGH INTENSITY RADIO TRANSMISSION AREA (HIRTA). Areas with a radius of 0·5NM or more are shown with name/effective altitude (in thousands of feet AMSL). ....

BIRD SANCTUARIES are shown with name/effective altitude (in thousands of feet AMSL). ....

GAS VENTING OPERATIONS pilots are advised to avoid flying over Gas Venting Sites (GVSs) below specified altitudes. A warning circle is shown on the chart to identify a GVS and the hazard altitude is shown in thousands of feet AMSL. See UK ENR 1.1. ....GVS/3·1

SMALL ARMS RANGES in the UK with a vertical hazard height of 500ft AGL do not attract UK Danger Area status. However, firing at some ranges may constitute a hazard to aircraft below 500ft AGL. Details of the Ranges are listed in the UK AIP at ENR 5.3. Pictorial depiction can be found on the CHART OF UK AIRSPACE RESTRICTIONS. ENR 6-5-1-1.

DANGER AREA CROSSING SERVICE (DACS) is available for certain Danger Areas. The relevant areas (identified on the chart by the prefix †) and Unit Contact Frequencies to be used are shown below. For availability of the services see UK AIP ENR 5.1.

✳D201 & D201B .... { ABERPORTH CONTROL 133·5MHz/ INFO. 122·15MHz
                          { LONDON MILITARY 135·15MHz
D402A, D402B & D403 ... { WEST FREUGH APP 130·05MHz
                          { SCOTTISH MIL VIA SCOTTISH INFO 119·875MHz
D402C & D403A .... WEST FREUGH APP 130·05MHz
D405 &D405A.................... WEST FREUGH APP 130·05MHz or KIRKCUDBRIGHT RANGE 122·1MHz
D406C .... ESKMEALS RANGE 122·75MHz
D411 .... WEST FREUGH APP 130·05MHz or DAAIS outside hours.
D508 .... NEWCASTLE APP 124·375MHz
D510 .... SPADEADAM 122·1MHz

DANGER AREA ACTIVITY INFORMATION SERVICE (DAAIS) is available for certain Danger Areas shown on this chart (identified by the prefix §). The Nominated Air Traffic Service Units (NATSUs) to be used are shown below. See UK AIP ENR 1.1.
Pilots are advised to assume that a Danger Area is active if no reply is received from the appropriate NATSU.

D207 .... LONDON INFORMATION 124·6MHz
D304 .... MANCHESTER APP 119·4MHz
D307 .... DONNA NOOK RANGE CONTROL 122·75MHz
D308 .... WAINFLEET RANGE CONTROL 122·75MHz
D314 .... MANCHESTER APP 119·4MHz
✳D406 &D406B .... LONDON INFORMATION 125·475MHz
✳D407 & ✳D407A .... PENNINE RADAR 128·675MHz
✳D408, ✳D409 .... LEEMING APP 127·75MHz or LONDON INFO 125·475MHz
D411 .... Outside times for DACS, SCOTTISH INFO 119·875MHz
D412 .... LONDON INFORMATION 125·475MHz
D441 .... LINTON APP 129·15MHz
D509 .... WEST FREUGH APP 130·05MHz or SCOTTISH INFO 119·875MHz
D510 .... NEWCASTLE APP 124·375MHz or CARLISLE TOWER 123·6MHz
✳D512 & ✳D512A .... SCOTTISH INFORMATION 119·875MHz
D513, D513A & D513B...... SCOTTISH INFORMATION 119·875MHz
D607, D608 & D609 .... SCOTTISH INFORMATION 119·875MHz

                                                        PORTREE ASR
ALTIMETER SETTING REGION BOUNDARY (ASR) ......⊶ ⊶ ⊶ ⊶ ⊶
NOTE: The airspace within (and below) all Control Zones,   BELFAST ASR
Terminal Control Areas and Control Areas (with the exception of the Worthing and Daventry CTAs) during their notified hours of operation, does not form part of the forecast QNH Altimeter Setting Region System . Pilots flying below the Transition Altitude, should use a QNH of an aerodrome situated within the lateral boundaries of that airspace. Alternatively, when flying within an aerodrome circuit, aerodrome QFE may be used. See UK AIP ENR 1.7.

■ *Figure 2-14* **Airspace and hazard information (sample only)**

MILITARY LOW FLYING SYSTEM This occurs in most parts of the UK at any height up to 2,000 ft above the surface. However, the greatest concentration is between 250 ft and 600 ft above the surface and civil pilots are advised to avoid this height band whenever possible. Geographic details are given in the UK AIP (ENR 6-5-2-1) on a combined chart called *UK Areas of Intense Air Activity (AIAA), Aerial Tactics Areas (ATA) and Military Low Flying System*.

A BIRD SANCTUARY is airspace of defined dimensions within which large colonies of birds are known to breed. Pilots are requested to avoid these areas, especially during any stated breeding season, and are warned of the high risk of bird strikes. Figure 2-15 shows an example of a bird sanctuary that exists at the mouth of the Severn River from the surface up to 4,000 ft amsl between September and April.

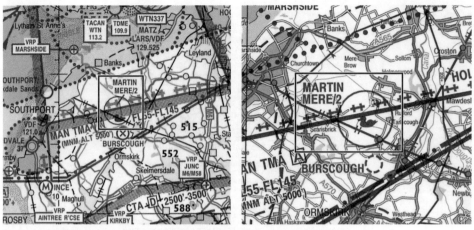

■ Figure 2-15 **Depiction of the same bird sanctuary on the half- and quarter-million aeronautical charts**

RADIO FACILITIES are also depicted on aeronautical charts, but these will not be significant until you commence training for instrument navigation. Note that the VOR compass roses on the chart are aligned with magnetic north and not true north.

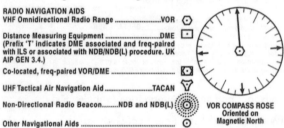

■ Figure 2-16 **Radio facilities marked on the 1:500,000 series (sample only)**

Position Information

The latitude-longitude graticule is clearly marked on charts.

The east–west parallels of latitude indicating degrees north or south of the equator (north in the UK and Europe) are labelled at either side of the 1:500,000 chart in 1° intervals (i.e. 60 nm intervals). Each degree is divided into 60 minutes, with marks each 5′ and 10′, and a full line across the chart at 30′. In the Northern Hemisphere, latitude is measured up from the bottom of the chart.

The north–south meridians of longitude (which gradually converge as they near the North Pole as a result of the 1:500,000 chart being a conical projection) are labelled at the top and bottom of the chart in degrees east or west of the prime meridian (in the UK, longitudes are both east and west). Each degree is divided into 60 minutes, with marks each 5′ and 10′, and a full line up the chart at 30′. Longitude is measured east or west from the Greenwich meridian. (Do not confuse the meridian with an isogonal.)

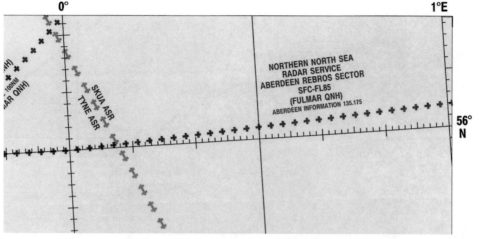

■ *Figure 2-17* **Graticule of the 1:500,000 series (not to scale)**

HIGH INTENSITY RADIO TRANSMISSION AREA (HIRTA). Airspace of defined dimensions within which there is radio energy of an intensity which may cause interference or damage to radio equipment in the aeroplane. They are best avoided.

AREA OF INTENSE AERIAL ACTIVITY (AIAA). Airspace of defined dimensions, not otherwise protected by Regulated Airspace (Controlled or Special Rules), within which the intensity of civil and/or military flying is exceptionally high, or within which unusual manoeuvres are frequently carried out. Examples are the Vale of York AIAA and the Lincolnshire AIAA.

Airspace Restriction Information is available on the legend of the 1:500,000 chart, and further information can be found in the Aeronautical Information Publication AIP ENR 5, *Chart of UK Areas of Intense Air Activity (AIAA), Aerial Tactics Areas (ATA) and Military Low Flying System* (ENR 6-5-2-1) and on the *Chart of UK Airspace Restrictions and Hazardous Areas* (ENR 6-5-1-1), which is included in the AIP. If necessary, the AIP should be referred to on the ground at the flight planning stage.

To obtain information in flight concerning the activity status of a particular Danger Area, the pilot should call on the appropriate Nominated Air Traffic Service Unit (NATSU) frequency, as listed on the chart legend. (If there is no reply, then assume that the Danger Area is active.)

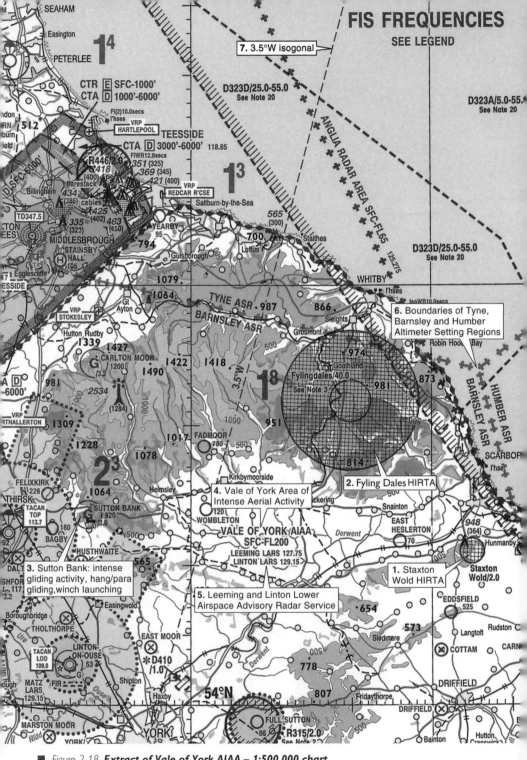

■ Figure 2-18 **Extract of Vale of York AIAA – 1:500,000 chart**

Figure 2-18 shows:

- a High Intensity Radio Transmission Area (HIRTA) at Staxton Wold extending up to 2,000 ft amsl (1);
- a High Intensity Radio Transmission Area (HIRTA) at Fylingdales, extending up to 40,000 ft (2), which has special conditions specified in Legend Note 3;
- intense gliding activity at Sutton Bank, together with hang/para gliding and winch launch activity (3). Note that winch cables may be carried up to altitudes of 3,000 ft amsl.
- generally intense aerial activity throughout the area, since it lies in the Vale of York AIAA (4).
- Other points of interest (though not hazards) in Figure 2-18:
- Lower Airspace Advisory Radar Service frequencies of 127.75 MHz for Leeming and 129.15 MHz for Linton (these are contact frequencies within the Vale of York AIAA) (5);
- the boundaries of the Humber, Barnsley and Tyne Altimeter Setting Regions (ASRs) (6);
- the 4.5°W isogonal (7).

Magnetic Information on the 1:500,000 Chart

ISOGONALS. or isogonic lines (lines joining places of equal magnetic variation, are indicated on the 1:500,000 chart by dashed blue lines. The UK experiences *variation west – magnetic best,* while in Eastern Europe there is *variation east – magnetic least.* For calculation purposes, use the whole degree variation either side of the half-degree isogonal, as appropriate.

THE AGONIC LINE. (where true north and magnetic north are the same direction, and variation is zero) lies in between the areas experiencing west variation and those areas experiencing east variation. The agonic line passes through southern France.

Because the magnetic poles are gradually moving, the amount of variation at a particular place will also gradually change over a period of years. Every year the isogonic information on the charts is updated, and the year of the information shown on the chart.

CAA 1:250,000 Topographical Air Charts

The 1:250,000 Topographical Air Charts, published by the CAA, show much more detail, because of their larger scale. This may be useful, especially in busy terminal areas, when you may be operating below 5,000 ft amsl. They show topographical and cultural information, together with low-level aeronautical information (up to 5,000 ft amsl); including:

- **all items up to 5,000 ft** amsl shown on the 1:500,000 series;
- **controlled airspace** with a lower limit at or below 5,000 ft amsl or FL55;

- **approximate runway layout** at aerodromes, and the main, final instrument approach course at aerodromes outside controlled airspace.

AERODROMES - Field limits with hard runway pattern   Civil ....
                                                      Government ....

- Showing disused runways as solid patterns ....

CUSTOMS AERODROMES are distinguished by a pecked line   MANCHESTER
around the name of the aerodrome   257

AERODROME LIGHT BEACON .... ☆ FIG ⁚⁚ ☆ FIR ⁚⁚

HELIPORT .... Ⓗ Ⓗ

MINOR AERODROME with runway pattern unknown or
not portrayable ....

MICROLIGHT FLYING SITES - Intense Activity also takes place at certain
Licensed and Unlicensed Aerodromes. See UK AIP ENR 1.1.5 .... Ⓜ

DISUSED or ABANDONED Aerodrome - shown for navigational
landmark purposes only. See AIC 17/97 (Pink 135).......................... ⊙

ELEVATIONS of Active Aeronautical Sites are shown adjacent to the symbol.
Shown in feet above Mean Sea Level (AMSL).   250 250

GLIDER LAUNCHING SITES - See UK AIP ENR 1.1.5
a. Primary activity at locations showing Maximum Altitude of winch launch. AMSL. .... Ⓖ

b. Additional activity at locations showing Maximum Altitude of
winch launch. AMSL. .... ◖G/2.5

c. Additional activity without cables .... Ⓖ/2.5

HANG/PARA GLIDING - Winch Launch Sites showing Maximum Altitude
of winch launch. AMSL. See UK AIP ENR 1.1. .... ◐G /2.5

WINCH LAUNCHED ACTIVITIES. Maximum Altitude of cables is represented in thousands and
hundreds of feet above mean sea level, calculated using a minimum cable height of 2000ft AGL
plus site elevation. At some sites the cable may extend above 2000ft AGL. Due to the ground-based
cable, aircraft should avoid over flying these sites below the indicated altitude.

Symbols depicting Non Winch Launch Hang/Para Gliding sites have been removed
as they were not an accurate representation of the activity on any given day. Airspace users
should be aware that single or groups of soaring or motorised Hang/Para Gliders can be
found flying anywhere in the open FIR up to 15,000ft.

FREE-FALL PARACHUTING DROP ZONE - See UK AIP ENR 1.1.5
Parachutists may be expected within the airspace contained in a   ▽
circle radius 1.5NM or 2NM of the DZ up to FL150. Night parachuting
may take place at any of the sites shown on this chart ....

FOR CURRENT STATUS, AVAILABILITY, RESTRICTIONS AND WARNINGS APPLICABLE TO
AERODROMES SHOWN ON THIS CHART CONSULT AIR INFORMATION PUBLICATIONS
AND AERODROME OPERATORS OR OWNERS. PORTRAYAL DOES NOT IMPLY ANY RIGHT
TO USE AN UNLICENSED AERODROME WITHOUT PERMISSION.

Controlled Airspace or ATZ with active surface level as lower limit. ....

AIRSPACE RESTRICTIONS Prohibited 'P', Restricted 'R' and Danger
Areas 'D' are shown with identification number/effective altitude
(in thousands of feet AMSL) except D216 where a limit is expressed
as a Flight Level. Areas activated by NOTAM are shown with a
broken boundary line.

For those Scheduled Danger Areas whose Upper Limit changes at specified times during
its period of activity, only the higher of the Upper Limits is shown.
Areas which may be active up to levels below the indicated Upper Limit are depicted by ↑.
Areas whose identification numbers are prefixed with an asterisk (⁎) contain airspace
subject to byelaws which prohibit entry during the period of activity. See UK AIP ENR 1.1.

DANGER AREA CROSSING SERVICE (DACS) is available for certain Danger Areas. The
relevant areas (identified on the chart by the prefix †) and Unit Contact Frequencies to be
used are shown below. For availability of the services see UK AIP ENR 5.1.

⁎D201, D201A & D201B .... { ABERPORTH INFORMATION 119·65MHz or
                                               { LONDON MILITARY 135·15MHz
D202... LLANBEDR RANGE 122·5MHz
D406C.. ESKMEALS RANGE 122·75MHz

DANGER AREA ACTIVITY INFORMATION SERVICE (DAAIS) is available for certain Danger
Areas shown on this chart (identified by the prefix §). The Nominated Air Traffic Service
Units (NATSUs) to be used are shown below. See UK AIP ENR 5.1. Pilots are advised to
assume that a Danger Area is active if no reply is received from the appropriate NATSU.

D213 .... COVENTRY ATIS126·05MHz, APP 119·25MHz
D304 & D314 .... MANCHESTER APP 119·525MHz
⁎D406 & D406B .... LONDON INFORMATION 125·475MHz

PRE-FLIGHT INFORMATION is available for certain Danger Areas. Information on notifiable
activities can be obtained by telephone H24 from AIS Heathrow, Tel: 020 8745 3451. Pilots
are advised to obtain an airborne update of the activity status and obtain a crossing
clearance using DACS unit contact frequencies.

RADIO NAVIGATION AIDS
VHF Omnidirectional Radio Range ....VOR ⊙

Distance Measuring Equipment ....DME ⊡
(Prefix 'T' indicates DME associated and freq-paired
with ILS or associated with NDB/NDB(L) procedure.
UK AIP GEN 3.4.3)
Collocated, freq-paired VOR/DME..................... ⊡

UHF Tactical Air Navigation Aid....................TACAN ▽

Non-Directional Radio
Beacon ....NDB and NDB(L)   VOR COMPASS ROSE
                                                              Oriented on
Other Navigational Aids .... ⊙   Magnetic North

ANNOTATION OF VERTICAL LIMITS FOR CONTROLLED
AIRSPACE WHICH HAVE AN UPPER LIMIT OF FL245 ARE   Ⓐ   B3 Ⓐ FL45+
SHOWN WITH A PLUS (+) AFTER THEIR BASE
LEVEL/ALTITUDE, eg 3000'-FL245 IS SHOWN AS 3000'+.   Ⓓ   CTA Ⓓ 2500'-3500'
WHERE THE UPPER LIMIT IS BELOW FL245 BOTH BASE
AND UPPER LIMITS ARE SHOWN.
AIRSPACE VERTICAL LIMITS ARE DEFINED BY   Ⓔ   TMA Ⓔ 2000'-6000'
ALTITUDE/FLIGHT LEVEL UNLESS OTHERWISE NOTED.
TINT BANDING DENOTES THE EXTREMITY OF
CONTROLLED AIRSPACE. LINES WITHOUT TINT   Ⓕ   N571D Ⓕ
BANDING DENOTE LEVEL CHANGES WITHIN AREA.
FOR CHART CLARITY ONLY CENTRE LINE........................... FL55-FL235
OF ADR's ARE SHOWN
ALL AIRSPACE NOT COVERED BY CLASSES A-F .... Ⓖ

NB. CONTROLLED AIRSPACE IS NOT DEPICTED ABOVE FLIGHT LEVEL 245 IN THE UK. ALL
CLASS Ⓑ AIRSPACE IS ABOVE FL245. NO AIRSPACE IS DESIGNATED CLASS Ⓒ IN THE UK.

Low Level Corridor or Special Route............................
                                                              750'-2500'
Radar Advisory Service Zone or Area. See UK AIP ENR 1.6...........

Reporting Point ....
Shown only for ADRs and certain Recommended Routes.   △

Special Access Lane Entry/Exit .... E/E
(⤴ indicates centre of lane.)   MERSEY LANE
Visual Reference Point (VRP). Notified in UK AIP   VRP
(Location identified by ⊕).   FLEETWOOD

MILITARY AERODROME TRAFFIC ZONES (MATZs)
have the following vertical limits: SFC to 3000ft AAL within the
circle and 1000ft AAL within the stub.
Zone configuration may vary, often two or more MATZs are   MATZ
amalgamated to produce a Combined Zone (CMATZ).   LARS
Controlling Aerodromes show the MATZ penetration   126·5
frequency to be used. See UK AIP ENR 2.2.
                                                              STANDARD MATZ WITH
                                                              TWO STUBS AND LARS
LOWER AIRSPACE RADAR SERVICE (LARS).
The abbreviation LARS has been added to the MATZ frequency to identify those participating
MATZ ATS Units. Other participating LARS Units are identified by a LARS frequency box.
The Service, Radar Advisory (RAS) or Radar Information (RIS), is available to all aircraft in
unregulated airspace up to and including FL95 within approximately 30NM of each participating
ATS Unit. See UK AIP ENR 1.6.

AREAS OF INTENSE AIR ACTIVITY (AIAA) ....
Areas are shown with name, vertical limits and where applicable contact frequency. Pilots
of aircraft who transit these areas are strongly advised to make use of the Radar Service.

                                                              PORTREE ASR
ALTIMETER SETTING REGION BOUNDARY (ASR)........... ⊹⊹ ⊹⊹ ⊹⊹
NOTE: The airspace within (and below) all Control Zones,   BELFAST ASR
Terminal Control Areas and Control Areas (with the exception of the Worthing and Daventry
CTAs) during their notified hours of operation, does not form part of the forecast QNH Altimeter
Setting Region System . Pilots flying below the Transition Altitude, should use a QNH of an
aerodrome situated within the lateral boundaries of that airspace. Alternatively, when flying
within an aerodrome circuit, aerodrome QFE may be used. See UK AIP ENR 1.7.

HIGH INTENSITY RADIO TRANSMISSION AREA (HIRTA). Areas with a
radius of 0·5NM or more are shown with name/effective altitude (in
thousands of feet AMSL).

BIRD SANCTUARIES are shown with name/effective altitude (in thousands
of feet AMSL) ....

SMALL ARMS FIRING RANGES. May be a hazard to aircraft flying below 500'AGL. Full
details are given in UK AIP ENR 5.3. Location of ranges is shown on UK AIP Chart
ENR 6-5-1-1.

GAS VENTING OPERATIONS pilots are advised to avoid flying over
Gas Venting Sites (GVSs) below specified altitudes. A warning   ◯
circle is shown on the chart to identify a GVS and the hazard altitude
is shown in thousands of feet AMSL. See UK AIP ENR 1.1.5 .... GVS/3·1

UK AERODROME TRAFFIC ZONES (ATZs)
SERVICES/RT FREQUENCIES (MHz). SEE UK AIP.

AERODROME TRAFFIC ZONE (ATZ), is airspace from the surface to 2000ft
AAL within a circle centred on the notified mid-point of the longest runway,
radius 2-0NM (RWY≤1850m) or 2·5NM (RWY>1850m), where Mandatory
Rules apply.
Most Government Aerodrome ATZs are H24.

   BARKSTON HEATH (EGYE) ....INITIAL CALL CRANWELL ATC 119·375
 ◆ BIRMINGHAM (EGBB)....................ATC 118·05
 ⁎ BLACKPOOL (EGNH).......................INITIAL CALL WARTON LARS 129·525
                                          BLACKPOOL ATC 119·95
   CAERNARFON (EGCK)....................INITIAL CALL VALLEY ATC 125·225, A/G 122·25
   CHURCH FENTON (EGXG) ....ATC 126·5
   COSFORD (EGWC)...........................ATC 135·875
   COTTESMORE (EGXJ) ....ATC 130·2
 ⁎ COVENTRY (EGBE) ....ATC 119·25
   CRANWELL (EGYD) ....ATC 119·375
   DERBY (EGBD) ....A/G 118·35
   DISHFORTH (EGXD)......................INITIAL CALL LEEMING ATC 127·5
 ◆ EAST MIDLANDS (EGNX) ....ATC 134·175
   FULL SUTTON (EGNU) ....A/G 132·325

■ Figure 2-19 **Sample excerpts of 1:250,000 chart (opposite) and legend**

Other Charts

There are other charts that are not used for position plotting or navigation, but to supply specific information. For example:

- Chart of United Kingdom Airspace Restrictions and Hazardous Areas (AIP ENR 6-5-1-1 and AIP ENR 5).
- Chart of United Kingdom Areas of Intense Air Activity (AIAA) and Aerial Tactics Areas (ATAs) (AIP ENR 6-5-2-1 and AIP ENR 5).

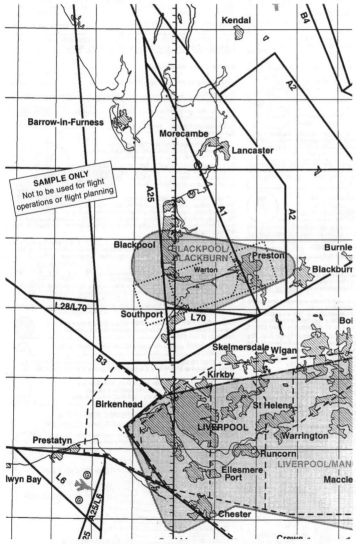

■ Figure 2-20 **Extract from the UK AIAAs and ATAs chart (sample only)**

Useful information regarding civil aerodromes in the United Kingdom can be obtained from *Pooley's Flight Guide*.

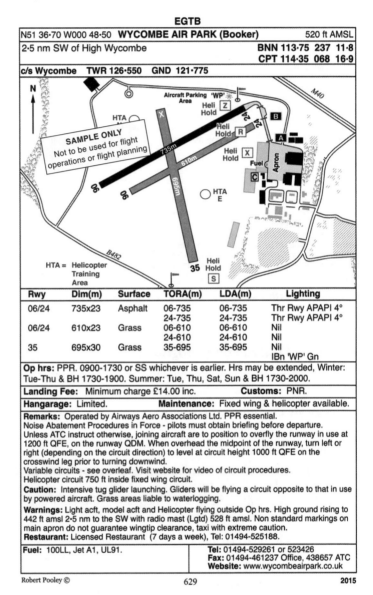

EGTB

N51 36·70 W000 48·50	**WYCOMBE AIR PARK (Booker)**		520 ft AMSL
2·5 nm SW of High Wycombe		**BNN 113·75 237 11·8**	
		CPT 114·35 068 16·9	

c/s Wycombe   TWR 126·550   GND 121·775

HTA = Helicopter Training Area

Rwy	Dim(m)	Surface	TORA(m)	LDA(m)	Lighting
06/24	735x23	Asphalt	06-735	06-735	Thr Rwy APAPI 4°
			24-735	24-735	Thr Rwy APAPI 4°
06/24	610x23	Grass	06-610	06-610	Nil
			24-610	24-610	Nil
35	695x30	Grass	35-695	35-695	Nil
					IBn 'WP' Gn

Op hrs: PPR. 0900-1730 or SS whichever is earlier. Hrs may be extended, Winter: Tue-Thu & BH 1730-1900. Summer: Tue, Thu, Sat, Sun & BH 1730-2000.

Landing Fee: Minimum charge £14.00 inc.	**Customs:** PNR.

Hangarage: Limited.	**Maintenance:** Fixed wing & helicopter available.

Remarks: Operated by Airways Aero Associations Ltd. PPR essential.
Noise Abatement Procedures in Force - pilots must obtain briefing before departure.
Unless ATC instruct otherwise, joining aircraft are to position to overfly the runway in use at 1200 ft QFE, on the runway QDM. When overhead the midpoint of the runway, turn left or right (depending on the circuit direction) to level at circuit height 1000 ft QFE on the crosswind leg prior to turning downwind.
Variable circuits - see overleaf. Visit website for video of circuit procedures.
Helicopter circuit 750 ft inside fixed wing circuit.
Caution: Intensive tug glider launching. Gliders will be flying a circuit opposite to that in use by powered aircraft. Grass areas liable to waterlogging.
Warnings: Light acft, model acft and Helicopter flying outside Op hrs. High ground rising to 442 ft amsl 2·5 nm to the SW with radio mast (Lgtd) 528 ft amsl. Non standard markings on main apron do not guarantee wingtip clearance, taxi with extreme caution.
Restaurant: Licensed Restaurant (7 days a week), Tel: 01494-525188.

Fuel: 100LL, Jet A1, UL91.	**Tel:** 01494-529261 or 523426
	Fax: 01494-461237 Office, 438657 ATC
	Website: www.wycombeairpark.co.uk

Robert Pooley ©   629   2015

■ *Figure 2-21* **Wycombe Air Park (Booker) aerodrome, as shown in Pooley's Flight Guide**

**UNITED KINGDOM
PRIVATE AIRFIELDS**

It[...] SAMPLE ONLY [...]he airfields and landing fields in this section are mostly
u[...]Not to be used for flight[...]**TRICTLY BY PRIOR PERMISSION ONLY** or by
ar[...]operations or flight planning[...]ings are made entirely at pilot's own risk. No extracts or part
the[...]may be re-published without the Publisher's and Editor's consent in writing.

1   ABOYNE   N5704·50 W00250·00   460 ft.AMSL
1 nm W of Aboyne. (N of River Dee)   **Op hrs:** PPR
Two parallel tarmac strips 09/27, 540x7 m and 520 x 5·5 m
Remarks: Operated by Deeside Gliding Club, Waterside, Dinnet. Only aircraft
involved in gliding activities permitted. Field grazed by cattle at times. Windsock N of
runway. Gliding site – aerotow only.
Landing fee: £5.00 Gliding Club Business. £10.00 Non Gliding Club Business.
Accommodation: Hotels in Aboyne and Dinnet, both 2 miles.
Fuel: Nil.   **Tel:** Dinnet 013398-85339 or 885236

2   ALLENSMORE   N5200 W00250   300 ft. AMSL
4 nm SW of Hereford.   **Op hrs:** Strictly PPR.
Grass field N/S 550m.
Remarks: Operated by Willox Bridge, Allensmore, Hereford. Contact Mr. Powell.
Prior permission advisable. Care must be taken due to animals grazing. Large letter
'A' on white background on hangar roof at N end of strip. **Taxi:** 01432-351238
Fuel: Nil   **Tel:** Wormbridge 0198121-203

3   AVIEMORE (Kincraig)   N5706 W00353   850 ft. AMSL
1·5 nm SE of Loch Insh.
Rough grass strip 02/20 approx. 670m.
Remarks: Operated by Miss Jane Williamson, Blackmill, Kincraig, Kingussie,
Invernesshire and Cairngorm Gliding Club. Light aircraft welcome at pilot's own risk,
PPR. Beware steeply rising ground to 4000ft. to East of airfield. Glider flying.
Fuel: Nil.   **Tel:** Kincraig 246

■ *Figure 2-22* **Further sample of information included in Pooley's Flight
Guide**

Measuring Latitude and Longitude

As a pilot/navigator, you sometimes need to determine the
latitude and longitude of a place.

To Determine the Latitude of a Place:

1. Lay a straight-edge east–west through the place, parallel to the
parallels of latitude.

2. From the latitude scales running north–south down the page
you can read off the exact latitude. (It should be the same
latitude on the scale either side of the place – this ensures that
the straight-edge is placed correctly on the chart.)

NOTE In the Northern Hemisphere the latitude increases towards
the north and top of the chart, and the scale lines break up each
degree of latitude into 60 minutes, with large marks each 10
minutes. (Make sure that you count from the bottom and up the
page, in the direction of increasing latitude.)

To Determine the Longitude of a Place:

1. Lay a straight-edge north–south through the place, parallel to
the closest meridians of longitude.

2. From the longitude scales running east–west across the page you can read off the exact longitude. (It should read the same on the scales above and below the place – this checks that the straight-edge is placed correctly on the chart.)

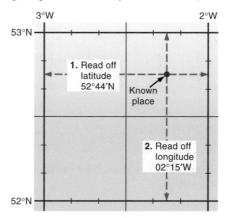

■ *Figure 2-23* **Finding the latitude-longitude of a place**

Plotting a Position

The reverse problem of plotting a given latitude and longitude on the chart is just as easy:

1. Find the approximate position of the place on the chart.

2. Mark the latitude given on the two nearest latitude scales either side of the position.

3. Mark the longitude given on the two nearest longitude scales north and south of the position.

4. Join the latitude marks and then join the longitude marks. Their point of intersection is the desired position.

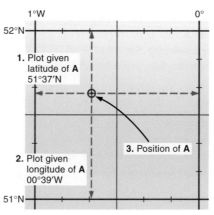

■ *Figure 2-24* **Plotting a known lat–long**

NOTE You are required to be able to specify or mark a position to an accuracy of 1 minute of arc.

Now complete: **Practice Questions - Aeronautical Charts**

1. Which navigation aid(s) is shown by the following ICAO chart symbol?

 (a) *NDB*

 (b) *VOR*

 (c) *Collocated VOR/DME*

 (d) *TACAN*

2. Which navigation aid(s) is shown by the following ICAO chart symbol?

 (a) *NDB*

 (b) *VOR*

 (c) *Collocated VOR/DME*

 (d) *TACAN*

3. What is shown by the following ICAO chart symbol?

 (a) *A Prohibited Area*

 (b) *A Military Air Traffic Zone (MATZ)*

 (c) *A UK Aerodrome Air Traffic Zone (ATZ)*

 (d) *A High Intensity Radio Transmission Area (HIRTA)*

4. What is shown by the following ICAO chart symbol

 (a) *A Gas Venting Site.*

 (b) *A Glider Launching Site where gliding is the primary activity with winch launches up to 2,500 ft AGL.*

 (c) *A Glider Launching Site where gliding is the primary activity with winch launches up to 2,500 ft AMSL.*

 (d) *A Glider Launching Site where activities in addition to gliding take place with glider winch launches up to 2,500 ft AMSL.*

5. What is shown by the following ICAO chart symbol?

 (a) *A civil aerodrome.*

 (b) *A customs aerodrome.*

 (c) *A government aerodrome available for civil use.*

 (d) *A government aerodrome normally restricted to military operations.*

6. Two blue numerals are shown in quadrangles bounded by each half degree of latitude and longitude on a 1:500,000 aeronautical chart. What do these ICAO chart symbols mean?

3^2

(a) *These are Maximum Elevation Figures (MEF) based on the highest known terrain and obstacles in the quadrangle allowing for errors. They are not a safety altitude.*

(b) *They represent a VFR safety altitude of 3,200 ft for the quadrant in which they reside.*

(c) *They indicate the maximum altitude at which controlled airspace is entered.*

(d) *These figures are the Minimum Safe Altitude (MSA) for the quadrant.*

Time

Time is of great importance to the air navigator, and the clock is one of the basic instruments used in the cockpit. Time enables you to:

- **regulate** affairs on board your aeroplane;
- **measure** the progress of your flight;
- **anticipate** arrival time at certain positions;
- **calculate** a safe endurance for flight;
- **estimate** when weather conditions at the destination are likely to improve;
- **measure** rest periods between flights ... and so on.

Time is also used to measure the earth's rotation. We relate the rotation of our planet Earth to the position of celestial or heavenly bodies, such as the sun and other stars. By using time we can specify the beginning of day, sunrise, noon, sunset, commencement of night, midnight, moonrise, moonset, and so on.

To all navigators – land, sea and air – time is of vital importance, and a subject that must be mastered, although much of this topic is beyond the scope of the PPL syllabus. However, if you are flying abroad in other time zones, then the relevance of this will be apparent.

Motion of the Earth

To measure the passage of time, we need to relate it to some repetitive event. For our ancestors, and indeed for us, a suitable recurring event is the apparent passage of the sun across our skies – its highest point in the sky simply indicated when the shadows that it casts are shortest. The sun appears to cross our skies once in every day.

On a longer time scale, we notice the regular passage of the seasons – spring, summer, autumn and winter – a complete cycle of these being called one year.

The sun has been used as a simple clock for thousands of years. Whereas early man thought that it was the sun which moved around the earth, we now know that this is not the case. It is, in fact, the rotation of the earth on its axis that causes the appearance of the sun travelling across our skies each day, hence the term 'apparent passage of the sun'.

As man's knowledge increased it was realised that one day is the approximate time span of one revolution of the earth on its own axis. One year is the approximate time span of one complete orbit of the earth about the sun.

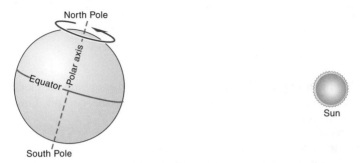

■ *Figure 3-1* **The earth rotates about its own axis once every 24 hours**

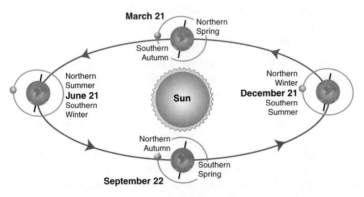

■ *Figure 3-2* **The earth rotates around the sun once a year**

There is a third fundamental type of time apart from the rotation of the earth about its own axis and the orbiting of the earth around the sun. It is **international atomic time (TAI),** where atomic vibrations, such as those occurring at very short time intervals in quartz crystals, are used to define the SI second and calibrate clocks extremely accurately. As this was endorsed internationally as recently as 1971 you can see that the subject of time is still not a closed book. In fact, only in 1985 was the international basis for standard time changed from Greenwich Mean Time (GMT) to Coordinated Universal Time (UTC).

Each day is divided into 24 hours, each hour further divided into 60 equal minutes, and each of these minutes further divided into 60 equal seconds.

To complete one orbit of the sun, the earth takes about 365 and ¼ solar days. It is convenient to have a whole number of days in a year, and so we define the civil year as 365 days. At the end of each 4 years, when the extra ¼ day each year adds up to one whole day, the extra day is added in to give a **leap year** of 366 days. This keeps the calendar reasonably in step with the seasons.

Measurement and Expression of Time

To measure time, use is again made of a repetitive event, such as the swinging of a pendulum, or the atomic vibrations within a quartz crystal, to design clocks that measure hours, minutes and seconds.

Each day is divided into 24 hours, which begins at midnight (00 hours 00 minutes), then proceeds through midday (1200) to midnight (2400), at which instant the next day begins (0000).

The hours are numbered from 00 hours to 24 hours (rather than 0 to 12 a.m. and 0 to 12 p.m.), and the 60 minutes of each hour are numbered from 00 min to 59 min. The term a.m. means *ante meridiem,* in the sense that the sun has yet to pass over your meridian of longitude, so the time is before noon; p.m. means *post meridiem,* because the sun has passed overhead and the time is afternoon.

For flight planning and navigation purposes we do not usually refer to the year or the month, but only the **day** of the month as the **date,** followed by the time in **hours** and **minutes.** As most air navigation occurs within a few hours, and only rarely in excess of 30 hours, we can be reasonably confident of which year and month we are talking about, so there is no need to specify them.

Seconds, which are $1/60$ of a minute, are too short a time interval for practical navigation, so date/time is usually expressed as a six figure date/time group.

Six-Figure Date/Time Group

In the six-figure date/time group:
- **the date** is a two-figure group for the day of the month from 00 to 31, and is followed by:
- **the time,** written as a four-figure group on a 24 hour clock – the first two figures representing the hours from 00 to 24, and the last two figures representing the minutes from 00 through to 59.

EXAMPLE 1 Express 13th of September, 2015, 10:35 a.m. as a six-figure date/time group.

date	time	
13	10	35
	hr	*min*

ANSWER 131035

EXAMPLE 2 Express 3:21 p.m. on March 17th, 2015, as a six-figure date/time group.

3:21 p.m. = 1200 noon
+ 321
1521 on the 24 hr clock

ANSWER 171521

Eight-Figure Date/Time Group

To specify the month, the six-figure date/time is preceded by two figures representing the month, and so is expanded into an eight figure time-group. This is often used in NOTAM (Notices to Airmen).

In the eight-figure date/time group:

- **the first two** numbers refer to month;
- **the second two** numbers refer to the date; and
- **the last four** numbers refer to the time.

EXAMPLE 3 5:45 p.m. on September 30th may be written as:

SEP 30 17 45
or 09 30 17 45
or 09301745

The Relationship Between Longitude and Time

In one day, the earth makes one complete rotation of 360° with respect to the chosen celestial body, which is the sun. The time of day is a measure of this rotation and indicates how much of that day has elapsed or, in other words, how much of a rotation has been completed.

As observers on the earth, we do not feel its rotation about its own axis, but rather we see the sun apparently move around the earth. In one mean solar day the sun will appear to have travelled the full 360° of longitude around the earth.

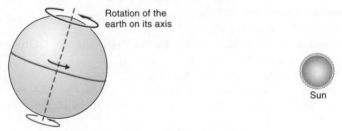

■ *Figure 3-3* **The earth rotates at 15° of longitude per hour**

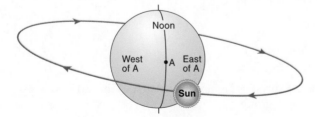

■ *Figure 3-4* **Apparent motion of the sun around the earth**

The angular difference between different longitudes is known as arc of longitude and has a direct relationship with time.

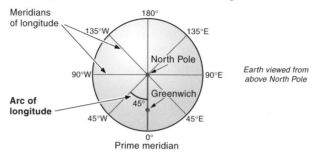

■ *Figure 3-5* **Arc of longitude**

The arc of longitude in degrees and minutes of arc is related to the time interval in hours and minutes as shown below.

ARC	TIME	
360°	24 hours	*(divide by 24)*
15°	1 hour	*(divide by 15)*
1°	4 minutes	*(divide by 4)*
15′	1 minute	*(divide by 15)*
1′	4 seconds	

Time to Arc Conversions

1. Multiply the hours by 15 to obtain degrees (1 hour = 15° arc of longitude).

2. Divide the minutes of time by 4 to obtain degrees (a minute of time = ¼° or 15′ arc) and then multiply the remaining minutes of time by 15 to obtain minutes of arc.

EXAMPLE 4 Convert 9 hr 23 min to arc units.

9 hr × 15 = 135°; as 1 hr = 15°

23 min ÷ 4 = 5°; as 4 min =1°

and the remaining 3 minutes of time × 15 = 45′ of arc as 1 minute = 15′

ANSWER Adding these, we get 140°45′

Arc to Time Conversions

1. Divide the degrees by 15 to obtain hours, and multiply the remaining degrees by 4 to obtain minutes of time.

2. Divide the minutes of arc by 15 to obtain minutes of time, and multiply the remainder by 4 to obtain seconds of time.

EXAMPLE 5 Convert 140°49′ of arc of longitude to time units.

140 ÷ 15 = 9 hr, with 5 left over × 4 = 20 min of time, i.e. 140° of arc = 9 hr 20 min.

49′ ÷ 15 = 3 min of time, with 4 left over × 4 = 16 sec of time.

Adding these: 140°49′ = 9 hr 23 min 16 sec.

ANSWER 9 hr 23 min 16 sec

Local Time

Time is a measure of the rotation of the earth, and any given time interval can be represented by a corresponding angle through which the earth turns. Suppose that the sun (the celestial reference point) is directly overhead, i.e. it is noon. For every point along that same meridian of longitude, the sun will be at its highest point in the sky for that day.

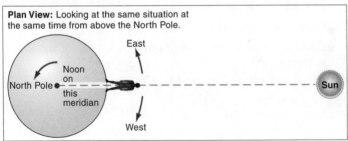

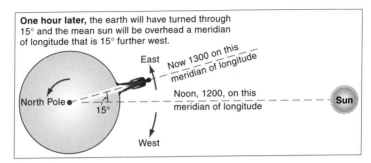

One hour later, the earth will have turned through 15° and the mean sun will be overhead a meridian of longitude that is 15° further west.

East

Now 1300 on this meridian of longitude

North Pole

15°

Noon, 1200, on this meridian of longitude

Sun

West

■ *Figure 3-6* **Noon is when the sun is at its highest point in the sky**

Meridians of longitude further east are ahead in local time.
Meridians of longitude further west are behind in local time.

EXAMPLE 6 Place A is 45° of longitude west of place B. How much earlier or later will noon occur at A compared to B?

45° arc of longitude = 3 hours, and because A is to the west of B, noon will occur three hours later at A.

Local Mean Time (LMT)

LMT uses the sun as its celestial reference point, and the local meridian of longitude as its terrestrial (earthly) reference point. Therefore, all points along the same meridian of longitude will have the same local mean time.

The local mean time along one meridian of longitude will differ from the local mean time along another meridian of longitude, and this difference will equal the difference (or change) in longitude expressed in time units. The further east the place is, the further ahead it is in LMT.

EXAMPLE 7 If it is noon LMT in Kingston upon Hull (00°20′W longitude) with the sun passing over the 00°20′W meridian of longitude, how much earlier or later will it be noon LMT in Blackpool (3°W longitude)?

Kingston upon Hull longitude:00°20′W
Blackpool longitude:03°00′W
difference, or change, of longitude =02°40′

which, in time units, is:
2° = 8 min (as 1° = 4 min of time)
40′ = 2 min 40 sec (as 1′ = 4 sec of time)

Therefore 2°40′ = 10 min 40 sec of time.

ANSWER Because Blackpool is to the west of Kingston upon Hull, noon at Blackpool with the sun passing over its meridian will be 10 minutes 40 seconds later than at Kingston upon Hull.

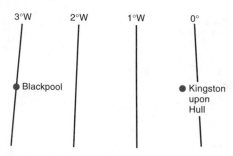

■ Figure 3-7 **Example 7**

In air navigation, the main use of local mean time (LMT) is in extracting data from tables in the Air Almanac on the rising and setting of celestial bodies such as the sun, moon and stars. We can use these tables to determine sunrise, sunset, twilight and so on.

Coordinated Universal Time (UTC)

UTC is the **local mean time** (LMT) at the meridian of longitude that runs through the observatory at Greenwich, near London. The Greenwich meridian is longitude 0, also known as the **prime meridian**. The international time standard used to be Greenwich Mean Time (GMT), but this term has now been replaced by **coordinated universal time** (UTC). UTC has a more academic definition and is slightly more precise than GMT.

UTC is a 'universal time', and all aeronautical communications around the world are expressed in UTC. For this reason, pilots need to be able to convert quickly and accurately from their local time to UTC, and vice versa.

Meridians to the east are ahead in time, thus:

Longitude east, universal least.

Meridians to the west are behind in time:

Longitude west, universal best.

EXAMPLE 8 If it is 231531 LMT on the 150°E meridian of longitude running through Sydney, Australia, what is the time in UTC (i.e. in the UK on the Greenwich meridian)?

150° = 10 hours, as 15° of arc = 1 hour
and *longitude east, universal least.*

23 15 31 LMT at 150°E
− 10 00   arc to time
23 05 31 UTC

ANSWER 230531 UTC

NOTE Australian Eastern Standard Time is based on the 150°E longitude, which is 10 hours ahead of UTC. Standard Time in Vancouver, British Columbia, Canada, is based on 120°W longitude and is therefore 8 hours behind UTC.

EXAMPLE 9 If it is 282340 on the 138°15′W meridian of longitude, express this LMT in Coordinated Universal Time (UTC).

Converting arc to time: 138°15′ = 9 hr 13 min
and *longitude west, universal best.*

28 23 40 LMT	at 138°15′W
+ 9 13	arc to time
28 32 53	32 hr = 1 day + 8 hr
29 08 53 UTC	

ANSWER 290853 UTC

EXAMPLE 10 Convert 300825 UTC to LMT at the 138°15′W meridian.

138° 15′ = 9 hr 13 min
and *longitude west, universal best.*

30 08 25 UTC	
− 9 13	arc to time (9 from 32 (24 + 8), and carry
29 23 12 LMT	1 over into *days* column)

ANSWER 292312 LMT at 138° 15′W

Zone Time

Obviously Local Mean Time (LMT) is not practical in day-to-day life, because every different meridian of longitude has its own LMT. Ships at sea set their clocks to the LMT of the nearest meridian divisible by 15 (which means that, as 15° = 1 hour, these times will differ from UTC by a whole number of hours).

Even though the ship may not be precisely on that meridian, it means that its clocks will be set to read the same time as the clocks of all the ships in that area or zone, and they will not be too far out of step with the sun – noon at the ship's actual meridian occurring at, or close to, 1200 zone time.

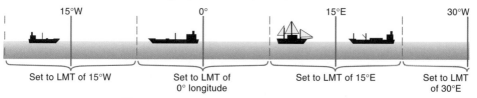

Figure 3-8 **Ships set their clocks according to the local time zone**

For example, a ship at longitude 145°27′E, when considered in proximity to the nearest meridian divisible by 15, is closest to the 150°E meridian of longitude. It would therefore set the LMT at 150°E on its clocks, and as this zone time differs from UTC by (150 ÷ 15) = 10 hours, and (longitude east, universal least) UTC will be 10 hours behind this.

The 150°E zone is called 'zone minus 10' because:

- **the zone meridian** is divisible by fifteen 10 times; and
- **minus 10,** because you need to subtract 10 from this zone time to obtain UTC (remember that east longitudes are ahead in time).

Zone times are not widely used in aviation.

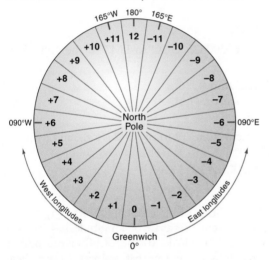

■ *Figure 3-9* **Longitudes as seen from a north polar satellite**

The Date-Line

Suppose that the time at the Greenwich meridian is 261200 LMT (i.e. 261200 UTC). Now, if you instantaneously travel *eastwards* from Greenwich to the 180° East meridian, the Local Mean Time there is 12 hours ahead of the LMT at Greenwich, that is 262400 LMT at 180°E, or midnight on the 26th LMT at 180°E.

If, however, you travel *westwards* from Greenwich to the 180° West meridian, then the time there is 12 hours behind Greenwich, i.e. 260000 or, as it is usually written, 252400 LMT at 180°W, midnight on the 25th. Note that the time is midnight in both cases, but on one side of the 180° meridian it is midnight on the 25th, and on the other side it is midnight on the 26th.

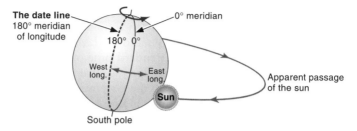

■ *Figure 3-10* **The date-line runs basically along the 180° meridian**

The 180°E and 180°W meridians are one and the same meridian – the anti-meridian to Greenwich. We have the situation of it being midnight in its vicinity, but on different dates, depending on which side of the 180° meridian you are on. Making a complete trip around the world, you would lose a day travelling westwards or gain a day travelling eastwards.

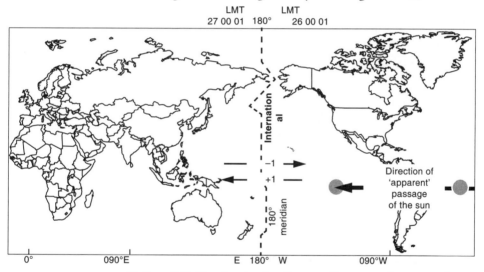

■ *Figure 3-11* **Crossing the date-line travelling east, subtract one day; travelling west, add one day**

To prevent the date being in error and to provide a starting point for each day, a date-line has been fixed by international agreement, and it basically follows the 180° meridian of longitude, with minor excursions to keep groups of islands together. Crossing the date-line, you alter the date by one day – in effect changing your time by 24 hours to compensate for the slow change during your journey around the world.

Standard Times or Local Times

Standard times operate in a similar way to zone time in that all clocks in a given geographical area are set to the LMT of a given standard meridian. This is known as **standard time** or **local time** (not to be confused with Local Mean Time) for that area.

Standard time in the UK is based on the Greenwich meridian. In other words, 1545 standard time in the UK is also 1545 UTC. Standard time in Germany is based on the 15°E meridian of longitude, and so is 1 hour ahead of the UK. At 1545 UTC, the time in London is 1545, and in Hamburg it is 1645 German standard time. In Tokyo, which is 9 hours ahead of UTC, it is 2445, i.e. 0045 Japanese standard time the next morning.

When flights involve travel between different time zones, it is easiest to work entirely in UTC and convert the answer to local time at the end.

EXAMPLE 11 You depart Prestwick, Scotland on a flight of 3 hours 40 minutes duration to Bremen in Germany at 0945 UK standard time, i.e. 0945 UTC. At what time should your German friends meet you in Bremen?

Departure Prestwick:	09 45 UTC
Flight Time:	3 40
ETA Bremen:	13 25 UTC
arc to time:	+1 00 (to convert British to German time)
	14 25

ANSWER 1425 MEZ (German standard time)

Light from the Sun

The sun's rays strike different parts of the earth at different angles depending on latitude and season.

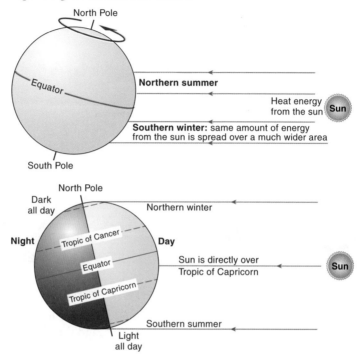

■ *Figure 3-12* ***The sun does not shine evenly on the earth***

Sunrise occurs when the upper limb of the sun (the first part visible) is on the visible horizon. **Sunset** occurs when the upper limb of the sun (the last part visible) is just disappearing below the visible horizon. Sunlight occurs between sunrise and sunset.

As we have all observed when waking early, it starts to become light well before the sun actually rises, and it stays light until well after the sun has set. This period of incomplete light, or if you like, incomplete darkness, is called **twilight**, and the period from the start of morning twilight until the end of evening twilight is called **daylight**.

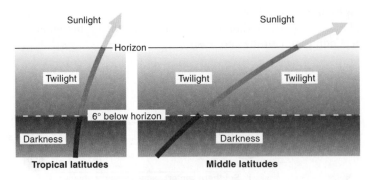

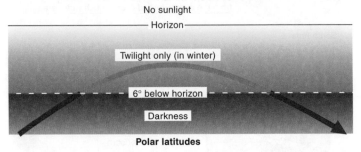

■ *Figure 3-13* **The higher the latitude, the longer the twilight**

In the tropics the sun rises and sets at almost 90° to the horizon, which makes the period of twilight quite short, and the onset of daylight or night dramatically rapid.

In the higher latitudes, towards the North and South Poles, the sun rises and sets at a more oblique angle to the horizon, consequently the period of twilight is much longer and the onset of daylight or darkness far more gradual than in the tropics.

At certain times of the year inside the Arctic and Antarctic Circles, the period of twilight occurs without the sun actually rising above the horizon at all during the day. This is the winter situation.

While to an observer at sea level the sun may appear to have set and the earth is no longer bathed in sunlight, an aeroplane directly overhead may still have the sun shining on it. In other words, the time at which the sun rises or sets will depend on the altitude of the observer.

In fact it is possible to take off after sunset at ground level and climb to an altitude where the sun appears to rise again and shine a little longer on the aeroplane. This is especially noticeable in polar regions when the sun might be just below the horizon, as seen from sea level, for long periods of time (twilight).

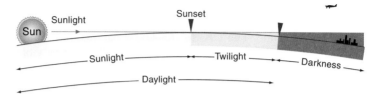

■ *Figure 3-14* **An aeroplane at altitude can be in sight of the sun after it has set on the earth below**

It is easy to be deceived by brightness at altitude only to find a few minutes later after a descent to near ground level, and possibly under some cloud cover, that it has become dark. High ground to the west of the aerodrome will also reduce the amount of light from the sun reaching the vicinity of the aerodrome as night approaches.

■ *Figure 3-15* **Local sunrise and sunset is affected by terrain**

Time of Sunset and Sunrise

The times at which sunrise and sunset occur depend on two things:

- **The date:** In summer sunrise is earliest and sunset later, i.e. the daylight hours are longer in summer. The reverse occurs in winter.
- **The latitude:** In the northern summer for instance, place B in Figure 3–16 experiences sunrise while place A is already well into the day, and it is still night at place C, yet all are on the same meridian of longitude. Because of this they all have the same Local Mean Time (LMT), but are experiencing quite different conditions of daylight due to being on different latitudes.

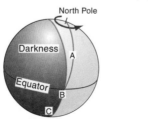

■ *Figure 3-16* **Places A, B and C, although on the same meridian, experience different sunrise and sunset times because they are on different latitudes**

Effect of Latitude on Sunrise and Sunset

The Local Mean Time of sunrise and sunset on a particular date depends on latitude. The *UK Air Almanac* (an annual publication of The United Kingdom Hydrographic Office) contains tables that give Local Mean Time for the occurrence of sunrise and sunset at ground level at different places in the UK. (The *UK Air Almanac* also contains tables for Morning and Evening Civil Twilight, but these are of no significance to air navigation in the UK.)

Effect of Longitude on Sunrise and Sunset

The Local Mean Time of sunrise and sunset depends further on the longitude of the place. Sunrise at places on a particular latitude occurs at the same Local Mean Time at each place but different places on the same latitude will have a different Local Standard Time for the event, depending on their *longitude*. The same applies to sunset.

Fishguard in Wales and Ipswich in Suffolk are both on the same latitude (52°N) but, because their arc of longitude difference is 6° (5°W to 1°E), the sun will rise 6/15 of an hour (24 minutes) earlier at Ipswich than Fishguard. It will set the same amount of time later in Fishguard than Ipswich on Local Standard Time – be it UTC or, in summer, British Summer Time (BST). Also, the sun will rise 1/15 of an hour (4 minutes) earlier at Ipswich than Greenwich.

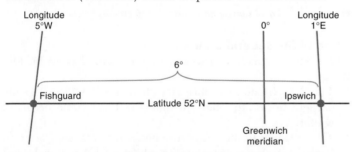

■ *Figure 3-17* **Fishguard and Ipswich experience sunset at the same LMT, but at different local standard times (UTC or BST)**

Sunrise and sunset times are available in the UK AIP GEN 2-7-1 and from ATS Units and Met Offices throughout the UK. Common sense dictates to err on the conservative side, especially for sunset.

Sunrise/sunset tables are published in *Pooley's Flight Guide*.

Robert Pooley ©

824

SUNRISE – SUNSET TABLES

All times are Local, allowances have been made for British Summer Time — 29 March to 25 October 2015

	Jersey	London/ Heathrow	Cardiff	Manchester	Belfast/ Aldergrove	Durham Tees Valley	Glasgow	Inverness	
	EGJJ	EGLL	EGFF	EGCC	EGAA	EGNV	EGPF	EGPE	
Jan 1	0804 1621	0807 1603	0818 1615	0824 1601	0848 1609	0828 1551	0848 1554	0858 1542	Jan 1
8	0802 1629	0805 1612	0816 1624	0822 1610	0845 1618	0825 1600	0845 1604	0854 1552	8
15	0758 1638	0801 1622		0817 1620	0839 1630	0819 1611	0839 1616	0847 1605	15
22	0752 1649		1645	0809 1633	0831 1643	0811 1624	0829 1630	0837 1619	22
28	07		1655	0801 1644	0822 1654	0802 1636	0820 1642	0826 1633	28
Feb 3	07		1706	0751 1655	0811 1707	0752 1648	0809 1655	0814 1646	Feb 3
9	07		1717	0740 1707	0800 1719	0740 1700	0757 1708	0801 1701	9
15	07		0728 1728	0728 1719	0747 1733	0728 1713	0743 1721	0747 1715	15
21	070	0704 1727	0716 1739	0715 1731	0734 1744	0714 1725	0729 1734	0732 1729	21
27	0656 1748	0652 1738	0703 1750	0702 1742	0720 1756	0701 1737	0715 1747	0716 1743	27
Mar 5	0644 1758	0639 1749	0651 1800	0648 1754	0706 1808	0646 1749	0700 1800	0700 1756	Mar 5
11	0631 1807	0626 1759	0637 1810	0634 1805	0651 1820	0632 1801	0644 1812	0644 1810	11
17	0619 1816	0612 1809	0624 1821	0620 1816	0636 1832	0617 1813	0629 1825	0628 1823	17
23	0606 1826	0559 1819	0610 1831	0605 1827	0621 1844	0602 1824	0613 1837	0611 1836	23
29	0653 1935	0645 1929	0657 1941	0651 1938	0706 1955	0647 1936	0657 1949	0654 1949	29
Apr 4	0641 1946	0631 1939	0643 1951	0636 1949	0651 2007	0632 1947	0642 2001	0638 2002	Apr 4
10	0628 1955	0618 1949	0630 2001	0622 2000	0636 2018	0617 1959	0626 2013	0621 2015	10
16	0616 2004	0605 1959	0617 2011	0608 2011	0621 2030	0602 2010	0611 2025	0605 2028	16
22	0605 2013	0552 2009	0604 2021	0555 2022	0607 2041	0548 2021	0556 2038	0549 2042	22
28	0553 2022	0540 2019	0552 2031	0542 2032	0553 2053	0535 2033	0542 2050	0534 2055	28
May 4	0543 2031	0529 2029	0541 2041	0530 2043	0541 2104	0522 2044	0529 2102	0520 2108	May 4

(watermark across table: SAMPLE ONLY – Not to be used for flight operations or flight planning)

■ *Figure 3-18* **Sample excerpt of the sunrise/sunset tables in Pooley's Flight Guide**

Flight operations of light aircraft in the UK, especially by pilots without a night rating, are closely geared to the times of sunrise and sunset. The earliest time at which basic PPL holders can legally fly with passengers is sunrise minus 30 minutes, and they must be on the ground again no later than sunset plus 30 minutes, irrespective of the length of twilight time. (This stems from the Air Navigation Order definition of **night,** which commences at sunset plus 30 minutes and ends at sunrise minus 30 minutes, both times being taken at surface level.)

NOTE Good airmanship may dictate to use an earlier time than SS+30 when planning a flight, if, for example, the destination aerodrome has high ground to the west of it, or the weather forecast indicates poor visibility, or cloud cover approaching from the west, as in a cold front.

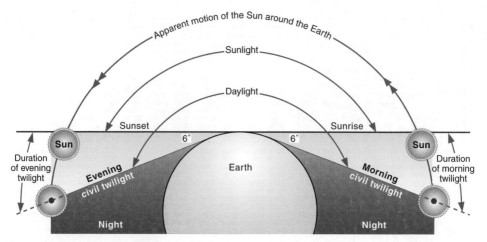

■ Figure 3-19 **In the UK, official night commences at sunset plus**
30 minutes and ends at sunrise minus 30 minutes

Another important consideration related to sunset is that many
smaller airfields in the UK (and throughout Europe) close at
sunset. This may also apply to the alternate aerodrome(s) chosen
for a flight. UK aerodrome operating hours are given in the AD
section of the UK AIP and also in *Pooley's Flight Guide* – the latter
contains details on most private airfields also.

Summer Time
To take advantage of the longer daylight hours and better weather
in summer, the clocks in many countries are put forward, usually
by one hour, to give a new standard time known as **summer time.**

Now complete: **Practice Questions - Time**

1. With the sun coming up, sunrise is said to occur when the:

(a) *Upper limb of the sun (the first bit to become visible) is on the observer's horizon.*

(b) *Centre of the earth's disc is 6° below the observer's horizon.*

(c) *Centre of the earth's disc is on the observer's horizon.*

(d) *Lower limb of the sun is on the observer's horizon.*

2. With the sun's altitude decreasing, sunset occurs when the:

(a) *Upper limb of the sun is on the observer's horizon.*

(b) *Centre of the earth's disc is 6° below the observer's horizon.*

(c) *Centre of the earth's disc is on the observer's horizon.*

(d) *Lower limb of the sun is on the observer's horizon.*

3. Regarding sunset, which of these statements is correct?

(a) *Twilight duration is 60 minutes everywhere in the world.*

(b) *Daylight can end earlier than the published night time when there is cloud cover.*

(c) *Daylight can end earlier than the published night time when there is high ground to the east of the location.*

(d) *Twilight duration increases as latitude reduces.*

4. The earliest time a PPL holder can legally fly in the United Kingdom with passengers is:

(a) *Sunrise.*

(b) *Sunrise minus 30 minutes.*

(c) *When centre of the rising sun's disc is 6° below the horizon.*

(d) *When centre of the rising sun's disc is 6° above the horizon.*

The Magnetic Compass and Direction

Direction is obviously of prime importance to accurate navigation. As aircraft navigate with reference to the earth's surface, we will begin with a brief look at the earth itself.

There is a geographical axis passing through two physical points on the surface of the earth about which the planet rotates. These points are the *geographic* North and South Poles. Any 'straight' line drawn around the earth's surface joining these two points is aligned in a true north–south direction.

By convention, the basic reference direction is **north**, and other directions are measured clockwise from this reference in degrees (°). Since there are 360° in a circle, **east** is described as 090°, **south** as 180°, **west** as 270°, and **north** as 000° or 360°. Any direction (be it the desired track of an aeroplane, or the direction from which the wind is blowing) can be defined in this way.

True Direction

If direction is described with reference to **true north** (the direction to the geographic North Pole), it is called the **true direction,** symbolised by 'T'. East is therefore written as 090°T or 090T. The track between town A and town B illustrated below is 327°T.

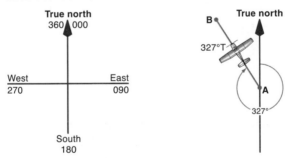

■ *Figure 4-1* **True direction**

A more approximate means of describing direction is using the **cardinal points,** which are the four chief directions of north, south, east and west – further divided by the **quadrantal points** north-east, south-east, south-west and north-west. If necessary, these can be divided even further to give, for instance, NNW (nor-nor-west). Obviously, the 360° method is superior for aeronautical navigation.

True direction, however, is a problem for pilots, because most aeroplanes do not have an instrument that can determine the direction of true north. The magnetic compass, the prime source of directional information in the cockpit, aligns itself with **magnetic north,** rather than with true north.

NOTE As you will see, this statement does not hold true if there are extraneous magnetic fields, say due to radios or nearby magnetic materials, that are strong enough to affect the magnet within the compass. At this stage, we will assume that the magnet is influenced only by the earth's magnetic field and none other.

Magnetic Direction

Near to the true (geographic) North Pole is an area from which the earth's magnetic field emanates, known as the **north magnetic pole** to avoid confusion with the geographic pole. Similarly, there is a **south magnetic pole** located near the true South Pole.

A small magnet that is suspended and free to move will seek to align itself with these roughly north–south lines of magnetic force. This is the basis of the **magnetic compass.** If a compass card is attached to a magnetic 'needle', then the magnetic heading of an aeroplane can be read-off against a **lubber line,** or index, on the compass face.

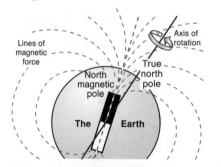 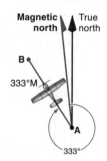

■ Figure 4-2 **Magnetic direction**

A direction defined by reference to the north-seeking end of a magnetic compass is known as a **magnetic direction.** In Figure 4-2, the direction between the same two towns, A and B, is now described as 333°M.

The actual direction between the two towns of course has not changed, only our description of it has, because of the two different reference directions, TN and MN. In the above case, 327°T and 333°M are the same physical direction described differently.

Direction Related to Magnetic North

Why introduce the complication of degrees related to magnetic north? Because the simple magnetic compass is the most reliable source of directional information. Instruments that display direction relative to true north are both complicated and expensive, and subject to certain operational limitations not associated with the conventional magnetic compass. Even in the most sophisticated aircraft flying today, a simple magnetic compass is installed.

In most light aircraft, the magnetic compass is the primary source of directional information, to which other heading or direction indicators (often gyroscopic) are aligned.

■ *Figure 4-3* **The magnetic compass**

To obtain accurate directional information from the magnetic compass, you must understand how it operates, and also its inaccuracies while the aeroplane is turning or changing speed. This is covered fully in the *Flight Instruments* section of Vol. 4 of this series. A summary follows here.

A bar magnet that is freely suspended horizontally will swing so that its axis points roughly north–south. The end of the magnet that points towards the earth's north magnetic pole is called the **north-seeking pole** of the magnet.

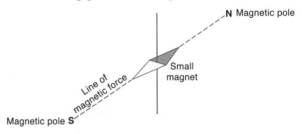

■ *Figure 4-4* **Simple bar magnet**

The Earth's Magnetic Field (Terrestrial Magnetism)

The earth acts like a very large and weak magnet. Its surface is covered by a weak magnetic field – lines of magnetic force that begin deep within the earth near Hudson Bay in Canada and flow towards a point deep within the earth near South Victoria Land in Antarctica. Because of their proximity to the *geographic* North and South Poles, the magnetic poles are referred to as the **north magnetic pole** and the **south magnetic pole**.

Variation

The latitude-longitude grid shown on charts is based on the geographic poles at either extremity of the earth's axis of rotation, so the **meridians of longitude** run true north and true south, and the **parallels of latitude** run true east and true west.

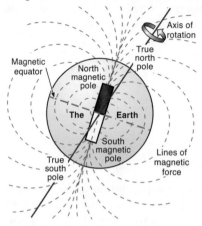

■ *Figure 4-5* **The earth has a magnetic field**

Our small compass magnet, however, does not point exactly at true north and true south. A magnetic compass, if it is working perfectly and is influenced only by the earth's magnetic field, will point at the north *magnetic* pole, near Hudson Bay in Canada. At most points on the earth this is a different direction from true north. The angular difference between true north and magnetic north at any particular point on the earth is called the **magnetic variation** at that point.

If the magnet points slightly east of true north, the variation is *east*. If the magnet points to the west of true north, the variation is *west*. West variation is experienced over the entire UK.

Variation at any point on the earth is measured from true north to magnetic north. For example, a magnetic compass in London will point ½° west of true north, i.e. the magnetic variation is ½°W, since magnetic north lies ½° west of true north. In Liverpool the magnetic variation is 2°W.

Variation is the angular difference from true north to magnetic north.

NOTE Because the earth's magnetic poles are not stationary, variation changes over time. In the British Isles variation reduces by 7–8 minutes annually (about 1° every 8 years).

Isogonals

As well as the lines forming the latitude-longitude grids, maps have other lines joining places that have the same magnetic variation. These lines are known as **isogonals** or **isogonic lines**. On the UK 1:500,000 aeronautical chart, the isogonals are shown as dashed lines coloured blue.

The 2° west isogonal joins all the places having a variation of 2° west. If you are anywhere on this line, then the message that your compass is giving you about magnetic north can be related to true north; your compass will point at magnetic north, which will be 2° west of true north.

> **Isogonals** are lines on a chart joining places of equal magnetic variation.

To assist you in choosing the magnetic variation in your area, CAA 1:500,000 UK aeronautical charts show half-degree isogonals. Between these lines you use the appropriate whole number of variation, as shown in Figure 4-6. Please note that this diagram is not a true representation of the position in 2015, but has been included for illustration purposes only.

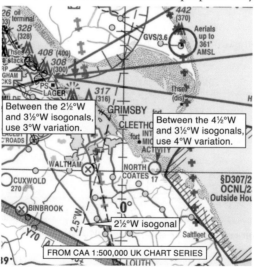

■ Figure 4-6 **Variation is the angle between true and magnetic**

If magnetic north is to the west of true north (west variation), then °M will exceed °T. Conversely, if magnetic north is to the east of true north (east variation), then °M will be less than °T. An easy way to remember the relationship between true and magnetic is:

> Variation west, magnetic best.   Variation east, magnetic least.

EXAMPLE 1 You are steering your aircraft on a heading of 300°M with reference to the magnetic compass. From an aeronautical chart you determine that magnetic variation in the vicinity is 4°W. What is the true heading of the aircraft?

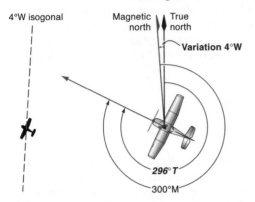

■ *Figure 4-7* **Variation west, magnetic best; answer 296°T**

EXAMPLE 2 Convert 100°T to a magnetic direction in an area where variation is 10°E.

100°T
−10°E (Variation east, magnetic least)
090°M *(Answer)*

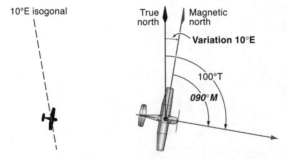

■ *Figure 4-8* **Variation east, magnetic least; answer 090°M**

The Agonic Line
The isogonal that joins places that have zero variation (i.e. magnetic north and true north coincide) is called the **agonic line.** It passes through Europe.

Compass Deviation
Unfortunately, the magnet in the magnetic compass is affected not only by the magnetic field of the earth, but by any magnetic field that exists in its vicinity, such as the magnetic fields surrounding the metal structure of the aeroplane, rotating parts in the engine,

the radios, etc. The effect of these additional magnetic fields in a particular aeroplane is to deviate or deflect the compass from indicating magnetic north precisely. This imprecision is known as **compass deviation.**

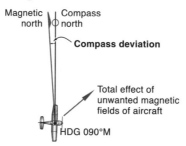

■ *Figure 4-9* **Compass deviation**

Deviation varies according to the heading that the aeroplane is on, since these unwanted extra magnetic fields are related to the aeroplane itself. If their resultant is diagonal to the longitudinal axis of the aeroplane (Figure 4-10) then, when the aeroplane is steering 045°, or its reciprocal 225°, it will be aligned with the earth's magnetic field and will not cause the compass needle to deviate. In other words, on these headings, compass deviation is zero.

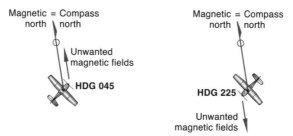

■ *Figure 4-10* **Compass deviation nil in this aeroplane on these headings**

If, on the other hand, the aeroplane is heading east, the alignment of the unwanted magnetic fields will deviate the compass as shown by the deviation card in Figure 4-13. The compass needle will then point towards a *compass north* that is slightly to the east of magnetic north in this case (by 1°). Even though the magnetic heading might be 090°M, the compass will indicate 089°.

An easy way to remember the relationship between magnetic and compass directions is:

Deviation east, compass least.   Deviation west, compass best.

EXAMPLE 3 An aircraft is flying with a heading of 257° indicated on the magnetic compass in the cockpit. If, on that heading, deviation is 3°W, what is the aeroplane's magnetic heading?

257°C (compass)
$\underline{-3}$ (Deviation west, compass best)
254°M *(Answer)*

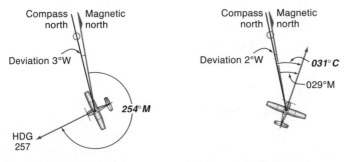

■ *Figure 4-11* **Example 3**   ■ *Figure 4-12* **Example 4**

EXAMPLE 4 What compass direction must be steered to achieve a magnetic heading of 029°M, if the compass deviation is 2° west?

Deviation west, compass best: 029°M + 2 = 031°C *(Answer)*

The Compass Deviation Card

Rather than continually having to carry out deviation corrections to the compass headings, a simpler approach is for each aircraft to have a small placard known as the deviation card displayed near the compass. This card shows the pilot what corrections need to be made to the actual magnetic compass reading (described as °C, for compass) in order to obtain the desired magnetic direction in °M. This correction usually involves no more than a few degrees (and in fact, the correction may be so small that the pilot does not apply it).

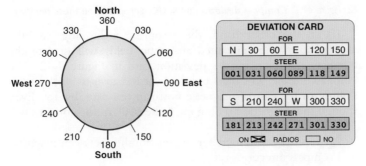

■ *Figure 4-13* **A compass rose and compass deviation card. To achieve a magnetic heading of 270° using this compass, steer 271°C.**

> **Deviation** is the angular distance from magnetic north to compass north for that particular compass, with the aircraft on that particular heading.

Precautions When Carrying Magnetic or Metal Goods

The compass deviation card is filled out by an engineer who has checked the compass in that particular aeroplane with it pointing in different directions. It may be done with electrical services off, or with them on (which is the normal in-flight situation). Electrical services, such as radios, often generate their own magnetic fields and may affect the compass indication.

The compass deviation correction card allows only for the magnetic influences in the aeroplane that were present when the engineer calibrated the compass in a procedure known as *swinging the compass*.

Any other magnetic influences introduced into the aeroplane at a time following the swinging of the compass will not be allowed for, even though they can significantly affect the compass. Therefore, as pilot, ensure that no metal or magnetic materials, such as metal pens, clipboards, books with metal binders, key rings, headsets, electronic calculators, transistor radios, or other devices that generate magnetic fields are placed anywhere near the compass.

Such magnetic or metal materials placed near the compass may introduce large and unpredictable errors. Many pilots have been lost or 'temporarily uncertain of their position' as a result of random deviations in the compass readings caused by these extraneous magnetic fields.

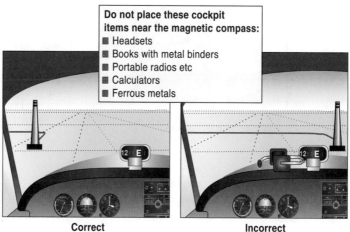

Do not place these cockpit items near the magnetic compass:
- Headsets
- Books with metal binders
- Portable radios etc
- Calculators
- Ferrous metals

Correct   Incorrect

■ Figure 4-14 **Keep foreign objects away from the magnetic compass**

Relating True, Magnetic and Compass Headings

1. **HDG(C) is the actual heading** that you observe on the magnetic compass in the cockpit. It relates to compass north for that particular compass in that particular aeroplane on that particular heading.

2. **Either refer to the deviation card,** or apply 'Deviation east, compass least; deviation west, compass best', to convert HDG(C) to HDG(M). The aeroplane has not changed its direction in space, but its heading is now related to *magnetic north* rather than *compass north* (since the peculiarities of that particular compass have been accounted for and corrected). Usually this correction for deviation is insignificant and is often disregarded.

3. **Apply variation** (found on a chart) to HDG(M) to convert it to HDT(T), which is the heading of the aeroplane related to the geographic poles, known as the North and South Poles or the *true poles*. The correction for variation can be large and should always be applied (and in the right sense – applying 6°W variation as if it were 6°E variation will give you a 12° error). Remember: 'Variation east, magnetic least; variation west, magnetic best.'

The above process takes you from *degrees compass* to *degrees magnetic* to *degrees true*. It is just as easy to carry out the reverse process to go from °T to °M to °C.

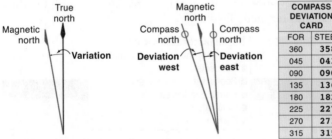

■ *Figure 4-15* **Variation and deviation**

EXAMPLE 5

Aircraft heading	020°T	
Variation	7°W	
Aircraft heading	027°M	
Deviation	2°E	
Aircraft heading	025°C	*(Answer)*

EXAMPLE 6

Aircraft heading	025°C
Deviation	2°E
Aircraft heading	027°M
Variation	7°W
Aircraft heading	020°T *(Answer)*

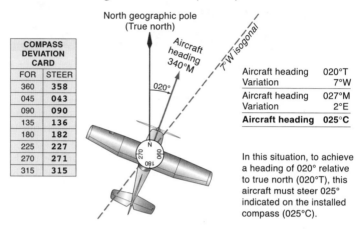

COMPASS DEVIATION CARD	
FOR	**STEER**
360	**358**
045	**043**
090	**090**
135	**136**
180	**182**
225	**227**
270	**271**
315	**315**

North geographic pole
(True north)

Aircraft heading 340°M

020°

7°W isogonal

Aircraft heading	020°T
Variation	7°W
Aircraft heading	027°M
Variation	2°E
Aircraft heading	**025°C**

In this situation, to achieve a heading of 020° relative to true north (020°T), this aircraft must steer 025° indicated on the installed compass (025°C).

■ *Figure 4-16* **The relationship of compass heading, magnetic heading and true heading with variation and deviation**

The maximum accuracy we consider practical in navigation is 1°, hence there is no need for us to consider the further subdivision of 1° into 60 minutes and each of these minutes into 60 seconds. Only apply a variation or deviation correction accurate to the nearest degree.

Pilot Serviceability Checks on the Magnetic Compass

- **Pre-flight,** check that the compass is securely installed and can be read easily. The liquid in which the magnet is suspended should be free of bubbles and should not be discoloured. The glass should not be broken, cracked or discoloured, and it should be secure.
- **Check the position** of the compass deviation card.
- **Check that the compass indication** is at least approximately correct. Runways are named according to their magnetic direction (e.g. a runway pointing 243°M is called Runway 24), so when pointing in the same direction as this runway, your compass should indicate this, at least approximately.
- **When taxiing out** prior to take-off, turn the aircraft left and right and check that the response of the magnetic compass is correct. Remember that the magnet should remain in the same north–south direction, and the aeroplane turn around it.

■ *Figure 4-17* **Always cross-check compass direction**

Magnetic Dip and Compass Errors

The earth's magnetic field is weak, and varies in strength and direction over the entire surface of the earth. The strength of the magnetic field can be resolved into two components:

- **a horizontal component** parallel to the surface of the earth, which is used to align the compass needle with magnetic north; and
- **a vertical component,** which causes the magnetic needle to dip down.

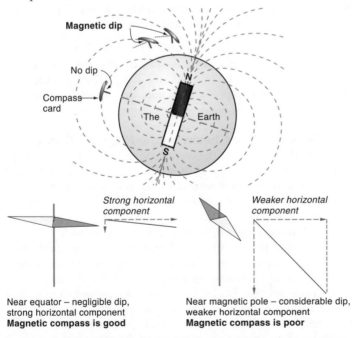

Near equator – negligible dip, strong horizontal component
Magnetic compass is good

Near magnetic pole – considerable dip, weaker horizontal component
Magnetic compass is poor

■ *Figure 4-18* **The horizontal component of the earth's magnetic field is strong near the equator and weak near the poles**

A magnetic compass indicates direction more accurately at middle and low latitudes than near the poles.

At the so-called 'magnetic equator' (roughly mid–way between the magnetic poles), the lines of magnetic force are parallel with the earth's surface (i.e. they are horizontal). Consequently, the horizontal component of the earth's magnetic field is at its strongest here and so the magnetic compass is stable and accurate in these areas.

At the higher latitudes near the magnetic poles, where the lines of magnetic force run in through the earth's surface, the vertical component of the earth's magnetic field causing dip is stronger, and the horizontal component parallel to the surface of the earth is weaker. This makes the compass less effective as an indicator of horizontal direction in the polar regions compared with its performance at the lower latitudes.

At latitudes higher than 60 degrees north or south (i.e. closer to the poles than 60°N or S), the magnetic compass is not very reliable at all.

As a means of avoiding the compass needle *dipping* down in line with the magnetic force, it is suspended in a manner that displaces its centre of gravity (CG) from the pivot point at which it is suspended (and indirectly attached to the aeroplane structure).

The greater the dip, the more the needle dips down towards the nearer magnetic pole, and the more its CG is displaced. This causes the weight force to *balance* the dip force and to keep the needle approximately horizontal.

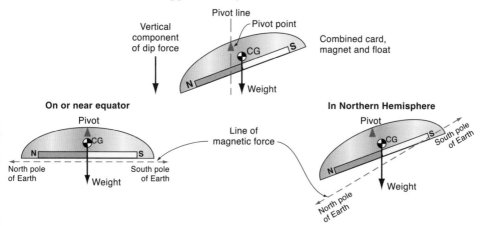

■ Figure 4-19 **To minimise the effect of magnetic dip, the needle's CG is displaced**

Turning and Acceleration Errors

Any acceleration of the aeroplane will be transmitted to the compass needle via its pivot. The needle's CG will tend to continue at its previous velocity and so will be left behind in an acceleration, and will move ahead in a deceleration. In a turn, the aeroplane (and the pivot) is accelerating towards the centre of the turn, with the CG trying to 'fly off at a tangent'.

Indication errors in the magnetic compass and what causes them is covered in detail in Vol. 4 of *The Air Pilot's Manual*. It will suffice here to summarise the effect of these errors on the magnetic compass indications (which you should know for the examination in this subject):

TURNING ERRORS. are greatest when turning through headings of magnetic north or south (and zero when turning through headings of east or west).

When heading towards the nearer magnetic pole, the magnetic compass is 'sluggish' and will under-indicate the amount of turn (for both left and right turns). You should stop the turn before the magnetic compass indicates your desired heading. Once settled into steady straight and level flight, the compass will settle down and (hopefully) indicate your desired heading. If not, make minor adjustments to your heading.

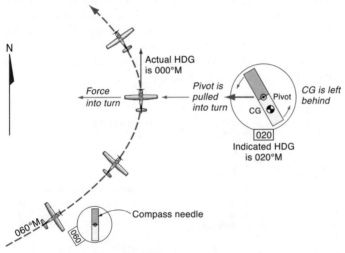

■ *Figure 4-20* **The compass is sluggish and lags behind when turning through north (in the northern hemisphere)**

In the case illustrated in Figure 4-20, an aeroplane flying initially on a heading of 060°M is turning left through north. The CG tends to fly off at a tangent and so the compass card rotates anticlockwise, thereby under-indicating the amount of turn. For example, when the aeroplane is turning through 000°M (magnetic north), the compass is only indicating 020°M.

When heading towards the more distant magnetic pole, the magnetic compass is 'lively' and will over-indicate the amount of turn. You should continue the turn through your desired heading as indicated on the magnetic compass during the turn. Once settled into steady straight and level flight, the compass will settle down and (hopefully) indicate your desired heading. If not, make minor adjustments to your heading.

ACCELERATION ERRORS are maximum on east and west magnetic headings (and zero on north and south headings).

Acceleration produces a false indication of turning towards the nearer magnetic pole (i.e. towards north in the northern hemisphere). Increasing speed (accelerating) towards the east will cause the compass needle and its attached card to rotate clockwise, causing a false indication of say 080° (instead of 090°). Another way of looking at this is that, on accelerating in an easterly direction, the centre of gravity is left behind, causing the compass card to rotate to the right. This gives a *false* indication of a turn towards north.

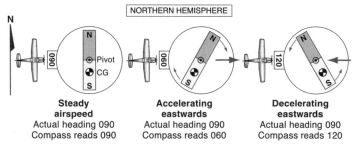

Steady
airspeed
Actual heading 090
Compass reads 090

Accelerating
eastwards
Actual heading 090
Compass reads 060

Decelerating
eastwards
Actual heading 090
Compass reads 120

■ *Figure 4-21* **Acceleration east produces a false indication of a turn towards the north**

Considering an acceleration on a westerly heading, again the centre of gravity is left behind, the compass card in this case turning anticlockwise and indicating (incorrectly) a turn towards north.

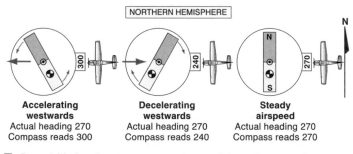

Accelerating
westwards
Actual heading 270
Compass reads 300

Decelerating
westwards
Actual heading 270
Compass reads 240

Steady
airspeed
Actual heading 270
Compass reads 270

■ *Figure 4-22* **Acceleration west produces a false indication of a turn towards north**

Conversely, deceleration on an easterly or westerly heading produces a false indication of turning towards the further magnetic pole (i.e. towards south in the northern hemisphere).

If the aeroplane is heading north or south, the pivot supporting the compass needle and the needle's centre of gravity are in line, and so the needle will not be displaced by accelerations or decelerations in the north–south directions.

On intermediate headings, the acceleration error will increase with the proximity of the aeroplane's heading to east or west.

EXAMPLE 7 You are flying in the UK. When turning from 150°M through south onto a heading of 220° using the magnetic compass, because it will over-indicate the amount of turn, you should continue the turn beyond a compass indication of 220 (say by 10°) and then level the wings and allow the compass to settle down.

EXAMPLE 8 You are flying in Scotland and accelerating from 80 kt to 150 kt on an easterly heading. Even though, by reference to a point on the horizon, you are still heading east, the needle of the magnetic compass will swing in a clockwise direction and indicate an apparent turn to the north. Once you attain a steady speed and allow the compass to settle down, it should indicate the correct heading again.

The Direction or Heading Indicator

Most light aircraft instrument panels include a gyroscopic **direction indicator (DI)**. This instrument is also known as the **heading indicator (HI)** or **directional gyro (DG)**.

Being a gyro-based instrument, its indication is steady compared to that of the magnetic compass but, due to the fact that the earth is rotating (at 15° per hour) and the direction indicator's axis is fixed in space by the gyroscope, the direction indicator has to be re-aligned with a known reference direction at regular intervals.

The magnetic compass is used as the reference for the direction indicator and so, when aligned with the compass, the DI will indicate the heading of the aircraft in degrees magnetic.

■ *Figure 4-23*
Direction indicator (DI)

NOTE Do not align the direction indicator (DI) with the magnetic compass if you are changing speed or direction, as the magnetic compass will be experiencing acceleration or turning errors, i.e. keep the wings level and maintain a constant speed when aligning the DI with the compass.

One of the advantages of a direction indicator is that it is not subject to turning or acceleration errors. Its accuracy depends on it being correctly aligned with magnetic north, so this must be done when the magnetic compass is indicating correctly.

Now complete: **Practice Questions - Magnetic Compass**

1. The angle between the earth's magnetic field and the horizontal is referred to as:

(a) *Deviation.*
(b) *Variation.*
(c) *Slip or 'z'.*
(d) *Dip or 'z'.*

2. As latitude decreases, the effect on the earth's magnetic field is that the:

(a) *Horizontal component increases; dip angle decreases.*
(b) *Vertical component increases; dip angle decreases.*
(c) *Horizontal component decreases; dip angle increases.*
(d) *Vertical component decreases; dip angle increases.*

3. A magnetic compass is designed to use the horizontal component of the earth's magnetic field. The compass will be most accurate:

(a) *At mid-latitudes, around 45° north or south.*
(b) *At low latitudes.*
(c) *At either 33°N or 33°S.*
(d) *Over the magnetic pole.*

4. An aircraft is maintaining a compass heading of 315°C, the deviation is 1°E, the true heading is 324°T. What is the magnetic variation?

(a) *8°E*
(b) *10°E*
(c) *10°W*
(d) *8°W*

5. You are flying and maintaining a heading of 179°C. From the compass card you know that the deviation is 4° W, the magnetic variation in the area is 9°W. What is the aircraft's true heading?

(a) *177°T*
(b) *166°T*
(c) *192°T*
(d) *190°T*

6. You are flying and maintaining a true heading of 255° T. The magnetic variation in the area is 6° E, and from the compass card you know that the deviation is 2° W. What is the aircraft's compass heading?

(a) *248°C*
(b) *248°T*
(c) *251°C*
(d) *244°C*

Section **Two**

Pre-Flight Planning

Introduction to Pre-Flight Planning

Cross country routes must always be flown with reference to a written route plan and a current aeronautical chart clearly marked with route segments. This applies whether or not you intend to supplement dead reckoning navigation with radio navigation aids including GPS.

Pre-flight planning commences by identifying a route using the principles of threat and error management whilst aiming to minimise the distance flown for economic and environmental reasons. The route is generally broken down into route segments or 'legs' that will be discussed in the next section. Additional information is then added to the chart to facilitate in-flight navigation, e.g. wind information and drift lines to assist you to maintain your planned track.

The written route plan is usually captured using a pilot or flight log form. There are various forms of flight log and your flying school will generally provide you with the type it prefers.

Pilot: *P.Pilot*					Aircraft: *GABCD*			Date: *21 09 2015*				Depart' Time:		
From/To	Safety Alt.	Alt. Temp.	CAS	TAS	W/V	TRK °T	Drift	HDG °T	Var.	HDG °M	GS	Dist	Time	ETA
											Total			

■ *Figure 5-1* **Typical Flight Log Form**

We have included a number of typical flight logs in this section. The flight log must contain, at the very least, for each leg of the route:

• Magnetic headings that take into account the impact of magnetic and compass deviation and wind speed and direction on the aircraft.
• The minimum safe VFR altitude and the planned altitude.
• The intended true airspeed to be flown and the corresponding groundspeed.
• The distance, time and fuel required including the time available on reserve fuel. This should also be totalled for the entire flight.

- The facility to enter the estimated time of arrival (ETA) and actual time of arrival (ATA) at check points and turning points.

It is important that, in addition to the main route to the destination airfield, the above considerations are extended to diversion routes to alternate aerodromes.

This section will consider each element of the pre-flight planning process, in turn. The aim is to explain how to prepare a chart and flight log for a VFR cross country flight.

The Route Plan

E nsure that you are using the latest chart edition and that you have updated the information on the chart from the CAA website at **www.caa.co.uk**. Erase all information marked on the chart from previous flights carefully.

Planning the Route

Draw in your intended route, divided into segments, each terminating in a turning point, the final destination aerodrome or an alternate aerodrome. Suitable diversion aerodromes should be identified and built into the planning process in case of deteriorating weather, radio or mechanical failure.

Preferred turning points have line features that lead you to them, e.g. rivers, valleys, railways, roads, ridges and tree lines. Large built-up areas make poor turning points, due to their size and the need to glide clear in the event of engine failure.

Using threat and error management principles, analyse the route to see whether it crosses the following features:

- Major hazards, e.g. high ground or remote areas
- Controlled airspace
- Aerodromes with or without active Aerodrome Traffic Zones (ATZ) and Military Aerodrome Traffic Zones (MATZ)
- Prohibited, Restricted or Danger Areas
- ATS Advisory Routes
- The extended centre line of a runway supporting an instrument approach procedure indicated by a 'feather' or 'cone' symbol.
- Sites supporting gliding, parachuting, paragliding, hang gliding and microlight operations
- Air navigation obstructions, e.g. radio transmission masts
- High Intensity Radio Transmission Areas (HIRTA)
- Bird sanctuaries
- Temporary restrictions communicated by Mauve Air Information Circulars or NOTAMS, e.g. air displays.

If any of these features affect the route, either by being overflown or by being selected as turning points, it may be sensible to change the route. Certain route features, e.g. controlled airspace, may require permission to access and contingency diversion routes will need to be planned in the event that access is denied.

Vertical navigation will be dealt with in Chapter 7, however it is also important to check the route for high ground and air navigation obstructions. A slightly longer track to avoid high ground and obstructions is prudent, particularly for flights in poor visibility and low cloud also where weather conditions might deteriorate.

The Measurement of Bearings on Charts

The track between two points on your route, e.g. the departure and destination aerodromes or an intermediate turning point, will be an approximate great circle on Lambert's Conformal Conic Charts such as the ICAO 1:500,000 series commonly used in the UK.

The direction, or bearing, to fly will be the same as that of the rhumb line at the mid-meridian of longitude. It is therefore best practice to measure direction at the mid-meridian, usually taken at the closest meridian to the mid-point of the route segment or leg.

The true bearing, or direction, of the leg to fly is measured against true north, using either a protractor or a plotter, and described by the angle of the track relative to true north in the first instance. For practical navigation, the true bearing will be converted to a magnetic bearing to enable navigational aids based on the magnetic compass.

Measuring the direction requires strict attention and careful checking because an error can cause serious problems in flight. Always estimate the direction before measuring accurately with a protractor or plotter. For example, the track from Shoreham to Lydd is approximately 080°T. This estimate guides the accurate measurement and prevents errors associated with misreading an incorrectly aligned protractor or gross errors where the protractor is not properly aligned with true north.

Always estimate a direction before measuring accurately.

Measuring Direction with a Protractor

The best way to measure direction with a protractor is to align its north–south axis with true north along the mid-meridian and then to read off the direction on the outer scale. (You can also measure the direction by aligning the axis of the protractor with the track and measuring the direction against the inner scale.)

Once again it is vital that you have an approximate value in mind prior to using the protractor so that you avoid any gross errors, such as being out by 90° or 180°.

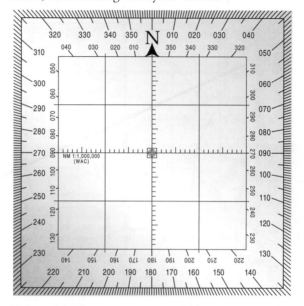

■ *Figure 6-1* **The square protractor is the type commonly used in aviation**

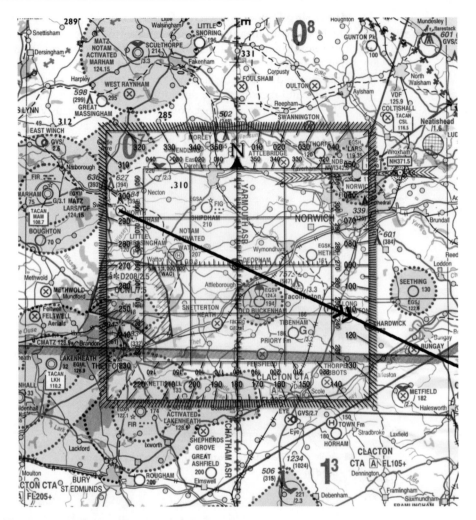

■ Figure 6-2 *Measuring direction with a protractor*

Measuring Direction with a Plotter

A plotter is a simple device that combines the functions of a scale rule and a protractor. An advantage is that only one instrument is required to measure track and distance, instead of two. This is significant for doing such measurements in the cockpit.

Prior to any accurate measurements of direction, you should always have an idea of the approximate direction (to within 20° or 30°) in mind. This avoids gross errors.

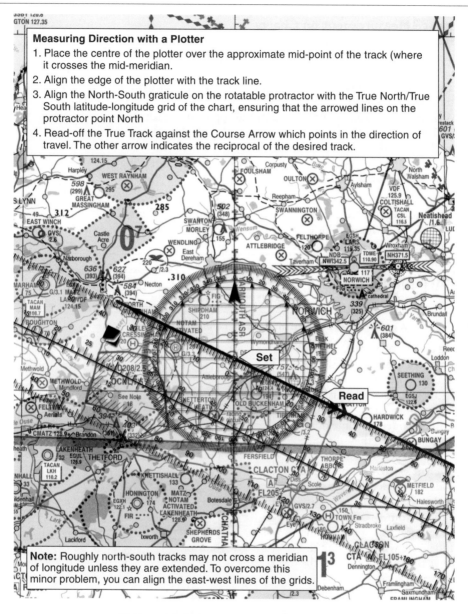

Measuring Direction with a Plotter

1. Place the centre of the plotter over the approximate mid-point of the track (where it crosses the mid-meridian.

2. Align the edge of the plotter with the track line.

3. Align the North-South graticule on the rotatable protractor with the True North/True South latitude-longitude grid of the chart, ensuring that the arrowed lines on the protractor point North

4. Read-off the True Track against the Course Arrow which points in the direction of travel. The other arrow indicates the reciprocal of the desired track.

Note: Roughly north-south tracks may not cross a meridian of longitude unless they are extended. To overcome this minor problem, you can align the east-west lines of the grids.

■ *Figure 6-3* **Measuring track direction with a plotter**
(note the scales for measuring distance)

Distance Measurement on Charts

Measuring distance is relatively straightforward. Again, it is good practice to estimate the distance and then measure it accurately using either:

- a scale rule or plotter, ensuring that the correct scale is used if more than one is available; or
- dividers, which can be placed against the appropriate scale line at the bottom of the chart or the latitude scale at the side

Distance can be measured with an accuracy to within 1 nm using one of the following methods:

1.THE GRADUATED SCALE LINE.   This is at the bottom of most charts. Using dividers, transfer the distance of the route segment on the chart down onto the scale line.

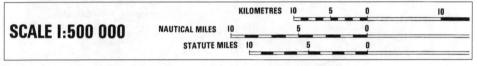

■ *Figure 6-4 **A graduated scale line is included on aeronautical charts***

2. THE LATITUDE SCALE. This is a graticule found on the side of each chart. At all points on earth for all practical purposes, 1 minute of latitude = 1 nm.

Using dividers or some other means, transfer the distance between the two positions on the chart across onto the latitude scale. (Because the scale over the whole chart may vary slightly from latitude to latitude, use that part of the latitude scale which is about the same as the mid–latitude of the track that you are considering.)

The number of minute divisions then gives you the distance in nautical miles.

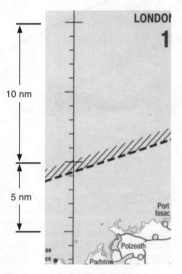

■ *Figure 6-5 **Latitude scales***

3. SCALE RULE. Navigation scales, rules and plotters are designed to measure distances on the 1:500,000 and 1:250,000 (and even 1:1,000,000) charts. Make sure that you are reading the distance off the chart against the correct scale line for that particular chart.

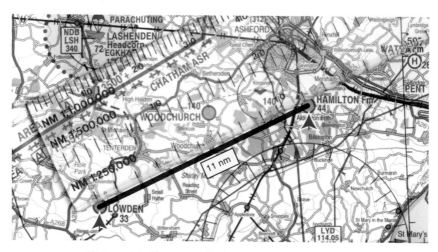

■ Figure 6-6 **Measuring the distance with a scale rule**

Conversion of True to Magnetic Bearings

Magnetic variation is required to convert true bearings to magnetic bearings. The magnetic variation is indicated on the chart by isogonals, a dashed blue line annotated with 0.5°W or whatever the local variation happens to be. Magnetic variation is generally rounded up: the whole number that applies between the isogonals is used, e.g. 1°W between the 0.5°W and 1.5°W isogonals.

This process step is often neglected in the UK where magnetic variation is small. It is good practice to get into the habit of making this correction as you may fly in regions where it is significant, e.g. Oregon in the US where magnetic variation is 17.0°E.

NOTE The conversion of magnetic heading to compass heading is good practice. This is discussed in Chapter 4 where use of the compass deviation card is explained. Normally, in well-maintained aircraft, compass deviation is small and usually neglected. It is important that you consult the aircraft's compass deviation card, located on or near the magnetic compass, to ensure that this approximation is valid.

Example Prepared Chart and Flight Log

Figure 6.8 shows a 1:500,000 aeronautical chart marked with a flight from Shoreham back to Shoreham via Lydd and Southend. Track lines have been added and the route direction is highlighted by the addition of double arrows pointing in the direction of flight.

In this case, the planner has determined that the magnetic variation is 1.5°W.

The route has been broken down into 4 legs. The initial leg to Lydd is direct, as is the case with the leg from Lydd to Southend. The planner has elected not to fly directly from Southend back to Shoreham which would involve penetration of Gatwick Class D airspace. Instead, and to avoid complication, the planner has introduced Uckfield as a turning point.

The associated flight log is shown in Figure 6.7

Pilot: *P Pilot*					Aircraft: *GABCD*			Date: *21 09 2015*				Depart' Time:		
From/To	Safety Alt.	Alt. Temp.	CAS	TAS	W/V	TRK °T	Drift	HDG °T	Var.	HDG °M	GS	Dist	Time	ETA
Shoreham *Lydd*						082			2°W			47		
Lydd *Southend*						346			2°W			38		
Southend *Uckfield*						212			2°W			42		
Uckfield *Shoreham*						241			2°W			17		
										Total		144		

■ *Figure 6-7* **Flight log with track, variation and distance details obained from the Aeronautical chart plot.**

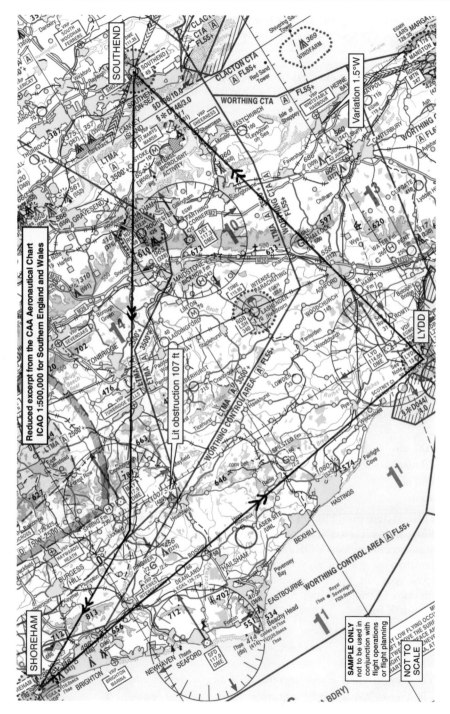

■ Figure 6-8 **Route of the flight on the 1:5000 000 chart (not to scale).**

Now complete: **Practice Questions - The Route Plan**

1. You plan a route segment (leg) from Gloucestershire (EGBJ) to Northampton/Sywell (EGBK). The true track for this leg is?

    (a) *064°T*
    (b) *084°T*
    (c) *244°T*
    (d) *044°T*

2. You plan a route segment (leg) from Gloucestershire (EGBJ) to Peterborough Sibson (EGSP). The magnetic track for this leg is?

    (a) *160°M*
    (b) *240°M*
    (c) *065°M*
    (d) *060°M*

3. The distance for the leg from Gloucestershire (EGBJ) to Northampton/Sywell (EGBK) is:

    (a) *102 nm*
    (b) *56 nm*
    (c) *112 nm*
    (d) *23 nm*

4. The distance from Norwich (EGSH) to Humberside (EGNJ) is:

    (a) *100 nm*
    (b) *80 nm*
    (c) *160 nm*
    (d) *40 nm*

5. You plan a route from Humberside (EGNJ) to Bridlington over two legs with a turning point at the Ottringham VOR/DME beacon. Rather than using a plotter, you use the VOR compass rose on the aeronautical chart to obtain track bearings. Which of the following statements is true?

    (a) *The VOR compass rose can only be used for IFR route planning.*
    (b) *The compass rose is aligned with magnetic north an gives magnetic bearings.*
    (c) *The compass rose is aligned with true north an gives true bearings.*
    (d) *The compass rose is aligned with grid north an gives grid bearings.*

6. You plan a route from Fenland (EGCL) to Humberside (EGNJ). Your route overflies RAF Coningsby. You should consider:

(a) *A detour via Mablethorpe to avoid the MATZ at Coningsby.*

(b) *The leg is satisfactory provided that you request MATZ penetration from Coningsby.*

(c) *The leg is satisfactory provided that you request MATZ and ATZ penetration from Coningsby.*

(d) *VFR routes through should never be planned through military or civil controlled airspace.*

Answers: 1a, 2d, 3b, 4b, 5b, 6c.

Vertical Navigation

V ertical navigation is important to pilots for three basic reasons:

1. For terrain clearance, to ensure that the aircraft will not collide with terrain or fixed obstacles on the ground.

2. For traffic separation, to allow pilots to cruise at an altitude different from that of nearby aircraft, to ensure safe vertical separation.

3. To calculate the performance capabilities of the aircraft and its engine, so as to operate safely and efficiently.

Vertical navigation is the guidance of flight in the vertical plane, and includes the science of measuring vertical distances in the atmosphere, known as *altimetry*.

Measuring vertical distance in the atmosphere is not as simple as it sounds. There are errors in the measuring instrument (the altimeter) and compromises in the principle on which it is built, with the result that the altimeter presents the pilot with approximate vertical information of the aircraft's position.

Altitude

Altitude is the vertical distance of a level, point, or object, measured from *mean sea level* (MSL). This definition appears in the UK Aeronautical Information Publication (AIP). The abbreviation for altitude is *alt* or ALT.

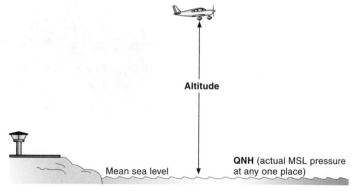

■ *Figure 7-1* **Altitude is the vertical distance above mean sea level (amsl)**

In the UK and the Western world the standard unit of height for aviation purposes is the *foot*. In many Eastern countries it is the *metre*.

The Altimeter

The basic instrument used to measure altitude is the pressure altimeter. This is simply a **barometer** – a device that measures atmospheric pressure. Barometers work on the principle that, in the atmosphere, air pressure decreases as height increases. This means that the higher you are in the earth's atmosphere, the lower the pressure – hence the need for most people to wear oxygen masks when they fly above 10,000 ft in unpressurised aeroplanes.

There are various types of pressure altimeter. The most compact and robust type suitable for installation in an aircraft is the **aneroid barometer,** which is similar to those seen in many homes. As the aeroplane goes higher, the atmospheric pressure of the air in which it is flying decreases, and the aneroid, which is an expandable and compressible metal capsule containing a fixed amount of air, is able to expand.

Through a system of linkages, a pointer is driven around a scale. This scale does not read directly in units of pressure, such as *hectopascals*, but rather in *feet*. Calculations by the designer have been made to relate the pressure to the altitude, and the scale reads in units of altitude, which is what pilots need. The altitude indication is known as **indicated altitude.**

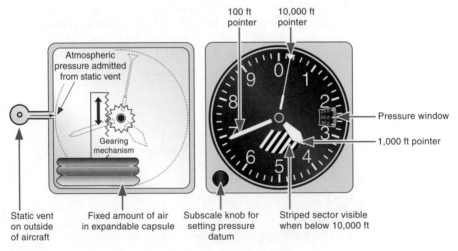

■ *Figure 7-2* **The altimeter is a pressure-sensitive instrument**

As the aeroplane climbs, the aneroid expands, driving the pointer to indicate a higher altitude. As the aeroplane descends, the static air pressure in the surrounding atmosphere increases, forcing the aneroid to contract and drive the pointer to indicate a lower altitude.

A number of errors are evident in altimeters, and these may be broken into two main types:

1. Errors in the particular altimeter.

2. Errors in the principle on which altimetry is based, i.e. by how much the pressure in the atmosphere decreases with height.

Errors in the Altimetry Principle

The rate at which air pressure decreases with height varies from time to time and from place to place. The simple barometric altimeter cannot cope with this because it has been calibrated according to a **standard atmosphere** in which a particular height **above mean sea level (amsl)** always corresponds with a particular pressure. Any variation of the actual atmosphere from the standard atmosphere will cause the altimeter to indicate an altitude different from the actual height amsl of the aeroplane.

The various gases surrounding the earth and forming its atmosphere are bound to it by gravity. A standard atmosphere is something that does not exist permanently, since this mixture of gases (or *air* as we call it) has constantly changing values of:

• **pressure**;
• **temperature**;
• **density**; and
• **water content (humidity)**.

Thus it is necessary to have a standard, against which to compare the actual atmosphere in our vicinity. That is the International Standard Atmosphere (ISA).

Lapse Rates

In the International Standard Atmosphere, pressure, temperature and density are defined as decreasing at specified rates with gain in height.

TEMPERATURE. The temperature lapse rate (rate of fall of temperature with increase in height) in the ISA is 1.98°C per 1,000 ft up to 36,090 ft, above which the temperature remains constant at minus 56.6°C (at least in the levels up to which commercial aeroplanes fly). For our purposes, in the ISA:

• **temperature falls** by 2°C per 1,000 ft up to 36,000 ft; and
• **above 36,000 ft,** remains constant at −57°C.

PRESSURE. The rate at which pressure in the ISA decreases with height varies, but is approximately 1 hPa per 30 ft up to about 5,000 ft. (This rate drops to about 1 hPa per 70 ft at high levels of the atmosphere, but this need not concern us here.) For our purposes, in the lower levels of the ISA, pressure decreases by 1 hPa for each 30 ft increase in altitude.

DENSITY. Air density decreases with height, so that at 20,000 ft the air density is about one-half of its MSL value, one-quarter at 40,000 ft, and one-tenth at 60,000 ft.

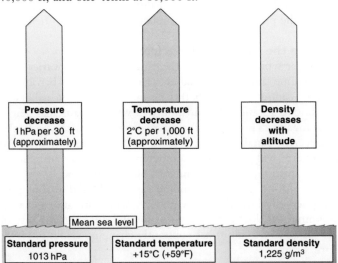

■ *Figure 7-3* **The International Standard Atmosphere (ISA)**

The main use of the International Standard Atmosphere is to calibrate altimeters. This is to provide a mathematical relationship between the air pressure measured by the aneroid barometer and the altitude calibrations placed on the scale around which the pointer is driven, so that all aircraft convert pressure to altitude by a standard method.

Pressure Altitude

Pressure altitude (called *pressure height* in some countries), is the height in the ISA above the 1013 hPa pressure datum at which the pressure equals that of the level under consideration. For example, the ISA pressure at a point 600 ft higher than the 1013 pressure level is approximately 993 hPa. If your aeroplane is flying in air whose pressure is 993 hPa, then its pressure altitude is 600 ft.

NOTE 1013.25 hPa is the precise value of standard or ISA MSL pressure. For our purposes, 1013 is sufficiently accurate. There is a Q-code for pressure altitude, QNE, but it is rarely used.

Pressure altitudes are often described in an abbreviated form as **flight levels,** where the final two zeros are omitted. For example, a pressure altitude of 4,500 ft (i.e. 4,500 ft higher than the 1013 pressure level) is also known as flight level 45 (written FL45). Flight levels are used for cruising at higher levels and are usually separated by at least 500 ft, e.g. FL55, FL60, FL65.

A flight level is a pressure altitude.

EXAMPLE 1 35,000 ft in the International Standard Atmosphere above the standard pressure level of 1013 may be referred to as:

- **pressure altitude** (or pressure height) of 35,000 ft; or as
- **flight level 350,** FL350 (where the last two zeros are dropped).

EXAMPLE 2 3,500 ft in the International Standard Atmosphere above the standard pressure level of 1013 may be referred to as:

- **pressure altitude** (or pressure height) of 3,500 ft, or as
- **flight level 35,** FL35, (where the last two zeros are dropped).

Air Pressure

The earth's atmosphere consists of molecules all moving at high speed and colliding with any object, be it another molecule or the earth's surface or a person that blocks their path. The force that these molecules exert as they collide gives rise to a *pressure,* or a 'force per unit area'. As these molecules are moving in all directions, the pressure at any point in the atmosphere will be exerted in all directions.

Because of gravity, the ambient pressure at any point in the atmosphere will depend on the weight of air that is above and pressing down. On a 'standard day', the column of air pressing down on the earth's surface exerts a pressure of 1013 hectopascals at sea level.

Low static pressure at altitude

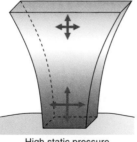

High static pressure
at mean sea level

■ *Figure 7-4* ***Pressure decreases with increase of altitude***

EXAMPLE 1 What temperature exists at 3,000 ft above the 1013 pressure surface (or pressure level) in the International Standard Atmosphere?

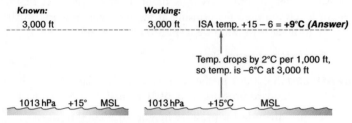

■ *Figure 7-5* **Example 1 answer: +9°C**

EXAMPLE 2 What temperature exists at 4,500 ft in the ISA?

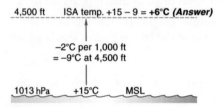

■ *Figure 7-6* **Example 2 answer: +6°C**

EXAMPLE 3 What temperature exists at 45,000 ft in the ISA?

ANSWER −57°C because in the ISA, temperature is constant at −57°C above 36,000 ft.

EXAMPLE 4 What temperature exists at 36,000 ft in the ISA?

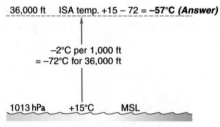

■ *Figure 7-7* **Example 4 answer: −57°C**

EXAMPLE 5 Calculate the ISA values of pressure and temperature for a pressure altitude of 6,000 ft.

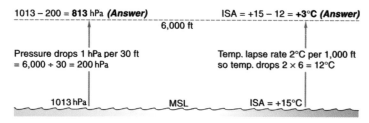

■ *Figure 7-8* **Example 5 answers: 813 mb and +3°C**

EXAMPLE 6 Calculate the ISA values of pressure and temperature for a pressure altitude of −1,500 ft (i.e. 1,500 ft below the 1013 pressure level).

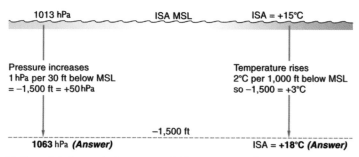

■ *Figure 7-9* **Example 6 answers: 1063 hPa and +18°C**

NOTE This sort of calculation for below ISA MSL is sometimes required because:

1. There are places on the earth's surface that are below mean sea level (e.g. Rotterdam, the Dead Sea, Lake Eyre in Australia).

2. The actual atmosphere is always different from our so-called standard atmosphere and negative pressure altitudes are not uncommon.

EXAMPLE 7 What is the pressure altitude of the 990 hPa pressure surface?

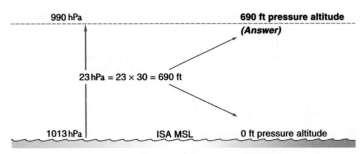

■ *Figure 7-10* **Example 7 answer: 690 ft pressure altitude**

Even though some of these exercises are simple, do not avoid them. A sound understanding of altimetry will stand you in good stead throughout your flying career!

Variations in Mean Sea Level Pressure – QNH

On maps and charts the height of terrain is given as height **above mean sea level (amsl).** It is therefore essential that a pilot knows the aircraft's height above mean sea level so that he can relate this to the height of terrain or obstructions and determine if there is sufficient vertical separation.

So far in our discussion the altimeter has only measured height above the ISA MSL datum of 1013 hPa. In reality, mean sea level pressure varies from day to day, and indeed from hour to hour, as the various high- and low-pressure systems move across the surface of the earth. You will notice this on daily weather maps.

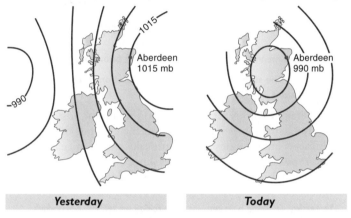

■ Figure 7-11 **Two different synoptic situations**

Consider the situations illustrated in Figure 7-11. Yesterday, a high-pressure system of 1015 hPa was sitting over Aberdeen. In 24 hours, the pressure system has moved on, and today Aberdeen is experiencing a lower pressure of 990 hPa. A profile of the atmosphere over Aberdeen on each of these days is shown in Figure 7-12.

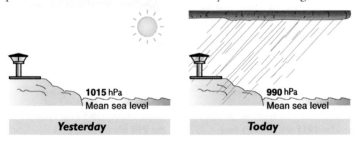

■ Figure 7-12 **Profile of MSL pressure situations – yesterday and today**

Figure 7-13 shows the position of the 1013 hPa pressure level in relation to each of these situations.

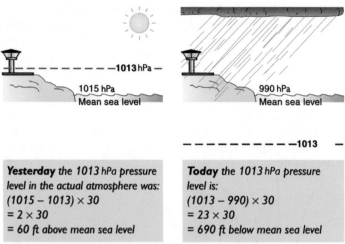

Yesterday the 1013 hPa pressure
level in the actual atmosphere was:
(1015 – 1013) × 30
= 2 × 30
= 60 ft above mean sea level

Today the 1013 hPa pressure
level is:
(1013 – 990) × 30
= 23 × 30
= 690 ft below mean sea level

■ Figure 7-13 **The standard pressure level in relation to the**
MSL pressure

Since height amsl is vital information to a pilot, instead of this
unwieldy calculation being required in the cockpit, the design of
the altimeter incorporates a small subscale and knob geared to the
altimeter pointer. By rotating the knob, the desired pressure
datum from which height will be measured is set in the subscale.

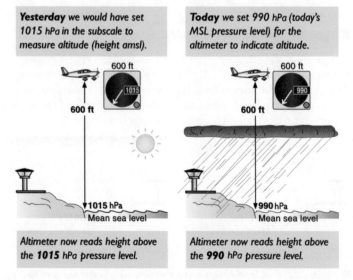

Yesterday we would have set
1015 hPa in the subscale to
measure altitude (height amsl).

Today we set 990 hPa (today's
MSL pressure level) for the
altimeter to indicate altitude.

Altimeter now reads height above
the **1015** hPa pressure level.

Altimeter now reads height above
the **990** hPa pressure level.

■ Figure 7-14 **When MSL pressure is set in the altimeter subscale, the**
altimeter indicates height amsl for that pressure situation

QNH

The Q-code name for the altimeter subscale setting which gives us this altitude is QNH (i.e. the MSL pressure level in the *actual* atmosphere). The QNH is the atmospheric pressure corresponding to mean sea level pressure at that place and time.

> An altimeter with **QNH** set on its subscale will indicate **altitude** – height above mean sea level (amsl).

From the previous example, we can see that yesterday in Aberdeen the QNH was 1015 hPa; today in Aberdeen the QNH is 990 hPa.

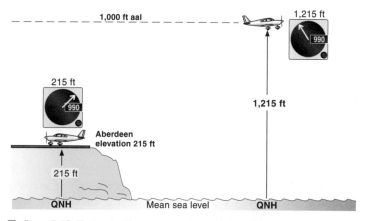

■ *Figure 7-15* **Today in Aberdeen the QNH is 990 hPa**

The official elevation of a particular aerodrome is that of the highest point on the landing area. Since most aerodromes are fairly level, it gives the pilot who is taxiing an opportunity to check his altimeter prior to take-off. With QNH set, the altimeter of an aeroplane on the ground should indicate close to aerodrome elevation.

The Altimeter Subscale

The altimeter subscale is controlled by a knob which the pilot can turn. It is connected to the pointer and mechanically geared in the ratio of approximately 1 hPa to 30 ft, i.e. altering the subscale setting by 1 hectopascal will alter the indicated height by about 30 ft. Altering the subscale setting by 10 hectopascals will alter the altimeter indication by about 300 ft.

An easy means of determining pressure altitude is simply to wind 1013 into the subscale. The altimeter will then indicate the height in the ISA above the 1013 hPa pressure level: pressure altitude.

EXAMPLE 8 Suppose that the MSL pressure is 1030 (i.e. QNH) and the aeroplane is 600 ft amsl. With QNH 1030 set in the subscale, the altimeter will indicate an altitude of 600 ft amsl. The pressure altitude can be found (without any calculation) by winding 1013 into the subscale. In this case the pressure altitude is 90 ft.

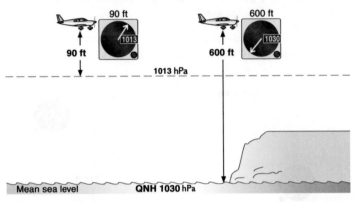

■ *Figure 7-16* **Example 8**

Wind on hectopascals, wind on height (and vice versa).

The correct QNH can be obtained from a number of sources, including Air Traffic Control, meteorological forecasts (at least approximately) and your own observations. By 'your own observations', we mean that if you are on the ground at an aerodrome whose elevation you know, then, after turning the knob until the altimeter indicates the aerodrome elevation, the reading in the subscale will be the current aerodrome QNH.

To illustrate this, suppose you arrive by car at a country aerodrome, elevation 1,290 ft, to go flying, and find that the altimeter indicates something quite different from 1,290. Simply by turning the knob until the pointers of the altimeter indicate 1,290 ft, which is the altitude (height amsl) of the aircraft, you will have wound the current QNH onto the subscale.

It is obvious that, for the altimeter indication to have any significance, the pilot must be aware of the setting on the subscale.

EXAMPLE 9 You are flying overhead Elstree aerodrome with the current QNH of 1020 set in the subscale, and the altimeter indicating 1,500 ft. What pressure altitude is that?

ANSWER 1,290 ft (Figure 7-17)

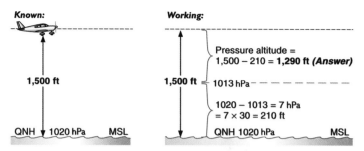

■ *Figure 7-17* **Example 9 answer: 1,290 ft**

EXAMPLE 10 Your aircraft is sitting on the tarmac at Compton Abbas airfield, elevation 810 feet. The altimeter reads 900 ft (i.e. 90 ft too high) with 1015 set on the subscale. What is the airfield QNH (i.e. what is the mean sea level pressure at Compton Abbas at that time, assuming the atmosphere extends down to MSL)?

ANSWER With 1015 set in the subscale, the altimeter over-reads the known elevation by 90 ft. By winding off this 90 ft, we wind off 3 hPa, i.e. QNH is 1012.

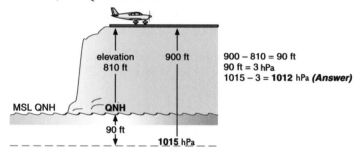

■ *Figure 7-18* **Example 10 answer: QNH 1012 hPa**

Height Above Aerodrome Level – QFE

It is very convenient for circuit operations if the altimeter can be set to indicate height **above aerodrome level (aal).** This means that a 1,000 ft circuit at, for example, Leicester airfield (elevation 469 ft) can be achieved with the altimeter indicating 1,000 ft, rather than 1,469 ft if QNH was set in the subscale. It is a satisfactory procedure in the UK to set QFE in the subscale when flying in the circuit.

QFE is the pressure at aerodrome level.

On the aerodrome, the altimeter should indicate within ±50 ft of zero with QFE set in the subscale. QFE is the pressure at aerodrome level. In flight, the altimeter, with QFE set, will indicate height above the runway. (Having departed the circuit area, however, QFE is of little value, since the surrounding terrain will probably be at a different level from the aerodrome.)

EXAMPLE 11 You plan to do some circuits at an aerodrome (elevation 749 ft amsl). On the ground you adjust the subscale of your altimeter until the altimeter indicates 0 feet, which it does with, say, 996 set in the subscale.

Calculate the current QFE, QNH and pressure altitude of this aerodrome, and the altimeter readings you would expect with these subscale settings when the aeroplane is on the ground.

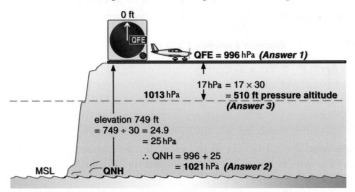

■ *Figure 7-19* **Example 11 answers: QFE 996 hPa, QNH 1021 hPa,**
pressure altitude 510 ft

Remember that the information your altimeter gives you depends on what you have set in the subscale.

For terrain clearance, use QNH.

Flying With Changing Sea Level Pressures

Consider an aeroplane flying from Land's End to Popham, with the barometric pressure over the south-west of England as shown in Figure 7-20.

We depart Land's End with the Land's End QNH of 995 set on the subscale (i.e. MSL pressure at Land's End), and cruise 3,000 ft above this with our altimeter indicating 3,000 ft.

Tracking towards Popham, we are flying into an area of higher pressure, and so the 995 pressure level will be gradually rising. If we maintain 3,000 ft indicated on the altimeter, with 995 set, we will in fact be climbing with respect to sea level.

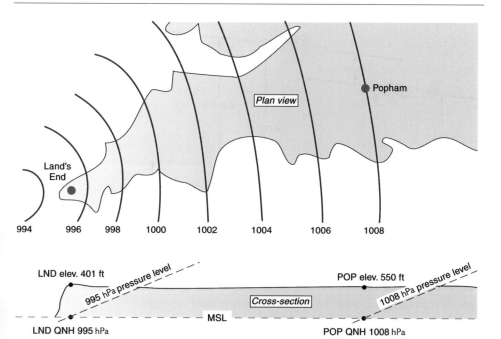

■ *Figure 7-20* **Plan and cross-section views of this synoptic situation**

Conversely, another aircraft flying in the opposite direction with the Popham QNH of 1008 set on its subscale and cruising at 4,000 ft will in fact be gradually descending. Can you spot the two inherent dangers?

Remember that two of the most important tasks for pilots are:
- **to avoid hitting the ground unexpectedly; and**
- **to avoid colliding with other aircraft.**

The aircraft coming from Popham, flying from a higher-pressure area towards an area of lower pressure, will actually be gradually descending if the altimeter reading 4,000 ft continues to have 1008 hPa set on the subscale. The aircraft will in fact be lower than 4,000 ft amsl, so terrain clearance could be a problem. When flying 'From *high* to *low*, beware below!' (Danger No. 1)

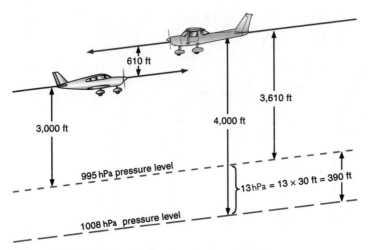

■ *Figure 7-21* **Flying from high to low, beware below!**

The two pilots may think that they have 1,000 ft vertical separation because the altimeter in one aeroplane indicates 3,000 ft, and the altimeter in the other indicates 4,000 ft. In fact, the vertical separation is only 610 ft, because 4,000 ft above the 1008 hPa pressure level is only (4,000 − 390) = 3,610 ft above the 995 hPa pressure level. (Danger No. 2)

Regional Pressure Setting (RPS)

The practical solution to both of these problems (terrain clearance and traffic separation) because of changing QNHs is to have all aircraft which are cruising in the same area, below the transition altitude, use the same altimeter subscale setting. For this reason the UK is divided into a number of Altimeter Setting Regions (ASRs) – see Vol. 2 of *The Air Pilot's Manual.*

Regional Pressure Setting can be obtained from:

- all aerodromes with Air Traffic Services;
- any Air/Ground ATC channel;
- by land-line (for pre-flight planning);
- the London and Scottish ATCCs; or
- the Manchester Sub-Centre.

When cruising en route, the appropriate subscale setting is the *Regional Pressure Setting* **(RPS)** (also sometimes known colloquially as the Regional QNH or the Area QNH) which is the current QNH for that region at that time. Its value will be updated by ATC at least every hour.

The QNH will in fact vary slightly throughout the Altimeter Setting Region, depending on the pressure pattern. To be on the conservative side, the Regional Pressure Setting is the lowest forecast QNH value for that hour, and so will be at sea level or slightly higher. This ensures that the aircraft will be at or slightly higher than the altitude indicated, and not lower.

For example, with Regional Pressure Setting set and the altimeter indicating 2,000 ft, the aeroplane should be 2,000 ft amsl or slightly higher. No Aerodrome QNH in that region will be lower than the value of the Regional Pressure Setting.

When cruising cross-country, set Regional Pressure Setting, and update it when you fly into another region, or whenever ATC communicates an amended value.

Altimetry Procedures for Cross-Country Flights

In the UK, a typical private cross-country flight in a light aircraft is usually conducted at or below 3,000 ft amsl. We will use a flight from Land's End to Popham as an example.

1. Set Aerodrome QNH or QFE for Take-Off

With Aerodrome QNH set, the altimeter indicates height amsl, which is useful information in the circuit area and during the climb-out, especially over high terrain or if ATC requires you to report altitude. On the ground, the altimeter should indicate aerodrome elevation, which at Land's End is 401 ft amsl.

If you choose to set QFE, the altimeter will indicate height aal, and this reading has little significance away from the vicinity of the aerodrome. On the ground, with QFE set, the altimeter should indicate close to zero (within ±50 ft).

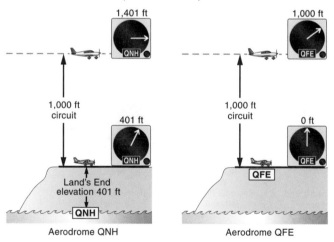

■ *Figure 7-22* **Set Aerodrome QNH, or Aerodrome QFE, for circuit operations**

2. Set Regional Pressure Setting if Cruising Below the Transition Altitude

On reaching cruising altitude 3,000 ft, the Scillies Regional Pressure Setting should be set. Flying with the altimeter indicating 3,000 ft should ensure that the height above mean sea level is 3,000 ft or slightly more (since the Regional Pressure Setting is always the lowest QNH for that area).

The Regional Pressure Setting should be updated as you cross each ASR boundary (shown on aeronautical charts) – in this case passing from Scillies ASR to the Wessex ASR to the Portland ASR, or whenever the appropriate Regional Pressure Setting is updated by ATC.

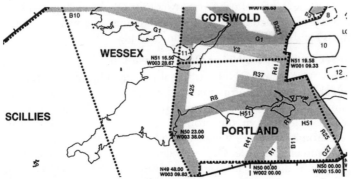

■ Figure 7-23 **Excerpt from the ASR map**

With Regional Pressure Setting set in the subscale, the pilot can evaluate:
- **terrain clearance** (the height of terrain is found from the aeronautical charts); and
- **vertical separation** from other aircraft.

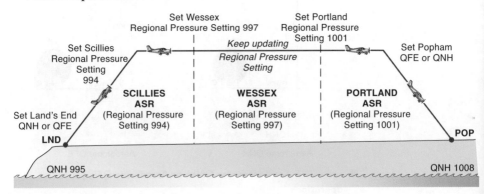

■ Figure 7-24 **When cruising below the transition altitude, set Regional Pressure Setting**

NOTE It is insufficient to assume that errors in horizontal tracking will safeguard you from other traffic in your vicinity operating at or near the same level. Modern tracking aids, such as VOR, GPS, and inertial navigation systems, have made extremely accurate tracking possible.

En route you may be required, when flying beneath a Terminal Control Area (TMA) or Control Area (CTA), to set the QNH of an aerodrome situated beneath that area, to assist in separation from other aeroplanes or to ensure that you do not inadvertently penetrate the controlled airspace above you. The Aerodrome QNHs will not differ greatly (if at all) from their Regional Pressure Setting.

When transiting a Military Aerodrome Traffic Zone (MATZ) where military aircraft may be operating, you may be required to set the MATZ Aerodrome QNH for separation purposes. Once clear of the MATZ, Regional Pressure Setting should be reset on the subscale.

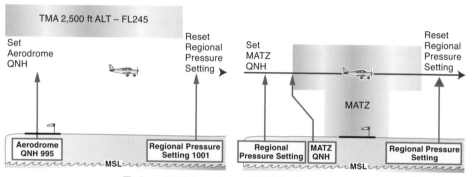

■ *Figure 7-25* **Aerodrome QNH (rather than Regional Pressure Setting) may be required en route**

3. Set QFE or Aerodrome QNH when Approaching for Landing

In preparation for joining the circuit, set the aerodrome QFE (or QNH if preferred) for the destination aerodrome as the circuit area is approached. For instance, approaching Popham, you would set QFE 990, or QNH 1008, on the altimeter subscale. (Note: In some countries only QNH is used.)

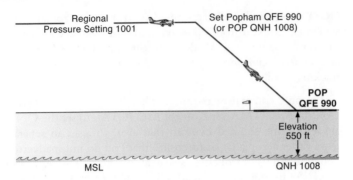

Regional Pressure Setting 1001   Set Popham QFE 990 (or POP QNH 1008)

POP
QFE 990

Elevation 550 ft

MSL   QNH 1008

■ Figure 7-26 *Approaching the circuit, set aerodrome QFE (or QNH if preferred)*

Cruising Above the Transition Altitude

The highest terrain in the UK is 4,406 ft amsl at Ben Nevis in Scotland. Obviously most of the UK is much lower than this. To avoid the need for continually updating the altimeter setting, it is common practice when flying at levels where high terrain is not a problem to set standard pressure 1013 mb on the subscale. All aircraft cruising at these levels, with 1013 set, thereby obtain adequate vertical separation from each other.

The altitude in the climb at which the transition from QNH to 1013 mb is made is called the **transition altitude.** In the UK, the transition altitude is generally 3,000 ft amsl. There are some exceptions to this in the vicinity of some major airports, where the transition altitude may be higher because traffic density is high and where the high rates of climb and descent of jet aircraft is a consideration.

In other parts of the world where the terrain is much higher, the transition altitude is much higher. In the USA the transition altitude is 18,000 ft; in Papua New Guinea (a mountainous country just north of Australia) it is 20,000 ft; in Australia it is 10,000 ft.

Exceptions, at the time of printing, to the usual UK transition altitude of 3,000 ft can be found in the United Kingdom AIP ENR 1.7.

Choice of Altimeter Setting for VFR Flights

Outside controlled airspace and above the transition altitude, VFR flights may cruise with Regional Pressure Setting, but it is advisable to use 1013 and cruise on flight levels as aircraft operating on Instrument Flight Rules are required to do.

In controlled airspace and above the transition altitude, aircraft should cruise at flight levels (with 1013 hPa set), rather than at altitudes (with QNH set).

The Transition Layer

There would be a possibility of conflict if aircraft cruising above the transition altitude were on Regional Pressure Setting and aircraft only slightly above it were on the 1013 reference datum. For this reason there is a layer above the transition altitude in which cruising flight should not occur, to ensure satisfactory vertical separation of at least 500 ft.

In practice, flight levels are nominated in 500-foot steps, e.g. FL35, FL40, FL45, FL50, FL55, etc. Since the 1013 hPa reference datum may not be at mean sea level, it is possible (indeed most likely) that the actual vertical spacing between a transition altitude of 3,000 ft and a transition level of FL35 will not be 500 ft, as illustrated in Figure 7-27.

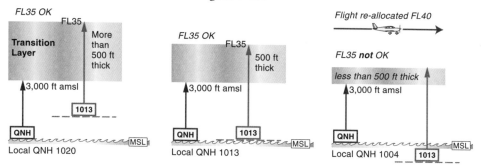

■ *Figure 7-27* **The thickness of the transition layer varies with QNH**

As you can see, the transition altitude remains fixed, but the transition level moves up or down according to the QNH. If the Regional Pressure Setting is less than 1013 hPa, FL35 is lower than 3,500 ft amsl and there is less than 500 ft vertical separation between a transition altitude of 3,000 ft and FL35. So you would need to cruise at FL40 to retain a 500 ft or better vertical separation from an aircraft cruising at 3,000 ft on Regional Pressure Setting.

Summary

THE TRANSITION ALTITUDE is the altitude at, or below, which the vertical position of aircraft is controlled by reference to altitudes, i.e. with regional QNH set. In the UK, it is usually 3,000 ft amsl.

THE TRANSITION LEVEL is the flight level at, or above, which the vertical position of aircraft is controlled with reference to flight levels, i.e. with 1013 set. In the UK, it is usually FL35 (or higher if QNH is less than 1013).

THE TRANSITION LAYER is the airspace between the transition altitude and the transition level. It varies in thickness, depending on the Regional Pressure Setting.

Cruising Level Selection above the Transition Altitude

As a student pilot, or basic −PPL holder (no Instrument Rating or IMC/Restricted Instrument Rating), you will be restricted to flying under Visual Flight Rules (VFR) and as such should always be clear of cloud and satisfy minimum visibility requirements.

It is not mandatory for VFR flights to cruise at any particular altitude or flight level, but it is recommended by the CAA that VFR flights adopt the Standard European Rules of the Air cruising level system.

- VFR flights on a magnetic track of 000 to 179 degrees should select odd thousands and intermediate 500 ft levels, e.g. FL35 and FL55, etc.
- VFR flights on a magnetic track of 180 − 359 degrees should select even thousands and intermediate 500 ft levels, e.g. FL45 and FL65, etc.

The current system is based on the semi-circular level system and replaces the quadrantal system bringing the UK into line with ICAO standards applied elsewhere in the world. VFR and IFR aircraft are allocated different levels at which to fly.

The Effect of Temperature Variations

So far we have only considered pressure variations from the International Standard Atmosphere. Temperature variations from ISA play a role not only in vertical navigation and altimetry, but also in aeroplane performance (see Vol. 4 of this series). ISA MSL temperature is +15°C, and the temperature lapse rate is 2°C/ 1,000 ft (decrease with altitude).

TEMPERATURE STRUCTURE IN THE ISA	
Pressure Altitudes	*ISA Temperatures*
above 36,000 ft	*constant at −57°C*
36,000 ft	*−57°C (ISA = +15 − [2 × 36] = +15 − 72 = −57°C)*
20,000 ft	*−25°C (ISA = +15 − [2 × 20] = +15 − 40 = −25°C)*
3,000 ft	*+9°C (ISA = +15 − [2 × 3] = +15 − 6 = +9°C)*
2,000 ft	*+11°C (ISA = +15 − [2 × 2] = +15 − 4 = +11°C)*
1,000 ft	*+13°C (ISA = +15 − 2 = +13°C)*
MSL 1013 hPa	*+15°C*

Temperature Deviation from ISA

Suppose that in the 'real' atmosphere, the temperature at 2,000 ft is not +11°C as in the ISA, but +16°C, i.e. it is 5°C warmer than in the ISA. This can be expressed as +16°C, a simple temperature, or as a deviation from the ISA, which in this case is ISA+5. In aviation it is common practice to use this ISA deviation means of describing temperature.

EXAMPLE 12 Express −10°C at FL80 as a deviation from the ISA.

At FL80, i.e. pressure altitude 8,000 ft ISA = +15 − (2 × 8)
$$= +15 - 16$$
$$= -1°C$$

ANSWER Now −10°C is colder than −1°C by 9°C, and this is expressed as ISA−9.

In Cold Air, the Altimeter Over-Reads

The altimeter is essentially a barometer that converts pressure measurements to altitude. It is calibrated according to the International Standard Atmosphere. On a cold day when the air is more dense, various pressure levels at altitude will be lower than on a warm day.

The 913 hPa pressure level that equates with a pressure altitude of 3,000 ft in the International Standard Atmosphere may be at only 2,900 ft. The altimeter, however, because it is calibrated according to the ISA, will indicate this as 3,000 ft even though the aeroplane is at 2,900 ft. On a day that is warmer than ISA, when the altimeter indicates 3,000 ft, the aeroplane may in fact be slightly higher.

This is not significant for separation between aircraft, since all altimeters will be affected identically. It is important for terrain separation, however, so when flying from a high to low temperature, beware below because the altimeter will read too high.

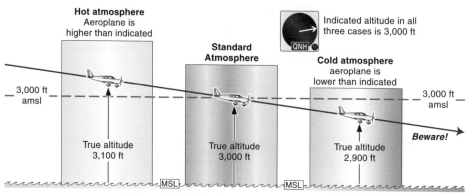

■ Figure 7-28 **When flying from high to low temperature, beware below!** **(Same rule as for pressure.)**

Density Altitude (or Density Height)

Density is the mass per unit volume, or if you like, the number of molecules in each unit volume, and is affected directly by variations in temperature. Aeroplane performance (the speed at which it can fly, and the height to which it can climb) depends, amongst a number of factors, mainly on the ambient air density. Consequently it is important to be able to calculate density altitude.

Density altitude is the atmospheric density expressed in terms of altitude in the International Standard Atmosphere which corresponds to that density.

If, for example, at 1,000 ft amsl in the actual atmosphere the density is the same as the density at 2,400 ft in ISA, i.e. our altitude is 1,000 ft amsl but our density altitude is 2,400 ft, the aircraft and engines will perform as if the aeroplane were at 2,400 ft.

How to Calculate Density Altitude

It is impractical for a pilot to have the equipment necessary to measure air density, so we make use of two pieces of information already available and on which density depends: pressure altitude and temperature. Density altitude can be calculated in three ways:

1. By correcting pressure altitude for ISA temperature deviation by 120 ft per 1°C.

2. Graphically, as in most aeroplane performance charts, on which both pressure altitude and temperature are the criteria used in entering the graph. Though density altitude itself may not be specified, it is implied by these other two parameters.

3. By navigation computer.

EXAMPLE 13 Calculate the density altitude at Huddersfield (Crosland Moor), elevation 825 ft, if the current QNH is 999, and the OAT (outside air temperature) +28°C.

ANSWER PA 1,245 ft, DA 3,105 ft

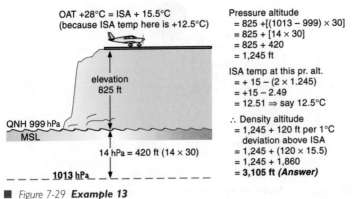

OAT +28°C = ISA + 15.5°C
(because ISA temp here is +12.5°C)

elevation
825 ft

QNH 999 hPa
MSL

14 hPa = 420 ft (14 × 30)

1013 hPa

Pressure altitude
= 825 +[(1013 − 999) × 30]
= 825 + [14 × 30]
= 825 + 420
= 1,245 ft

ISA temp at this pr. alt.
= + 15 − (2 × 1.245)
= +15 − 2.49
= 12.51 ⇒ say 12.5°C

∴ Density altitude
= 1,245 + 120 ft per 1°C
  deviation above ISA
= 1,245 + (120 × 15.5)
= 1,245 + 1,860
= 3,105 ft **(Answer)**

■ Figure 7-29 **Example 13**

NOTE Even though the aircraft is lower than 1,000 ft amsl, the engines will perform, and the aircraft will fly, as if it were at about 3,000 ft in the International Standard Atmosphere, i.e. it will have a much poorer performance. As a good pilot you should be aware of poor performance when hot and high.

EXAMPLE 14 Calculate the density altitude of Shoreham, elevation 7 ft, QNH 1031 hPa, OAT –2°C.

ANSWER PA – 533 ft, DA – 2,573, i.e. below msl

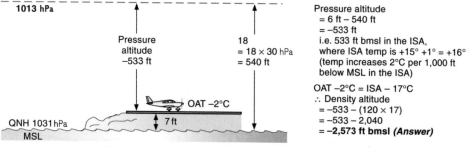

Pressure altitude
= 6 ft – 540 ft
= –533 ft
i.e. 533 ft bmsl in the ISA,
where ISA temp is +15° +1° = +16°
(temp increases 2°C per 1,000 ft
below MSL in the ISA)

OAT –2°C = ISA – 17°C
∴ Density altitude
= –533 – (120 × 17)
= –533 – 2,040
= **–2,573 ft bmsl (Answer)**

■ *Figure 7-30* **Example 14**

NOTE A high QNH (i.e. high air pressure) increases density as does the low temperature, with the temperature usually being the critical factor to watch out for. In this particular case of a low aerodrome elevation and a low temperature at Shoreham, we could expect the engines and the aeroplane to perform very well.

Any graph or table in an aeroplane Performance or Flight Manual that has both pressure altitude and temperature on it means that density height is being allowed for, and will not have to be calculated directly as above or by computer.

Determine Safety Altitudes and Select Cruising Levels

It is good airmanship to determine reasonable minimum safe cruising altitudes which will provide an adequate vertical clearance above obstacles on and near the planned route. There are various philosophies about how to estimate this safety altitude, and you should refer to your flying instructor on this point. Some methods are clearly more conservative than others.

In selecting an appropriate altitude at which to fly on a cross country flight in VMC and under VFR, it is useful to bear in mind the following:
• The need to comply with the requirements of the low flying rules (rule 5) including:
  – separation from obstacles,
  – suitable clearance over congested areas,
  – the glide-clear requirements;

- Selecting a higher altitude at which to fly gives you more options in the event of an in-flight emergency;
- Selecting altitude other than the obvious 1500, 2000, 2500 feet amsl is less likely to lead to a conflict with other traffic;
- It is useful to have calculated the safety altitude for the route that you are flying in order to have an awareness of the terrain clearance that would be required should you inadvertently become IMC.

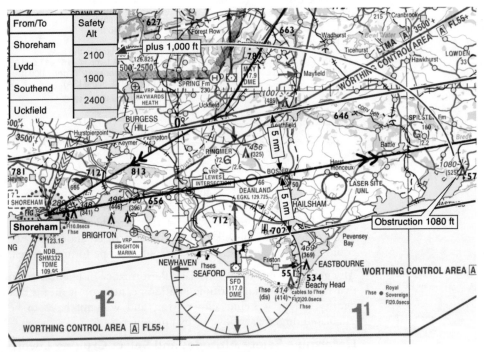

From/To	Safety Alt
Shoreham	2100
Lydd	1900
Southend	2400
Uckfield	

■ *Figure 7-31* **Study the chart and calculate a safety altitude**

It is certainly not necessary on a VFR cross-country route to fly at a calculated MSA since your separation from obstacles and terrain should be determined visually. The instrument flight rules specify a legal minimum of 1000 feet clearance from the highest fixed obstacle within 5 nm of the aircraft (or 2000 feet in mountainous terrain) but there is no requirement for PPLs flying VFR in VMC to adhere to those rules.

Remember that contours below 500 ft amsl and obstructions below 300 ft agl are not shown on aeronautical charts; in other words, an obstacle that is 799 ft amsl may not be shown, so always keep a sharp lookout, especially in poor visibility.

Having determined the minimum safe cruising altitude for each leg, then select the cruising level which you propose to use. You are constrained:

- **on the lower side** by the safety altitude; and
- **on the upper side** by perhaps cloud, controlled airspace or a markedly increasing headwind.

Aerodrome Traffic Zones extend up to 2,000 ft above aerodrome level (aal) and Military Aerodrome Traffic Zones extend up to 3,000 ft aal. You may fly through them, of course, but it is good airmanship in some situations to remain clear of an ATZ. There is also no point climbing to a high cruising altitude if your destination is nearby. As a pilot, you must think about vertical navigation as well as horizontal navigation.

While private pilots operating under Visual Flight Rules may cruise at altitude on QNH, they may also choose to fly at flight levels based on 1013 hPa when cruising above the transition altitude, to fit in with Instrument Flight Rules traffic observing the cruising level procedure in the United Kingdom AIP ENR 1.7 paragraph 5.2.

Example Prepared Chart and Flight Log

We return to the example flight from Shoreham to Shoreham passing overhead the Lydd and Southend aerodromes. The planner has drawn additional guidelines 5 nm either side of their track (see Figure 7.31 for an extract from the route).

Following the recommended practice, the planner has elected to calculate a safety altitude that assures a 1,000 ft clearance above obstacles and high terrain. This has the advantage that, in the event of entering IMC, the pilot simply needs to execute a 180° turn without changing altitude. In good visibility, 1,000 ft may be excessive and a lower altitude, compatible with Rule 5, could be considered.

The planner has chosen to fly at 2,400 ft at all times. This achieves three objectives:

- the flight is conducted above the safety altitude at all times.
- this is a 'non-obvious' altitude that should provide separation from aircraft being flown at popular, conventional altitudes, e.g. 2,000 ft.
- it ensures that the flight is conducted below the London TMA which is Class A airspace where VFR flights are prohibited. The lowest point of the London TMA along the route is 2,500 ft requiring particular attention to altitude-holding.

Vertical navigation information can now be added to the route information on the Flight Log as shown in Figure 7.32.

Pilot: *P. Pilot*				Aircraft: *GABCD*			Date: *21 09 2015*				Depart' Time:		
From/To	Safety Alt.	Alt. Temp.	CAS	TAS	W/V	TRK °T	Drift	HDG °T	Var.	HDG °M	GS	Dist	Time	ETA
Shoreham Lydd	*2100*	*2400*				*082*			*2°W*			*47*		
Lydd Southend	*1900*	*2400*				*346*			*2°W*			*38*		
Southend Uckfield	*2400*	*2400*				*212*			*2°W*			*42*		
Uckfield Shoreham	*1900*	*2400*				*241*			*2°W*			*17*		
										Total		*144*		

■ *Figure 7-32* **Flight log with safety and planned altitude details added.**

Now complete: **Practice Questions - Vertical Navigation**

1. Altitude is the vertical distance of a level, point or object measured from:

(a) *The Aerodrome Reference Point.*
(b) *Mean sea level.*
(c) *The indicated value on an altimeter.*
(d) *The altimeter reading with QFE set in the subscale.*

2. The International Standard Atmosphere defines a change in temperature with increasing height. This is:

(a) *15°C at mean sea level reducing by 1.98°C per 1,000 ft up to 36,090 ft where the temperature remains at a constant -57°C.*
(b) *0°C at mean sea level reducing by 15°C per 1,000 ft indefinitely.*
(c) *15°C at mean sea level reducing by 1.98°C per 1,000 ft indefinitely.*
(d) *0°C at mean sea level reducing by 1.98°C per 1,000 ft up to 36,090 ft where the temperature remains at a constant -57°C.*

3. With aerodrome QFE set on the altimeter subscale, the altimeter reads:

(a) *Altitude above mean sea level.*
(b) *Pressure altitude.*
(c) *The aerodrome elevation.*
(d) *The height above the aerodrome.*

4. An aerodrome has an elevation of 599 ft. With QNH set on the altimeter subscale, the altimeter will read:

(a) *0 ft*
(b) *599 ft*
(c) *1,013 ft*
(d) *Minus 599 ft*

5. The International Standard Atmosphere defines a change in pressure with increasing height. For general aviation pilots, operating in the lower airspace, the approximation is :

(a) *1013 hPa at mean sea level reducing by 1 hPa per 30 ft.*
(b) *1013 hPa at mean sea level reducing by 30 hPa per 1 ft.*
(c) *1000 hPa at mean sea level reducing by 1 hPa per 30 ft.*
(d) *1000 hPa at mean sea level reducing by 30 hPa per 100 ft.*

6. What temperature exists at 5,500 ft in the International Standard Atmosphere?

(a) -11°C
(b) +4°C
(c) -4°C
(d) +15°C

7. You are planning a cross-country flight and require the pressure altitude to calculate true airspeed (TAS). Your planned altitude is 2,400 ft and the regional QNH is 998 hPa. What is the pressure altitude for planning purposes (use 1hPa = 30ft)?

(a) 2,400 ft
(b) 1,982 ft
(c) 3,398 ft
(d) 2,850 ft

8. An aircraft is flying at FL60 over terrain which is 1750 ft AMSL where the local QNH is 998 hPa. If the temperature structure is the same as ISA, what is the aircraft's height above the terrain (use 1hPa = 30ft)?

(a) 4,250 ft
(b) 4,700 ft
(c) 3,800 ft
(d) 6,450 ft

9. An aircraft is flying at FL60 over terrain which is 1750 ft AMSL where the local QNH is 1020hPa. If the temperature structure is the same as ISA, what is the aircraft's height above the terrain (use 1hPa = 30ft)?

(a) 3,360 ft
(b) 4,460 ft
(c) 2,940 ft
(d) 3,800 ft

Airspeed

Airspeed

A sound understanding of the factors involved in *airspeed* is important if you are to become a competent pilot/navigator. The **true airspeed (TAS)** of an aircraft is its rate of progress or speed through the air mass in which it is flying. Whether the air mass is moving over the ground or is stationary is irrelevant to the true airspeed. TAS is simply the speed of the aircraft through the air.

In contrast, a hot-air balloon or a cloud has no horizontal driving force of its own and so just hangs in the air. This means the TAS of a balloon or a cloud is zero because it is not moving *relative* to the air mass.

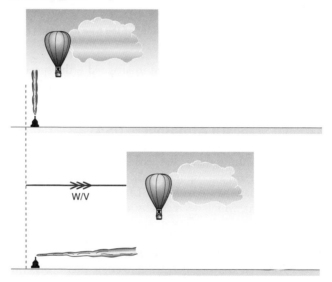

■ *Figure 8-1* ***An air mass can be stationary or move as wind***

If the air mass is moving relative to the ground (i.e. the wind velocity is other than zero), then the balloon or cloud will be carried by the air mass across the ground. Being static in the air mass, the balloon or the cloud could theoretically be used as a point against which to measure the true airspeed (TAS) of an aircraft. In other words, an aircraft will fly past a balloon, or a cloud, at its true airspeed.

The actual speed of an aircraft relative to the ground is called the **groundspeed (GS).** The resultant groundspeed is a combination of:

- **the true airspeed** (TAS – the movement of the aircraft relative to the air mass); and
- **the wind velocity** (W/V – the movement of the air mass relative to the ground).

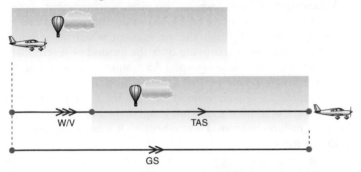

■ *Figure 8-2* **The groundspeed is the resultant of the true airspeed (TAS) and the wind velocity (W/V)**

At this stage we are only interested in airspeed – the speed of the aircraft through the air. (Groundspeed comes later in the book.)

International Standard Atmosphere (ISA)

A *standard atmosphere* is the standard state against which we can compare the actual atmosphere that exists at a given place on a given day. The standard atmosphere has:

- **A standard mean sea level (MSL) pressure** of 1013.25 hectopascals (hPa), which decreases by about 1 hPa for each 30 ft of altitude gained. For practical purposes, we use 1013 hPa.
- **A standard MSL temperature** of + 15°C, which decreases by about 2°C for each 1,000 ft of altitude gained.
- **The ISA MSL air density** is 1,225 gm/cubic metre, and this also decreases as altitude is gained.

NOTE The **hectopascal (hPa),** a standard unit of pressure for aviation, equivalent to millibars, has been adopted in many countries. Because 1 mb = 1 hPa, only the name change is significant. The UK recently adopted the hPa but many places still use millibars (mb) and the USA still uses inches and you will see hPa in the Republic of Ireland and in Europe.

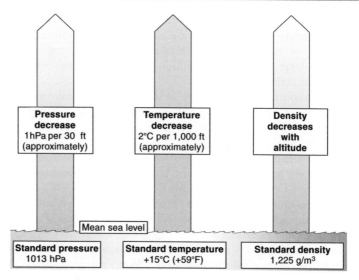

■ *Figure 8-3* **The International Standard Atmosphere (ISA)**

Speed Measurement

The basic instrument used to measure speed is the **airspeed indicator (ASI)** which is a pressure-operated instrument. The airspeed displayed is the **indicated airspeed (IAS).**

Due to the nature of the atmosphere – in which air pressure and air density decrease with altitude – and the design of the airspeed indicator, the indicated airspeed (IAS) is usually *less* than the true airspeed (TAS).

■ *Figure 8-4* **Airspeed indicator with a TAS correction scale**

The indicated airspeed shown on the airspeed indicator in the cockpit and the true airspeed of the aeroplane through the air will only be the same value when International Standard Atmosphere mean sea level (ISA MSL) conditions exist. Such conditions are usually not experienced.

In conditions other than ISA MSL, pilots must make simple calculations (either mentally or by navigation computer) to convert the IAS they read on the airspeed indicator to the TAS needed for navigation.

The fact that the word *airspeed* has a number of meanings in aviation may be confusing at first but you must understand the differences.

- **Performance** of the aeroplane is related to **indicated airspeed (IAS)** (i.e. whether the aircraft will stall or not, its rate of climb performance, lift/drag ratio etc.), and is a function of IAS. Indicated airspeed is related to dynamic pressure.
- **Navigation and flight planning** depend on **true airspeed (TAS), wind velocity (W/V)** and **groundspeed (GS)**. True airspeed is the actual speed of the aeroplane through the air.

To understand the difference between the two basic airspeeds: indicated airspeed (IAS), and true airspeed (TAS), we need to consider briefly certain properties of the atmosphere and the principles of fluid flow.

Static Pressure

Static pressure at any point in the atmosphere is exerted equally in all directions. It is a result of the weight of all the molecules composing the air above that point. At this very moment, static pressure of the atmosphere is being exerted at all points on the skin of your hand.

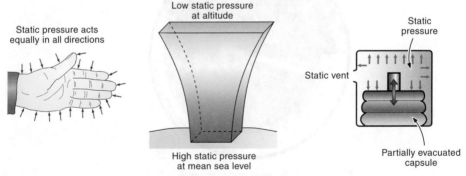

■ Figure 8-5 **Static pressure**

As its name implies, static pressure does not involve any motion of the body relative to the air.

Dynamic Pressure

If you hold your hand up in a strong wind or out of the window of a moving car, then an extra wind pressure, or 'moving pressure', is felt due to the air striking your hand.

This extra pressure, over and above the static pressure which is always present, is called **dynamic pressure,** or pressure due to relative movement. It is felt by a body that is moving relative to the air, i.e. it could be moving through the air, or the air could be flowing past it.

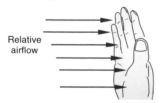

■ *Figure 8-6* **Dynamic pressure**

Just how strong dynamic pressure is depends on a number of things, the two main ones being:

1. The speed of the body relative to the air. The faster the car drives or the faster the wind blows, then the stronger the extra dynamic pressure that you feel on your hand. This is because of the greater number of air molecules that strike it per second.

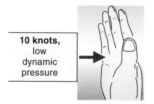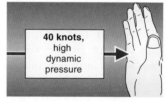

■ *Figure 8-7* **Dynamic pressure increases with airspeed**

2. The density of the air. In outer space, no matter how fast you travelled, you would not feel any dynamic pressure because there are practically no molecules to strike you. In contrast, at sea level, where the atmosphere is densest, your hand would be struck by many molecules per second – certainly many more than in the upper regions of the atmosphere. Even though you might be travelling at the same speed, you will feel a much lower dynamic pressure in the higher levels of the atmosphere, where the air is less dense, than in the lower levels.

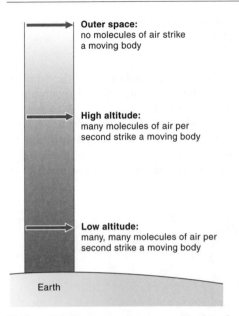

Outer space:
no molecules of air strike
a moving body

High altitude:
many molecules of air per
second strike a moving body

Low altitude:
many, many molecules of air per
second strike a moving body

Earth

■ *Figure 8-8 **Air density decreases with altitude***

So, for an aircraft moving at a constant true airspeed, less dynamic pressure is experienced the higher the altitude. The actual measure of dynamic pressure is written:

Dynamic pressure = $\frac{1}{2}$ × rho × V-squared

- *rho* represents air density, which decreases with altitude.
- *V* represents the speed of the body relative to the air, i.e. the true airspeed. (It does not matter whether the body is moving through the air, or the air blowing past the body, or a combination of both – as long as they are moving relative to one another there will be an airspeed and a dynamic pressure.)

Total Pressure
In the atmosphere some static pressure is always exerted, but only if there is motion of the body relative to the air will any dynamic pressure (due to relative motion) be felt by the surface exposed to the airflow. Thus:

Total pressure consists of static pressure plus dynamic pressure.

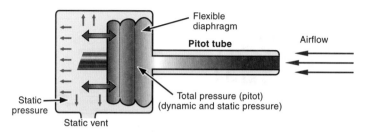

■ *Figure 8-9* **Total pressure is measured by a pitot tube**

Much of this theory about pressure was developed by the Swiss scientist Daniel Bernoulli, and is expressed in Bernoulli's equation, which, in simplified form, is:

Static pressure	**+**	**Dynamic pressure**	**=**	**Total pressure**
measured by static line (barometer or altimeter)		*½ rho × V-squared*		*measured by pitot tube*

An expression for dynamic pressure can be obtained by subtracting the term static pressure from both sides of this equation:

Dynamic pressure = total pressure − static pressure

Indicated Airspeed (IAS)

A measure of dynamic pressure can be found by starting with the total (pitot) pressure, and subtracting the static pressure from it. This is done using a diaphragm with total pressure from the pitot tube fed onto one side, and static pressure from the static line fed onto the other side.

The diaphragm in the airspeed indicator (ASI) system positions itself according to the difference between the total pressure and the static pressure, i.e. according to the dynamic pressure. A pointer connected to the diaphragm through a gearing mechanism then moves around the ASI scale as the diaphragm responds to these pressure variations.

If we assume that the density of air (*rho*) remains constant at its mean sea level value (which it does not), the scale around which the pointer moves can be graduated in units of speed. This results in an airspeed indicator that displays the airspeed accurately only under ISA MSL conditions, i.e. when the air density is 1,225 grams per cubic metre (the same as at + 15°C, pressure altitude zero).

If the air density (*rho*) is precisely 1,225 gm/cubic metre, then the airspeed indicator will show an indicated airspeed that is the same as the true airspeed of the aeroplane through the air.

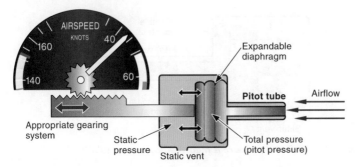

■ *Figure 8-10* **The flexible diaphragm in the airspeed indicator drives the pointer to display indicated airspeed (IAS)**

NOTE Airspeed indicators are usually calibrated in knots but you may see indicators graduated in statute miles per hour, the familiar mph.

Indicated airspeed (IAS) is what we read on the airspeed indicator (ASI).

Calibrated Airspeed (CAS)

A particular pitot-static system and its cockpit airspeed indicator (ASI) will experience some small errors. The main two are:

1. **Instrument error** – resulting from poor design and construction of the ASI itself, or from friction within it.

2. **Position error** – resulting from sensing errors inherent in the position on the aircraft of the static vent and the pitot tube. Their position with respect to the airflow is critical and may lead to somewhat incorrect readings when the airflow pattern is disturbed at certain airspeeds, angles of attack, or wing flap settings.

The pilot can correct the reading of indicated airspeed shown on the ASI by using a calibration table (found in the Pilot's Operating Handbook for the aeroplane) to obtain a value known **calibrated airspeed (CAS)** or **rectified airspeed (RAS)**.

The calculated CAS figure is what the ASI would read if the particular airspeed indicator system was perfect. CAS is therefore more accurate than IAS and, if you have taken the trouble to calculate CAS, it should be used in preference to IAS in navigation calculations.

The instrument and position errors of an airspeed indicator system are usually no more than a few knots and, for our purposes at PPL level, we can generally assume that indicated airspeed (IAS) and calibrated airspeed (CAS) are equal. To remind you we will occasionally write IAS (CAS).

Relating True Airspeed to Indicated Airspeed

The aeroplane will rarely be flying in an air mass that has the same density as that under ISA MSL conditions (1,225 gm/cubic metre), the basis of the calibration of the airspeed indicator. Generally an aeroplane flying at altitude will be experiencing an air density significantly less than this, because air density *(rho)* decreases with altitude. This will also be the case when there is an increase in temperature.

The indicated airspeed (even if it has been corrected for instrument and position errors to give calibrated airspeed) will need to be further corrected for **density error** if the pilot is to know the exact speed at which the aeroplane is moving through the air – the true airspeed.

Whereas the position and instrument error (if any) will be different for each ASI system, the density error applies equally to all systems because it is a function of the atmospheric conditions at that time and place.

Air density varies for two main reasons:

1. **Temperature.** Cold air is dense, warm air is less dense, so on a warm day an aircraft must travel faster through the air for the same number of molecules per second to strike it, and for the same IAS to be indicated. TAS varying with temperature (for a constant IAS) is one reason why, on a warm day, an aeroplane requires longer take-off and landing distances. The TAS is higher to give you the same IAS, and the IAS is what you 'fly by'.

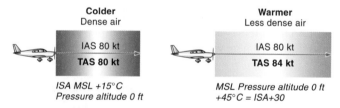

■ Figure 8-11 **Constant IAS (CAS): TAS varies with air temperature**

2. **Pressure.** The greater the pressure altitude (i.e. the lower the air pressure), the fewer the molecules per unit volume. For two aircraft with the same true airspeed (TAS), the higher aircraft will have a lower indicated airspeed (IAS) because it will strike fewer molecules of air per second than the lower aircraft.

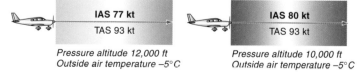

■ Figure 8-12 **Same TAS: the aircraft in less dense air has a lower IAS (CAS)**

Remember that IAS (CAS) is only equal to TAS under ISA MSL (International Standard Atmosphere mean sea level) conditions. At higher altitudes the IAS (or CAS) will be less than the TAS because the aircraft will be flying through the thinner air with an airspeed well in excess of that indicated on the ASI.

What Happens When We Climb at a Constant IAS?

As an aeroplane gains altitude, the air density (*rho*) decreases. If we adopt the usual climb technique of maintaining a constant IAS (a constant dynamic pressure '½ × *rho* × V–squared'), the decrease in *rho* is made up by an increase in *V* (the true airspeed).

> The higher we climb, when flying at a constant IAS, the greater the TAS.

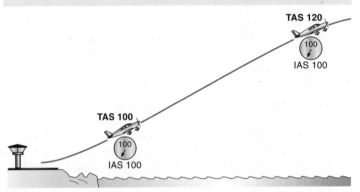

■ Figure 8-13 **The higher we climb, the greater the TAS for a constant IAS (CAS)**

Using the Navigation Computer to Find TAS from IAS

Finding TAS from IAS is simple with a navigation computer. The principles illustrated here apply to most types available.

On the calculator side of most navigation computers is an **airspeed correction window,** which allows us to:

- **match up** the *pressure altitude* and the *air temperature* (the main factors determining density); and then
- **from IAS** (or CAS/RAS) on the inner scale, read off TAS on the outer scale.

NOTE On many navigation computers the inner scale is labelled CAS or RAS (or IAS) and the outer scale TAS. Check your own computer.

Ensure that you use the Celsius temperature scale, as all temperatures in UK meteorology forecasts (and those for most other countries) are given in degrees Celsius (formerly centigrade).

EXAMPLE 1

1. Temperature is −10°C at pressure altitude 8,000 ft.

2. CAS (RAS) 115 kt gives TAS 127 kt.

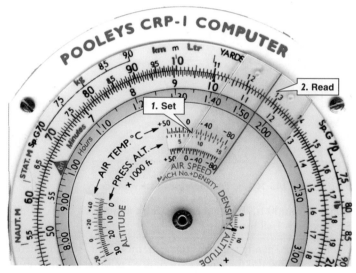

■ *Figure 8-14* **Example 1, finding TAS from IAS (CAS) and air temperature on the navigation computer**

As a further example, line up the ISA MSL conditions of +15°C and pressure altitude 0. The computer will then show that under these conditions IAS (inner scale) and TAS (outer scale) are the same.

Variation of TAS with Altitude

Assume that the recommended climb speed for your aeroplane is 100 kt IAS. Using your navigation computer, see if you can come up with similar answers for the TAS as we have in Figure 8-15, for a climb at IAS 100 kt from MSL to 20,000 ft. (Assume standard atmosphere conditions, where temperature decreases by 2°C for each 1,000 ft climbed.)

Pressure altitude	Temp.	IAS/RAS	TAS
20,000 ft	–25°C	100 kt	137 kt
15,000 ft	–15°C	100 kt	126 kt
10,000 ft	–5°C	100 kt	117 kt
5,000 ft	+5°C	100 kt	108 kt
ISA MSL	+15°C	100 kt	100 kt

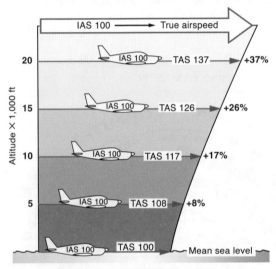

■ Figure 8-15 **IAS 100 kt: TAS increases with altitude**

NOTE At 5,000 ft, TAS exceeds IAS by about 8%. At 10,000 ft, TAS exceeds IAS by about 17%.

These are handy figures to remember for rough mental calculations and also for when experienced pilots are talking about the speeds at which their aeroplanes 'true-out'. If you are cruising at 5,000 ft with IAS 180 kt showing on the airspeed indicator, then your TAS will be approximately 8% greater (8% of 180 = 14), i.e. 194 kt TAS.

For a Constant TAS, What IAS is Required?

It is interesting to compare what indicated airspeed will be shown in the cockpit if a constant true airspeed is required at various levels. See if you can obtain the same answers as we do for IAS with a constant true airspeed of 200 kt at various pressure altitudes. Once again, assume a standard atmosphere to be present.

Pressure Altitude	Temp.	TAS	IAS/RAS
20,000 ft	−25°C	200 kt	146 kt
15,000 ft	−15°C	200 kt	159 kt
10,000 ft	−5°C	200 kt	172 kt
5,000 ft	+5°C	200 kt	185 kt
ISA MSL	+15°C	200 kt	200 kt

To fly the same TAS, IAS will decrease with higher altitudes as the air density decreases.

So, for the same TAS, the greater the pressure altitude, the lower the IAS.

The higher an aircraft flies, the more the TAS exceeds the IAS.

Variation of TAS with Outside Air Temperature (OAT)

Temperature at the one level in the atmosphere will vary from place to place and from time to time. Since temperature affects air density, it will also affect the relationship between IAS and TAS.

1. The mean sea level situation if temperature varies:

	Temp.	IAS/RAS	TAS	
	ISA+20 = +35°C	100 kt	104 kt	(less dense air)
Pressure	ISA+10 = +25°C	100 kt	102 kt	
altitude	ISA = +15°C	100 kt	100 kt	
0 ft	ISA−10 = +5°C	100 kt	98 kt	
	ISA−20 = −5°C	100 kt	96 kt	(more dense air)

The less dense the air, the greater the TAS, compared to IAS (CAS).

2. The situation at pressure altitude 10,000 ft, if temperature varies:

	Temp.	IAS/RAS	TAS	
	ISA+20 = +15°C	100 kt	121 kt	(less dense air)
Pressure	ISA+10 = +5°C	100 kt	119 kt	
altitude	ISA = −5°C	100 kt	117 kt	
10,000 ft	ISA−10 = −15°C	100 kt	115 kt	
	ISA−20 = −25°C	100 kt	113 kt	(more dense air)

True airspeed is important for navigation and flight planning because TAS is the actual speed of the aeroplane through the air mass.

More IAS to TAS Computer Calculations

EXAMPLE 2 At FL70, OAT −5°C, IAS (CAS) 105 kt. Find the TAS.

Working:

Set the pressure altitude 7,000 ft against −5°C OAT in the true airspeed (TAS) window.

Then, against CAS 105 kt on the inner scale, read off TAS 115 kt on the outermost scale.

TAS is 115 kt.

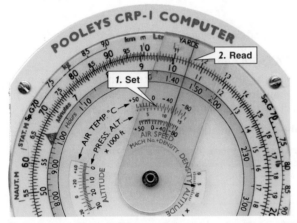

■ *Figure 8-16* **Example 2**

In some situations the required pieces of information are not always given directly, but have to be derived first from other information which is provided. We will take an example from a high flight level to illustrate the widening gap between IAS (CAS) and TAS as an aeroplane climbs.

EXAMPLE 3 A turboprop plans on flying at flight level 280 (FL280), where the temperature is forecast to be ISA+10°C. If its rectified airspeed (CAS) will be 150 kt, what TAS can be expected?

Working:

FL280 is pressure altitude 28,000 ft.

$$\text{At FL280, ISA} = +15 - (2 \times 28)$$
$$= +15 - 56$$
$$= -41°C$$
$$\text{so ISA+10} = -41 + 10$$
$$= -31°C$$

In the computer *airspeed* window, set *pressure altitude* 28,000 against OAT –31.

Against CAS 150 kt, read off TAS 240 kt on the outer scale.

Finding the Required IAS to Achieve a Particular TAS

The usual in-flight problem is to determine the TAS from the indicated airspeed read off the ASI. Sometimes, however, you need to be able to work these problems in reverse, say to achieve a certain desired TAS or GS for flight planning purposes, when you will start with these and work back to find the IAS (CAS/RAS) necessary to achieve this.

EXAMPLE 4 Cruising at FL100 and temperature ISA–10, what is the required CAS (RAS) to give you a true airspeed of 200 kt?

Working:

Pressure altitude is 10,000 ft,

$$\text{where ISA} = +15 - (2 \times 10)$$
$$= +15 - 20$$
$$= -5°C$$
$$\text{so ISA–10} = -5 - 10$$
$$= -15°C$$

In the computer *airspeed* window, set *pressure altitude* 10,000 against OAT –15°C.

Against TAS 200 on the outer scale, read off CAS 175 kt on the inner scale.

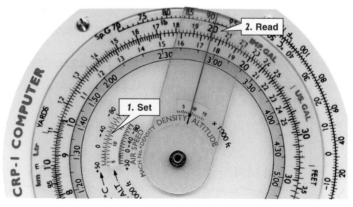

■ *Figure 8-17* **Example 4**

Airspeed Terminology

IAS: Indicated airspeed.

CAS OR RAS: Calibrated airspeed or rectified airspeed. Generally approximately equal to indicated airspeed.

TAS: True Airspeed. At higher altitudes, TAS is usually greater than IAS/CAS or RAS).

Example Prepared Chart and Flight Log
The calculation of true airspeed is a two-stage process:
* Firstly, calculate the pressure altitude;
* Secondly, knowing the pressure altitude and temperature at the intended cruising level, use the navigation computer to obtain true airspeed.

The mean sea level pressure (QNH) on the date of the flight is 1000 hPa. We can estimate the temperature of the cruising level either by the ISA lapse rate approximation of -2°C per 1000 ft of ascent based on the temperature on the ground. Alternatively, a more accurate estimate could be obtained from Met. Office Form 214 UK Spot Wind Forecast Chart. The planner has determined that the temperature is +10°C at the selected cruising level of 2400 ft.

The pressure altitude is calculated using the process in Chapter 7 – vertical navigation and is shown below:

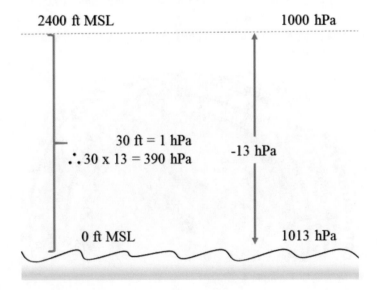

■ *Figure 8-18* **Calculation of pressure altitude**

With an indicated altitude of 2400 ft in a QNH of 1000 hPa, the pressure altitude is 2790 ft (based on an approximation of 30 ft per 1 hPa).

Using the navigation computer, and the selected cruising calibrated airspeed of 98 kt, the TAS at a pressure altitude of 2790 4ft at +10°C is 102 kt. This can now be entered into the flight log form:

Pilot: *P. Pilot*						Aircraft: *GABCD*			Date: *21 09 2015*				Depart' Time:		
From/To	Safety Alt.	Alt. / Temp.	CAS	TAS	W/V	TRK °T	Drift	HDG °T	Var.	HDG °M	GS	Dist	Time	ETA
Shoreham *Lydd*	*2100*	*2400* / *+10*	*98*	*102*		*082*			*2°W*			*47*		
Lydd *Southend*	*1900*	*2400* / *+10*	*98*	*102*		*346*			*2°W*			*38*		
Southend *Uckfield*	*2400*	*2400* / *+10*	*98*	*102*		*212*			*2°W*			*42*		
Uckfield *Shoreham*	*1900*	*2400* / *+10*	*98*	*102*		*241*			*2°W*			*17*		
										Total		*144*		

■ *Figure 8-19* **Example flight log form with airspeed added.**

Now complete: **Practice Questions - Airspeed**

1. You are flying at FL70 with an outside air temperature of - 10°C. The ASI indicates 100 kt and combined instrument and position error correction is zero kt. What is your TAS?

   (a) 109kt
   (b) 100kt
   (c) 112kt
   (d) 105kt

2. An aircraft is flying at an indicated air speed (IAS) of 130 knots at FL 100. The OAT is +10° C what is the aircraft's true airspeed (TAS)? Ignore position and instrument errors.

   (a) 150 kt
   (b) 134 kt
   (c) 162 kt
   (d) 156 kt

3. An aircraft is flying at an indicated air speed (IAS) of 110 knots at FL 40. The OAT is -5° C, what is the aircraft's true airspeed (TAS)? Ignore position and instrument errors.

   (a) 117 kt
   (b) 114 kt
   (c) 240 kt
   (d) 109 kt

4. An aircraft is flying at an indicated air speed (IAS) of 120 knots at FL 80. The OAT is 11° C greater than the ISA, what is the aircraft's true airspeed (TAS)? Ignore position and instrument errors.

   (a) 133 kt
   (b) 138 kt
   (c) 115 kt
   (d) 144 kt

5. An aircraft is cruising with an IAS of 95kt at FL70 where the outside air temperature is 10°C colder than in the ISA. If the combined ASI position and instrument error is -6kt, what is the TAS?

   (a) 93kt
   (b) 90kt
   (c) 97kt
   (d) 102kt

6. Your destination is 77 nm away; you must arrive in not less than 42 minutes. If you are flying at FL 50 and the OAT is + 10° C° what is the minimum Calibrated Airspeed CAS required to arrive at the desired time? Assume no head or tail wind component.

(a) *91 kt*

(b) *111 kt*

(c) *101 kt*

(d) *97 kt*

7. An aircraft is approaching Waypoint A en-route to Waypoint B. For air traffic reasons, the ETA at B must be 15 minutes after arrival over A. The distance A to B is 25nm, the flight is at FL60 where the temperature is 0°C. Ignoring wind, what is the appropriate CAS to fly from A to B?

(a) *87kt*

(b) *95kt*

(c) *92kt*

(d) *89kt*

Drift

An aeroplane flies in the medium of air. Its motion relative to the air mass is specified by its:
- **direction** (known as **heading**); and
- **speed** through the air mass (**true airspeed**).

HEADING (HDG). When flown in balance (as it normally is) the aeroplane will travel *through* the air in the direction in which it is heading. If the aeroplane is heading east (090), then its passage relative to the air mass will be easterly (090) also.

TRUE AIRSPEED (TAS). This is the actual speed of the aeroplane *relative* to the air mass. True airspeed is normally abbreviated to TAS, but occasionally to V when used in aerodynamic formulae. (See *Principles of Flight* in Vol. 4 of *The Air Pilot's Manual*.)

When considered together, HDG/TAS constitute a **vector** quantity, which requires both *magnitude* (in this case TAS) and *direction* (here HDG) to be completely specified. HDG/TAS is the velocity (direction and speed) of the aeroplane through the air.

> The **HDG/TAS** vector fully describes the motion of the aeroplane relative to the air mass.

HDG/TAS is symbolised by a single-headed arrow ——▷—— ; the direction of the arrow indicates the direction of movement along the vector line.

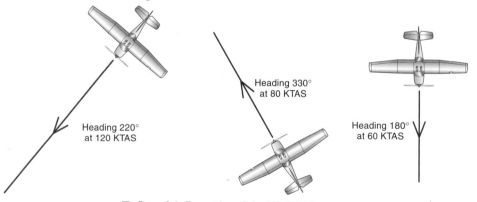

Heading 220°
at 120 KTAS

Heading 330°
at 80 KTAS

Heading 180°
at 60 KTAS

■ *Figure 9-1* **Examples of the HDG/TAS vector**

An Air Mass can Move Relative to the Ground (a Wind can 'Blow')

The general movement of air relative to the ground is called **wind velocity** and is abbreviated to **W/V**. Like HDG/TAS, W/V is a vector quantity because both direction and magnitude are specified.

By convention, the wind direction is expressed as the direction *from* which it is blowing. For example, a northerly wind blows from the north towards the south. W/V is symbolised by a triple-headed arrow ——⟫—— .

> The **W/V** vector fully describes the horizontal motion of the air mass relative to the earth's surface.

| A westerly wind of 30 knots, i.e. 270/30 | A wind blowing from 030° at 10 knots, i.e. 030/10 | A southerly wind of 15 knots, i.e. 180/15 | A wind blowing from 210° at 20 knots, i.e. 210/20 |

■ *Figure 9-2* **Examples of the wind vector**

With a W/V of 230/20, the air mass will be moving relative to the earth's surface from a direction of 230° at a rate of 20 nautical miles per hour.

In a 6 minute period, for example, the air mass will have moved 2 nm (6 minute = $^1/_{10}$ hour; $^1/_{10}$ of 20 nm = 2 nm) from a direction of 230°, and therefore towards (230 – 180) = 050°.

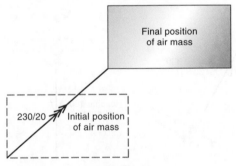

■ *Figure 9-3* **A wind of 230/20**

The motion of the aeroplane relative to the surface of the earth is made up of two velocities:
- **the aeroplane** moving relative to the air mass (HDG/TAS); and
- **the air mass** moving relative to the surface of the earth (W/V).

Adding these two together gives the resultant vector of:
- **the aeroplane** moving relative to the surface of the earth. This is the track and groundspeed (TR/GS), which is symbolised by a double-headed arrow ———⟫——— .

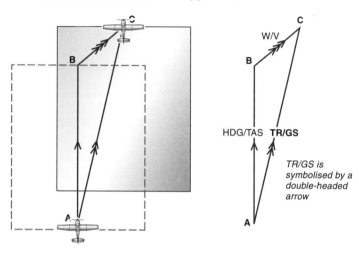

■ Figure 9-4 **HDG/TAS + W/V = TR/GS**

An aeroplane flying through an air mass is in a similar situation to you swimming across a fast flowing river. If you dive in at A and head off through the water in the direction of B, the current will carry you downstream towards C. To an observer sitting overhead in the branch of a tree, you will appear to be swimming a little bit 'sideways' as you get swept downstream, even though in fact you are swimming straight through the water.

In the same way, it is common to look up and see an aeroplane flying somewhat 'sideways' in strong wind situations. Of course the aeroplane is not actually flying sideways through the air, rather it is flying straight ahead relative to the air mass (HDG/TAS). It is wind velocity (W/V) which, when added to the aeroplane's motion through the air (HDG/TAS), gives it the resultant motion over the ground (track/groundspeed).

To fly from A to C in the above situation, the pilot must fly on a HDG of A–B through the air, i.e. maintain the nose of the aeroplane in a direction parallel to A–B. The wind will have the effect of B–C. The combined effect of these, known as the resultant, will give the aeroplane a track over the ground of A–C.

The TR/GS vector fully describes the motion of the aeroplane relative to the earth's surface.

The Triangle of Velocities

The two velocities:

- **HDG/TAS:** the aeroplane moving through the air mass; and
- **W/V:** the air mass moving over the ground;

when added together as vectors, give the resultant:

- **TR/GS (track/groundspeed)** – the aeroplane moving over the ground.

These three vectors form the **triangle of velocities.** It is a pictorial representation of the vector addition:

HDG/TAS + W/V = TR/GS

i.e. the combined effect of HDG/TAS plus W/V will give the resultant TR/GS (Figure 9-5).

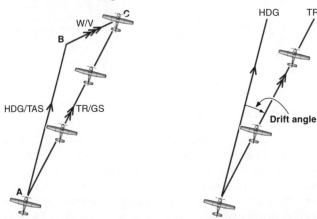

■ Figure 9-5 **The triangle**
of velocities

■ Figure 9-6 **Drift is the angle**
between heading and track

We add the two vectors for HDG/TAS and W/V 'head to tail', i.e. starting from A, the head of the HDG/TAS vector at B is the starting point for the tail of the W/V vector which then ends up at C.

The resultant effect of the two combined is the TR/GS vector starting at A and finishing at C. This is the path that the aeroplane would fly over the ground. The angle between the HDG and the track (TR) is called the **drift angle** (Figure 9-6).

You may have already seen this triangle of velocities illustrated on a navigation computer, as in Figure 9-7.

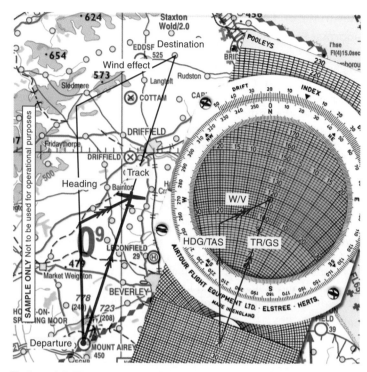

■ Figure 9-7 **The triangle of velocities laid on the wind side of a navigation computer**

At the flight planning stage:
• **you will know the desired track** (track required); and
• **will obtain a forecast wind velocity**.

Using the known true airspeed, you will be able to calculate:
• **the heading required** to 'make good' the desired track; and
• **the expected groundspeed.**

Later on during the flight you may find that, even though you have flown the HDG/TAS accurately, your actual **track made good (TMG)** over the ground differs from your desired track; in other words there is a **track error.** It is most likely to be caused by the actual wind being different from the forecast wind that you used at the flight planning stage. You will then have to make some adjustments to the HDG to carry out the navigation task of rejoining your desired track and continuing to the destination.

This is what air navigation is all about. The essential principles are simple and have now been covered. All we have to do is expand on them in the following chapters and combine them into practical navigation operations.

Summary of Terminology

HDG/TAS: Heading **(HDG)** is the actual heading of the aeroplane in degrees steered by the pilot. It may be related to true north, magnetic north or compass north.

True airspeed **(TAS)** is the actual speed of the aeroplane through the air. It will differ significantly from the airspeed indicated on the airspeed indicator (the indicated airspeed) due to the air being less dense the higher the aeroplane flies. The pilot will need to complete a small calculation to convert indicated airspeed (IAS) to true airspeed (TAS) when flying at altitude.

The normal unit for airspeed is the knot. IAS is useful for aerodynamics, but TAS is necessary for navigation. The normal unit of distance for navigation is the nautical mile (nm) and if it is distance relative to the air, we call it an air nautical mile (anm).

TR/GS: Track **(TR)** is the path of the aeroplane over the surface of the earth, and is usually expressed in degrees true or magnetic.

Groundspeed **(GS)** is the actual speed of the aeroplane over the ground and is measured in knots. A GS of 120 kt means that 120 ground nautical miles would be covered in 1 hour at that GS.

DRIFT is the difference between the HDG steered by the pilot and the track of the aeroplane over the ground. The wind blows the aeroplane from its HDG/TAS through the air onto its TR/GS over the earth's surface.

Drift is measured from the HDG (the nose of the aeroplane) to the TR, and is specified in degrees left (port) of HDG or right (starboard) of HDG.

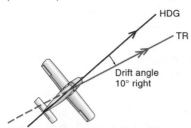

■ *Figure 9-8* **Drift is the angle between heading and track**

W/V: Wind direction is expressed in degrees *true* or *magnetic* and is the direction *from* which the wind is blowing. Wind speed is measured in knots (kt). 1 kt = 1 nm per hour.

TRACK ERROR: The actual **track made good** (TMG) over the ground will often differ from the *desired track*. The angular difference between the desired track and the TMG is called **track**

error and is specified in degrees left (port) or right (starboard) of the desired track.

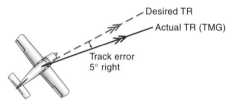

■ Figure 9-9 **Track error is the angle between desired track and the track made good (TMG)**

NOTE Track error is totally different from *drift*.

LATITUDE: The distance of a place north or south from the equator, measured in degrees.

LONGITUDE: The distance of a place from the prime meridian (0°), through Greenwich, also measured in degrees.

NAUTICAL MILE: The length of 1 minute of latitude measured along a meridian, i.e. down the side of a chart.

KNOT: Unit of speed equal to 1 nautical mile per hour.

GREAT CIRCLE: Intersection of the earth's surface and a plane passing through the earth's centre.

Heading, Drift and Speed Calculations

The slide navigation computer allows you to handle navigation problems involving the **triangle of velocities** quickly and accurately. The three vectors in the triangle can be marked on the plotting disc so that they appear in the same relationship, one to the other, as in flight, making it easier to visualise the situation and check that the vectors have been applied correctly.

Components of the **wind side** of a navigation computer are:

• A **circular, rotatable compass rose** (or azimuth) set in a fixed frame which is marked with an **index** at the top.

• A **transparent plastic plotting disc** attached to the rotatable compass rose, marked with a **centre-dot.**

• A **slide plate** printed with concentric *speed arcs* and radial *drift lines*. This plate slides through the frame and compass rose assembly, hence the name 'slide' navigation computer.

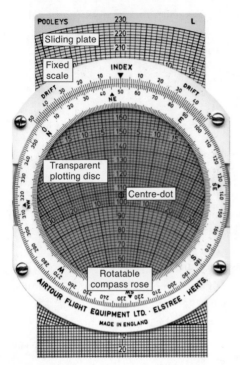

■ Figure 9-10 **Wind side of a slide navigation computer**

The Triangle of Velocities

Before you can use the navigation computer effectively, you must understand the triangle of velocities which, of course, has three sides. The first two are:

1. The motion of the aeroplane through the air – heading/true airspeed.

2. The motion of the air over the ground – wind velocity (direction and speed).

When these two are added together, the third side of the triangle, which is their resultant effect, is:

3. The motion of the aeroplane over the ground – track/ groundspeed.

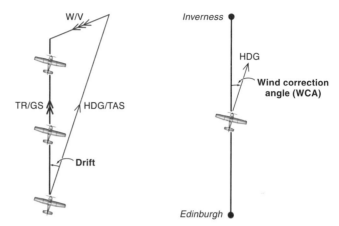

■ *Figure 9-11* ***The triangle of velocities and wind correction angle***

Note that the wind always blows the aeroplane from its heading to its track. In other words, the wind vector must start at the HDG/TAS vector and end at the TR/GS vector. If you have this firmly fixed in your mind, then computer solutions will follow easily and correctly.

A wind from the right will carry an aeroplane onto a track that is to the left of its heading. This is known as left drift or port drift. The drift angle is measured from HDG to TR. In Figure 9-11, 10° left drift is shown.

To achieve a particular track, say between two towns, the aeroplane must be steered into-wind on a heading that allows for the drift. In the above illustration, to achieve the track shown, the aeroplane is being steered on a steady heading 10° to the right of track. This can be described as a wind correction angle of 10° right. The wind correction angle is measured from TR to HDG and is, of course, equal and opposite to the drift angle.

Each of the three vectors in the triangle of velocities has two aspects: magnitude (size) and direction. This means that in the triangle of velocities there are six components:

VECTOR	MAGNITUDE	DIRECTION
HDG/TAS	TAS	HDG
W/V	Wind speed	Wind direction (from)
TR/GS	GS	TR

Typical navigation problems involve knowing four of these six elements and finding the other two.

Marking the Vector on the Plotting Disc

If you can sketch a triangle of velocities with the three vectors placed properly, then the wind side of the computer will create no difficulties at all.

While you are still learning how to use the computer, it is a good idea to mark each of the vectors with their arrowheads on the plotting disc to ensure that the triangle of velocities is portrayed correctly. Marks on the plotting disc can be removed quite easily at the end of each problem.

Once you become familiar with the use of the computer, however, the actual drawing in of each vector becomes unnecessary, and just one single mark (known as the wind-mark) to illustrate the extent of the wind velocity is all that is needed.

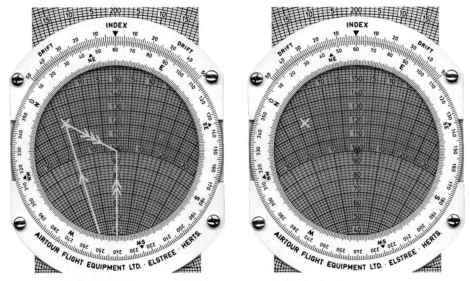

■ Figure 9-12 **Initially show the vectors (left); with practice you need only show the wind-mark**

Calculations in Degrees True and Magnetic

Calculations involving the navigation computer must be solved either in °T or °M. It is important not to mix the two in order to avoid errors. As wind direction is reported in °T, it is simpler to complete tasks using directions in °T and then apply magnetic variation to convert to °M. There is no reason why magnetic variation cannot be applied to the wind direction to allow solutions to be derived in °M. The examples that follow are calculated in °T.

Calculation Method

The wind side of the navigation computer can be used to calculate:

* the **heading** to steer; and
* the **groundspeed** that will be achieved

KNOWN:	FIND:
TR, W/V and TAS	HDG and GS

The navigation computer is used at the pre-flight planning stage and requires a knowledge of:

* the **track** in °T, measured on an aeronautical chart
* the **wind direction and velocity** in °T/kt, found using weather forecast resources
* the **true airspeed**

Whilst some texts describe the use of the navigation computer in flight, you should consider whether this practice is compatible with good airmanship principles, e.g. lookout and effective control of the aircraft. Techniques for en-route navigation are discussed in the next section which do not require involved mental arithmetic or use of the navigation computer.

Whilst there are now a plethora of computer applications designed to replace the navigation computer, it remains an absolutely reliable tool that does not require batteries or wireless internet access to function.

There are two common calculation methods described in user manuals and aviation literature: the **wind-up** and **wind-down** methods. The wind-up method is generally preferred over the wind-down method for two reasons: the calculation follows the triangle of velocities representation most closely and is simpler to use. For this reason, examples will follow based on the wind-up method and will be repeated based on the wind-down method starting on Page 172. The selection of method is generally made on the personal preference of the user or their flying instructor or training organisation. At this formative stage, the reader should consider both methods to develop their preference.

The Wind-Up Method

Determining HDG and GS When Flight Planning

EXAMPLE 1 *Find HDG and GS*

KNOWN:		FIND:
Required track (TR) *measured off chart*	**150°**	**HDG and GS**
True airspeed (TAS) *known, or calculated from* *expected RAS/CAS*	**100 kt**	
Wind velocity (W/V) *stated on forecast*	**360°T/30**	
Magnetic variation *shown on chart*	**5°W**	

An efficient way to record navigation data is to use a flight log, like that in Figure 9-13. The known information can be entered first as shown, with the results of your calculations following at a later stage.

From/To	Safety ALT	ALT		RAS	TAS	W/V	TR °T	Drift	HDG °T	Var	HDG °M	GS	Dist	Time	ETA	HDG °C
		Temp														
					100	360/30	150			5°W						

■ *Figure 9-13* **Typical flight log**

STEP 1. PLACE THE W/V ON THE PLOTTING DISC.

Wind direction and wind speed are known, i.e. both aspects of the W/V vector are known.

Rotate the compass rose until the wind direction 360 (north) is under the index. Mark the start of the W/V vector 30 kt above the centre-dot.

Since the track is known, show the W/V blowing towards the centre-dot, i.e. the wind vector will come from direction 360° and end at the centre-dot. Marking the starting point of the wind 30 kt above the centre-dot is most easily achieved by first setting one of the labelled wind arcs under the centre-dot, and then placing the wind-mark 30 kt above it.

At this early stage in your training, mark in the full W/V, showing the three arrowheads of the W/V vector pointing down towards the centre-dot. This will give you a clear picture as the whole triangle of velocities is developed.

STEP 2. PLACE THE TR/GS VECTOR ON THE PLOTTING DISC.

Track is known (having been measured on the chart); ground-speed is not known. In this case, only one aspect of the TR/GS vector is known – its direction, but not its magnitude.

Rotate the compass rose until the required TR of 150°T is under the index. (We cannot position the appropriate ground-speed arc under the centre-dot because we do not yet know its value.)

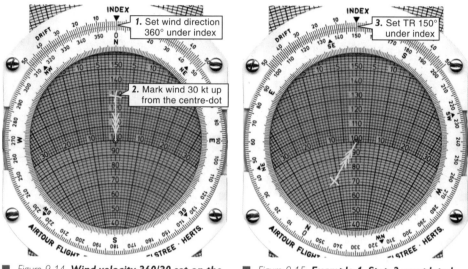

1. Set wind direction 360° under index

2. Mark wind 30 kt up from the centre-dot

3. Set TR 150° under index

■ *Figure 9-14* **Wind velocity 360/30 set on the computer at the flight planning stage: Example 1, Step 1**

■ *Figure 9-15* **Example 1, Step 2 completed**

STEP 3. PLACE THE HDG/TAS VECTOR ON THE PLOTTING DISC.

True airspeed is known, but the heading is not. In this case, only one aspect of the HDG/TAS vector is known – its magnitude.

Move the slide and place the TAS 100 kt speed arc under the wind-mark (which is the starting point of the W/V vector). This is where a clear understanding of the triangle of velocities is most important! The end of the HDG/TAS vector is where the W/V begins.

STEP 4. READ OFF THE ANSWERS FOR HDG AND GS.

The GS of 125 kt appears under the centre-dot. From the drift lines, the wind correction angle is 9° to the left of the track. This means that in order to achieve TR 150°T, the aeroplane must be pointed 9° into-wind and flown on a HDG of 141°T to allow for the 9° of right (starboard) drift.

The arithmetic (for determining HDG 141 from TR 150 and a wind correction angle of 9° into-wind) can be checked on the scale near the index mark.

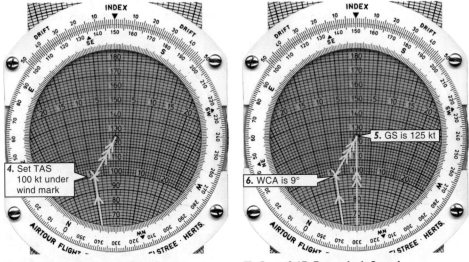

■ Figure 9-16 **Example 1, Step 3**   ■ Figure 9-17 **Example 1, Step 4**

ANSWER HDG 141°T, GS 125 kt

NOTE If magnetic heading is required, it is simply a matter of applying variation. If variation is 5°W, then 141°T is 146°M (variation west, magnetic best).

From/To	Safety ALT	ALT / Temp	RAS	TAS	W/V	TR °T	Drift	HDG °T	Var	HDG °M	GS	Dist	Time	ETA	HDG °C
			100	360/30	150	9°R	141	5°W	146	125				

■ Figure 9-18 **Example 1**

EXAMPLE 2 *Find HDG and GS*

Given a true airspeed of 174 kt, a forecast W/V of 240°T/40 kt, and a desired track of 290°T, calculate the true heading required and the groundspeed that will be achieved. What is the magnetic heading if variation in the vicinity of the flight is 6°W?

KNOWN:		FIND:
TAS.	174 kt	HDG and GS
Required TR	290°T	
W/V	240°T/40	

From/To	Safety ALT	ALT Temp	RAS	TAS	W/V	TR °T	Drift	HDG °T	Var	HDG °M	GS	Dist	Time	ETA	HDG °C
			174	240/40	290				6°W						

■ Figure 9-19 **Example 2**

STEP 1. PLACE THE W/V ON THE PLOTTING DISC.

Both wind speed and wind direction are known. Since the required TR is known, we show the W/V blowing down from the index towards the centre-dot.

Set wind direction 240 under the index. Mark in the wind strength 40 kt above the centre-dot.

STEP 2. PLACE THE TR/GS VECTOR ON THE PLOTTING DISC.

TR is known. GS is not known. Rotate the compass rose until the required TR 290°T is under the index. (We cannot position the appropriate speed arc under the centre-dot because we do not yet know the GS.)

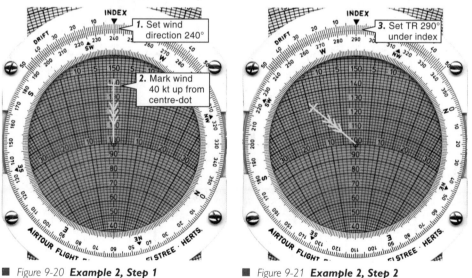

■ Figure 9-20 **Example 2, Step 1**   ■ Figure 9-21 **Example 2, Step 2**

STEP 3. PLACE THE HDG/TAS VECTOR ON THE PLOTTING DISC.

TAS is known. HDG is not known. Move the slide to place the TAS 174 kt under the wind-mark, which is starting point of the W/V vector (since the W/V vector begins where the TAS/HDG vector ends).

STEP 4. READ OFF THE ANSWERS FOR HDG AND GS.

The wind correction angle of 10° left can now be read off the drift lines, i.e. the aeroplane must be steered 10° into wind (i.e. left of the desired track to allow for the 10° right, or starboard, drift). In this case, to achieve the desired track of 290°T, the aeroplane must be steered on a heading of 280°T.

The groundspeed 145 kt lies under the centre-dot.

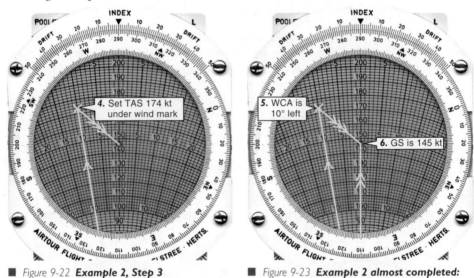

■ Figure 9-22 **Example 2, Step 3**   ■ Figure 9-23 **Example 2 almost completed: HDG 280°T, GS 145 kt**

Magnetic variation in the area is 6°W, so HDG 280°T is 286°M.

ANSWER HDG 280°T, variation 6°W, HDG 286M; GS 145 kt

From/To	Safety ALT	ALT Temp	RAS	TAS	W/V	TR °T	Drift	HDG °T	Var	HDG °M	GS	Dist	Time	ETA	HDG °C
			174	240/40	290	10°R	280	6°W	286	145				

■ Figure 9-24 **Example 2**

EXAMPLE 3 *Finding HDG/TAS to Achieve a Particular TR/GS*

Occasionally you may want to achieve a particular groundspeed, for instance to arrive overhead the destination at a particular time. This example is a variation on the previous one.

We want to know what true airspeed is required to achieve a groundspeed of 120 kt in Example 2.

KNOWN:		FIND:
TR	*290°T*	**TAS and HDG**
W/V	*240°/40 kt*	
GS	*120 kt*	

From/To	Safety ALT	ALT / Temp	RAS	TAS	W/V	TR °T	Drift	HDG °T	Var	HDG °M	GS	Dist	Time	ETA	HDG °C
					240/40	290			6°W		120				

■ *Figure 9-25* **Example 3**

STEP 1. PLACE W/V ON THE PLOTTING DISC.

Set wind direction 240° under the index. Place wind–mark 40 kt above the centre–dot, wind blowing down.

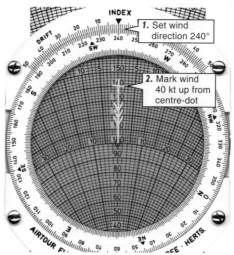

■ *Figure 9-26* **Example 3, Step 1**

STEP 2. PLACE THE TR/GS VECTOR ON THE PLOTTING DISC.

In this case both TR 290°T and GS 120 kt are known. Rotate the compass rose and set TR 290°T under the index. Set GS 120 kt under the centre-dot.

STEP 3. READ OFF TAS, AND DETERMINE HDG FROM DRIFT.

Read off TAS 150 kt under the wind-mark. Read off drift of 12°, therefore HDG is 12° left of TR. HDG is 278°T.

NOTE The wind is from the left, so the wind correction angle is 12° left of the desired track to allow for the expected 12° right (starboard) drift. You can check your arithmetic against the small scale near the index mark.

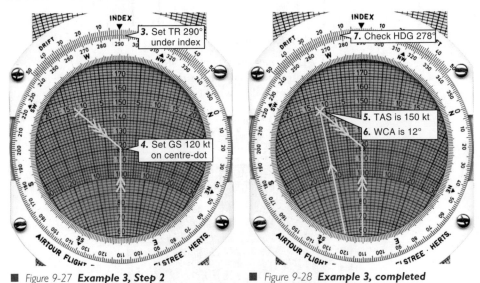

■ Figure 9-27 **Example 3, Step 2**   ■ Figure 9-28 **Example 3, completed**

ANSWER TAS 150 kt, HDG 278°T

From/To	Safety ALT	ALT Temp	RAS	TAS	W/V	TR °T	Drift	HDG °T	Var	HDG °M	GS	Dist	Time	ETA	HDG °C
				150	240/40	290	12°R	278	6°W	284	120				

■ Figure 9-29 **Example 3**

Calculating the Wind Velocity In Flight

It is also possible to determine the actual W/V when the pilot knows:

- the heading maintained;
- true airspeed;
- the track made good (TMG);
- the groundspeed.

These are four of the six items in the triangle of velocities and, using them, you can find the other two – wind direction and wind speed (i.e. wind velocity). This problem can be summarised as:

KNOWN:	FIND:
HDG/TAS and TR/GS	W/V

EXAMPLE 4 Finding the W/V

KNOWN:		FIND:
HDG	143°M	W/V
Variation	5°W, (HDG 138°T)	
TAS	120 kt	
TR	146°T	
GS	144 kt	

NOTE Another way of asking the same question is to give HDG 138°T and right drift 8° (rather than TR 146°T).

From/To	Safety ALT	ALT Temp	RAS	TAS	W/V	TR °T	Drift	HDG °T	Var	HDG °M	GS	Dist	Time	ETA	HDG °C
				120		146		138	5°W	143	144				

■ *Figure 9-30* **Example 4**

STEP 1. PLACE THE TR/GS VECTOR UNDER THE CENTRE-DOT.

Rotate the compass rose and set track 146°T under the index. Set GS 144 kt under the centre-dot.

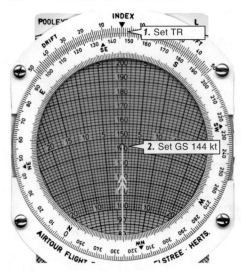

■ *Figure 9-31* **Example 4, Step 1**

STEP 2. PLACE THE HDG/TAS VECTOR ON THE PLOTTING DISC.

From HDG 138°T and TR 146°T, the drift is 8° to the right; the HDG is 8° to the left of TR (i.e. the wind correction angle is 8° left).

Mark in the HDG direction as the 8° drift line to the left of track. Mark the TAS where the 120 kt speed arc intersects the drift line; this indicates the HDG/TAS vector.

The W/V blows the aircraft from HDG to TR.

STEP 3. DETERMINE THE W/V.

Rotate the compass rose until the wind-mark is on the index line with the arrows pointing down towards the centre-dot. The direction the wind is blowing from, 360°T, is now indicated under the index.

Read off the wind strength of 30 kt. (Setting a definite speed arc under the centre-dot, 100 kt in this case, makes the wind strength easier to read.)

ANSWER W/V 360°T/30 kt

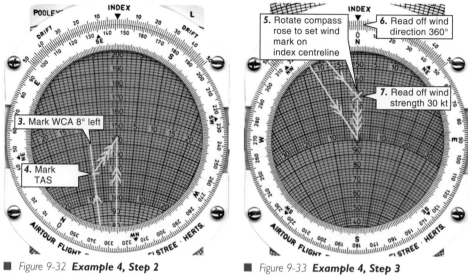

■ Figure 9-32 **Example 4, Step 2**   ■ Figure 9-33 **Example 4, Step 3**

From/To	Safety ALT	ALT / Temp	RAS	TAS	W/V	TR °T	Drift	HDG °T	Var	HDG °M	GS	Dist	Time	ETA	HDG °C
			120	360/30	146	8°R	138	5°W	143	144					

■ Figure 9-34 **Example 4**

> If you are satisfied with the above method of using the wind side of
> your computer, then it is not necessary to work through the next part
> (Method B), as the calculations are a repeat of what you have just
> completed.
>
> You should, however, complete the final part of this chapter, beginning
> on page 184, which shows how to work out wind components. This is
> important information for take-off and landing operations on runways
> where the wind is not blowing directly along the runway (often the case).

The Wind-Down Method (Method B)

Use Method B if your flying instructor recommends it. It is called
the 'wind-down' method because:

- **the wind direction** (from which it blows) is placed under the
  index;
- **the centre-dot** is used as the starting point of the W/V vector;
  and
- **the wind-mark,** in this case representing the end of the W/V
  vector, is drawn beneath the centre-dot ('down' from the
  centre-dot).

Since the W/V blows the aeroplane from its heading to its
track, and the heading vector ends where the W/V vector starts,
the heading/TAS vector should be placed up the centre of the
slide so that it ends at the centre-dot.

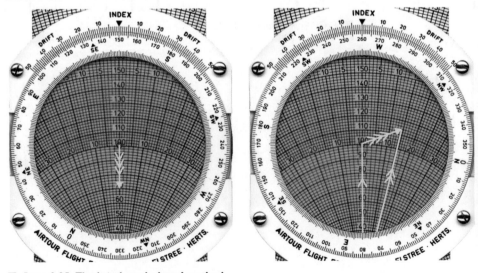

■ Figure 9-35 **The 'wind-mark-down' method**

The simplest type of problem to solve using the wind-down method is the in-flight situation of knowing the HDG, TAS and W/V, and then having to find the TR and GS. This situation could arise on an over-water flight, or a flight over barren terrain or in poor visibility, where it is difficult to obtain two position fixes to determine TR and GS. HDG is found from the compass, TAS is calculated from the indicated airspeed, and forecast W/V (in °T) is used.

Finding Track and Groundspeed In Flight

EXAMPLE 5 *Find TR and GS*

KNOWN:		FIND:
HDG	*050°T*	**TR and GS**
TAS	*120 kt*	
W/V	*140°T/30 kt*	

In practice, you would probably enter this data on a flight log to keep it neat and orderly.

From/To	Safety ALT	ALT / Temp	RAS	TAS	W/V	TR °T	Drift	HDG °T	Var	HDG °M	GS	Dist	Time	ETA	HDG °C
				120	140/30			050							

■ *Figure 9-36* **Example 5**

STEP 1. PLACE THE W/V ON THE PLOTTING DISC.

Rotate the compass rose until the wind direction 140°T is under the index. Set the centre-dot (in transparent window) on an easily noted value (100 in the illustration) and mark the end of the W/V vector 30 knots down from the centre-dot.

STEP 2. PLACE THE HDG/TAS VECTOR UNDER THE CENTRE-DOT.

Rotate the compass rose until the HDG 050°T is under the index. Move the slide so that the TAS 120 kt is under the centre-dot.

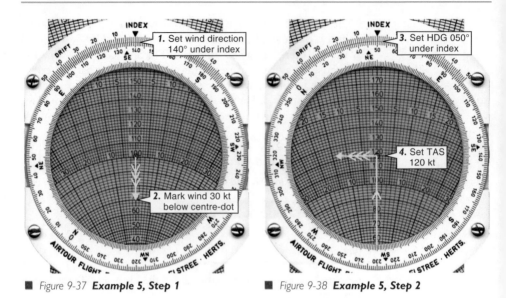

■ *Figure 9-37* **Example 5, Step 1**   ■ *Figure 9-38* **Example 5, Step 2**

STEP 3. READ OFF GS AND DRIFT, THEN CALCULATE TRACK.

The wind-mark now lies over the groundspeed 123 kt. The wind-mark lies over the 14° drift line, which means the wind blowing from the right will cause a HDG of 050°T to result in a track of (050 − 14) = 036°T. (You can check your arithmetic against the small scale near the index mark.)

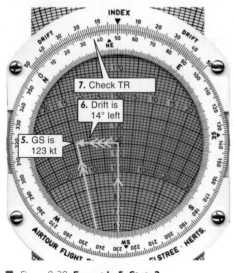

■ *Figure 9-39* **Example 5, Step 3**

ANSWER GS 123 kt, TMG 036°T added to the flight log.

From/To	Safety ALT	ALT Temp	RAS	TAS	W/V	TR °T	Drift	HDG °T	Var	HDG °M	GS	Dist	Time	ETA	HDG °C
			120	140/30	036			050			123				

■ *Figure 9-40* **Example 5**

Finding the Wind Velocity

EXAMPLE 6 Find W/V

When HDG and TAS are known, and you know the track made good and the groundspeed.

KNOWN:		FIND:
HDG	160°T	**W/V** *(direction*
TAS	145 kt	*and strength)*
TMG	168°T	
GS	157 kt	

From/To	Safety ALT	ALT Temp	RAS	TAS	W/V	TR °T	Drift	HDG °T	Var	HDG °M	GS	Dist	Time	ETA	HDG °C
			145			168		160			157				

■ *Figure 9-41* **Example 6**

NOTE The same question could have been asked differently, with HDG 160°T and drift 8° right given, rather than TR 168°T.

STEP 1. PLACE THE HDG/TAS VECTOR UNDER THE CENTRE-DOT.
Rotate the compass rose until the HDG 160°T appears under the index. Move the slide until TAS 145 kt is under the centre-dot.

STEP 2. PLACE THE TMG/GS ON THE PLOTTING DISC.
Mark in the 8° right drift line, since the drift is 8° to the right, calculated from the HDG 160°T and the TMG 168°T. Mark the point along this line where the GS is 157 kt. This point is the end of the TR/GS vector. (The wind has blown the aeroplane from the centre-dot to this point marked on the plotting disc.)

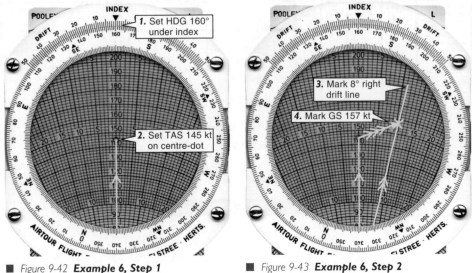

■ Figure 9-42 **Example 6, Step 1**   ■ Figure 9-43 **Example 6, Step 2**

STEP 3. READ OFF THE W/V.

Rotate the compass rose until the wind dot appears directly down from the centre-dot. The direction from which the wind is blowing appears under the index, i.e. 045°T.

The wind strength of 26 kt can be read from the distance beneath the centre-dot. (You can adjust the slide to make reading this easier.)

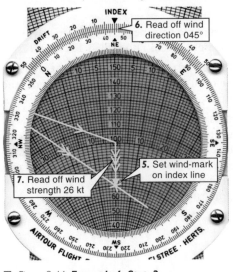

■ Figure 9-44 **Example 6, Step 3**

ANSWER W/V is 045°T/26 kt

From/To	Safety ALT	ALT Temp	RAS	TAS	W/V	TR °T	Drift	HDG °T	Var	HDG °M	GS	Dist	Time	ETA	HDG °C
			145	045/26	168		160			157					

■ *Figure 9-45* **Example 6**

The Flight-Planning Situation
EXAMPLE 7 Find HDG and GS, Knowing TR, TAS and W/V

This is the typical situation prior to flight. Since it is at the flight-planning stage when the navigation computer is used most, you must become adept at this sort of problem.

From the aeronautical chart, you can measure the desired track (and distance). The wind is known from the forecast. The aeroplane's performance in terms of true airspeed is known, or can be found from the Flight Manual or Pilot's Operating Handbook.

KNOWN:		FIND:
Desired track	295°T	**HDG and GS**
TAS	97 kt	
Forecast W/V	320°T/25	

From/To	Safety ALT	ALT Temp	RAS	TAS	W/V	TR °T	Drift	HDG °T	Var	HDG °M	GS	Dist	Time	ETA	HDG °C
			97	320/25	295										

■ *Figure 9-46* **Example 7**

STEP 1. PLACE THE W/V ON THE PLOTTING DISC.
Rotate the compass rose until the direction from which the wind is blowing is under the index, i.e. 320°T. Put a wind-mark 25 kt down from the centre-dot.

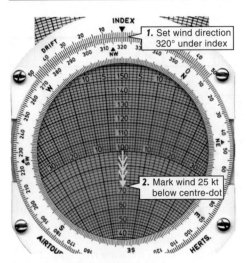

1. Set wind direction 320° under index

2. Mark wind 25 kt below centre-dot

■ *Figure 9-47* **Example 7, Step 1**

STEP 2. PLACE THE HDG/TAS UNDER THE CENTRE-DOT.

Since the W/V starts at the centre-dot and blows away from it, place the end of the HDG/TAS vector under the centre-dot.

Move the slide until TAS 97 kt appears under the centre-dot. Set approximate HDG 295°T under the index.

When we come to set the HDG under the index, we are faced with a problem – we do not know the HDG! To get started, use the desired track as an approximate HDG; i.e. assume that the HDG is approximately 295°T and rotate the compass rose until 295°T appears under the index.

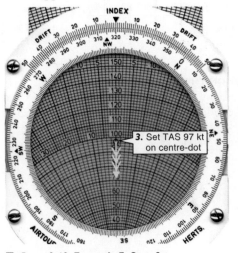

3. Set TAS 97 kt on centre-dot

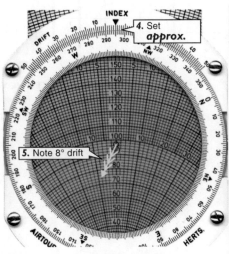

4. Set *approx.*

5. Note 8° drift

■ *Figure 9-48* **Example 7, Step 2a**   ■ *Figure 9-49* **Example 7, Step 2b**

STEP 3. ADJUST THE APPROXIMATE HDG TO ALLOW FOR DRIFT.

The W/V dot lies over the 8° left drift line, so, on a HDG of 295°T, the aeroplane should achieve a track 8° to the left of this.

Since the desired track is 295°, the aeroplane should be heading approximately 8° to the right of this to allow for the left drift, i.e. on a HDG of 303°T, with a wind correction angle of 8° right.

Rotate the compass rose until 303°T appears under the index, and check the drift (and calculate the track). The drift is now indicated to be only 6° (not the original 8°), so adjust the HDG to allow for only 6°, i.e. an adjusted HDG is 301°T.

Set the adjusted HDG 301°T under the index. By checking the position of the wind-mark, we see that this 'adjustment' of the compass rose has not appreciably altered the 6° drift. (In other words, the adjusted HDG and the expected 6° left (port) drift will allow us to achieve the desired track of 295°T.)

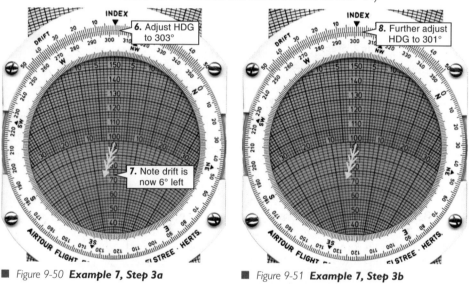

■ *Figure 9-50* **Example 7, Step 3a**   ■ *Figure 9-51* **Example 7, Step 3b**

STEP 4. READ OFF THE HDG AND GS.

The HDG 301°T appears under the index. The GS 73 kt appears under the wind-mark.

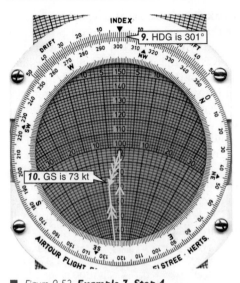

■ Figure 9-52 **Example 7, Step 4**

ANSWER HDG 301°T, GS 73 kt

| From/To | Safety ALT | ALT | RAS | TAS | W/V | TR °T | Drift | HDG °T | Var | HDG °M | GS | Dist | Time | ETA | HDG °C |
		Temp													
			97	320/25	295			301			73				

■ Figure 9-53 **Example 7**

NOTE Because there have to be some adjustments to the initial HDG by rotating the compass rose a few degrees this way and that, the above method is sometimes also known as the 'jiggle' method, as well as the 'wind-down' method. It still gives accurate answers.

To solve a slightly unusual flight-planning problem such as "What TAS is required to achieve a groundspeed of 80 kt?" the same procedure as above can be used, except that the wind-mark is placed over the appropriate GS arc, and then the TAS and HDG can be read off under the centre-dot.

EXAMPLE 8 Find HDG and GS, Knowing TR, TAS and W/V

This variation on the 'wind-down' method avoids having to adjust the compass rose when calculating HDG and GS at the flight-planning stage. It repeats the previous example. Check if your instructor recommends this method.

KNOWN:		FIND:
TR	295°T	HDG and GS
TAS	97 kt	
W/V	320°T/25 kt	

From/To	Safety ALT	ALT Temp	RAS	TAS	W/V	TR °T	Drift	HDG °T	Var	HDG °M	GS	Dist	Time	ETA	HDG °C
				97	320/25	295									

■ *Figure 9-54* **Example 8**

STEP 1. SET W/V ON THE PLOTTING DISC USING THE SQUARE GRID.

Rotate the compass rose until the wind direction 320°T appears under the index.

Set the zero point of the square grid under the centre-dot. Put a wind-mark 25 kt down from the centre-dot.

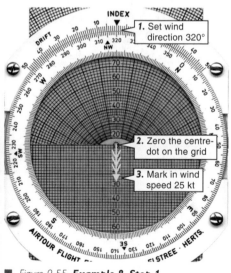

■ *Figure 9-55* **Example 8, Step 1**

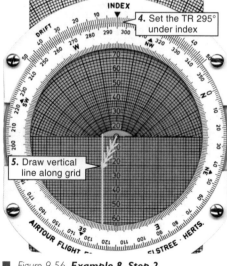

■ *Figure 9-56* **Example 8, Step 2**

STEP 2. SET TRACK, AND MARK IN CROSSWIND LINE.

Rotate the compass rose until the TR 295°T appears under the index. Run a vertical line down through the wind-mark, which is a 10 kt crosswind component. It is this crosswind component from the right that causes the left drift.

STEP 3. SET HDG/TAS ON THE PLOTTING DISC.

Move the slide and place TAS 97 kt under the centre-dot. Note that the crosswind effect line does not parallel the drift lines at this stage.

Rotate the compass rose until the crosswind effect line is parallel with one of the drift lines.

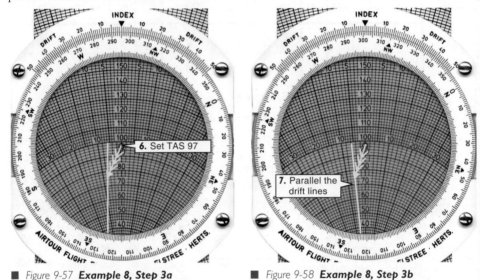

■ *Figure 9-57* **Example 8, Step 3a**   ■ *Figure 9-58* **Example 8, Step 3b**

STEP 4. READ OFF HDG AND GS.

HDG/TAS lies under the centre-dot. The TR/GS vector ends where the W/V vector ends.

Read off HDG 301°T under the index. Read off GS 73 kt under the wind-mark.

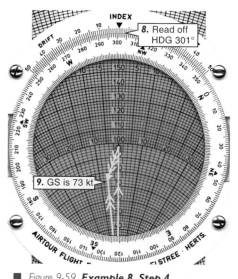

■ Figure 9-59 **Example 8, Step 4**

ANSWER HDG 301°T, GS 73 kt

From/To	Safety ALT	ALT Temp	RAS	TAS	W/V	TR °T	Drift	HDG °T	Var	HDG °M	GS	Dist	Time	ETA	HDG °C
			97	320/25	295			301			73				

■ Figure 9-60 **Example 8**

Example Prepared Chart and Flight Log

The calculation of drift is the next process.

An accurate estimate of the wind speed and direction is obtained from the Met. Office Form 214 UK Spot Wind Forecast Chart. At the planned time of this flight, the wind direction is 270°T and the velocity is 30 kt. This information is entered on the flight log form and annotated on the aeronautical chart:

Pilot: *P. Pilot*					Aircraft: *GABCD*			Date: *21 09 2015*					Depart' Time:		
From/To	Safety Alt.	Alt. Temp.	CAS	TAS	W/V	TRK °T	Drift	HDG °T	Var.	HDG °M	GS	Dist	Time	ETA
Shoreham *Lydd*	*2100*	*2400* *+10*	*98*	*102*	*270/30*	*082*			*2°W*			*47*		
Lydd *Southend*	*1900*	*2400* *+10*	*98*	*102*	*270/30*	*346*			*2°W*			*38*		
Southend *Uckfield*	*2400*	*2400* *+10*	*98*	*102*	*270/30*	*212*			*2°W*			*42*		
Uckfield *Shoreham*	*1900*	*2400* *+10*	*98*	*102*	*270/30*	*241*			*2°W*			*17*		
										Total		*144*		

■ *Figure 9-61* **Example flight log form with wind speed and direction details added.**

Using the wind side of the navigation computer and the preferred method of calculation (the wind-up or wind-down method), the drift, true heading and groundspeed can be obtained. These are then added to the flight log form.

Pilot: *A. Johnson*					Aircraft: *GABCD*			Date: *21 09 2015*					Depart' Time:		
From/To	Safety Alt.	Alt. Temp.	CAS	TAS	W/V	TRK °T	Drift	HDG °T	Var.	HDG °M	GS	Dist	Time	ETA
Shoreham *Lydd*	*2100*	*2400* *+10*	*98*	*102*	*270/30*	*082*	*-2*	*080*	*2°W*		*132*	*47*		
Lydd *Southend*	*1900*	*2400* *+10*	*98*	*102*	*270/30*	*346*	*-17*	*329*	*2°W*		*91*	*38*		
Southend *Uckfield*	*2400*	*2400* *+10*	*98*	*102*	*270/30*	*212*	*+14*	*226*	*2°W*		*83*	*42*		
Uckfield *Shoreham*	*1900*	*2400* *+10*	*98*	*102*	*270/30*	*241*	*+8*	*249*	*2°W*		*75*	*17*		
										Total		*144*		

■ *Figure 9-62* **Example flight log form with drift, heading and groundspeed details added.**

The final stage in the process is to convert the true heading into a compass heading which is used to fly the route. Many flight log forms assume that compass deviation is minimal and so the magnetic heading is flown as a reasonable approximation to the compass heading. The validity of the approximation must be checked with reference to the compass deviation card on the magnetic compass in the aircraft.

Pilot: *A. Johnson*					Aircraft: *GABCD*			Date: *21 09 2015*				Depart' Time:		
From/To	Safety Alt.	Alt. Temp.	CAS	TAS	W/V	TRK °T	Drift	HDG °T	Var.	HDG °M	GS	Dist	Time	ETA
Shoreham *Lydd*	*2100*	*2400* *+10*	*98*	*102*	*270/30*	*082*	*-2*	*080*	*2°W*	*082*	*132*	*47*		
Lydd *Southend*	*1900*	*2400* *+10*	*98*	*102*	*270/30*	*346*	*-17*	*329*	*2°W*	*331*	*91*	*38*		
Southend *Uckfield*	*2400*	*2400* *+10*	*98*	*102*	*270/30*	*212*	*+14*	*226*	*2°W*	*228*	*83*	*42*		
Uckfield *Shoreham*	*1900*	*2400* *+10*	*98*	*102*	*270/30*	*241*	*+8*	*249*	*2°W*	*251*	*75*	*17*		
										Total	*144*			

■ *Figure 9-63* **Example flight log form with true headings converted to magnetic heading using magnetic variation.**

Wind Components

Often a wind needs to be broken down into its two components:
- **the headwind or tailwind** component; and
- **the crosswind** component.

This is especially the case when taking off and landing, because:

1. For performance reasons, you often need to know the headwind or tailwind component to determine the take-off or landing distance required.

2. For safe aeroplane handling, you always need to know (at least approximately) the crosswind component on the runway that you intend using. The crosswind component is very important and every aeroplane has a maximum crosswind limit specified in its Flight Manual. This crosswind limit should never be exceeded.

Winds found on forecasts, which are most likely to be used for flight-planning purposes, are given in degrees true, whereas the wind in take-off and landing reports broadcast by Air Traffic Control are given in degrees magnetic, so that they can be easily related to runway direction, which is always in °M. This applies to the direction of the wind given to you by the Tower, or as broadcast on the Automatic Terminal Information Service (ATIS).

A runway whose centreline lies in the direction 074°M will be designated Runway 07. A runway whose centreline lies in the direction 357°M will be designated Runway 36. A wind of 350°M/25 kt would favour RWY 36, which is almost directly into-wind. RWY 07 would experience a strong crosswind from the left; the pilot should determine just how strong before using this particular runway.

Since both wind direction and runway direction are measured from the same datum (magnetic north), there is no need to convert into degrees true for your computer manipulations. When using your computer, work either totally in °T or totally in °M.

In Vol. 4 of *The Air Pilot's Manual,* when discussing take-off and landing performance, we illustrate a simple way of determining wind components mentally. Here we show you how to do it using the **square grid** on your navigation computer.

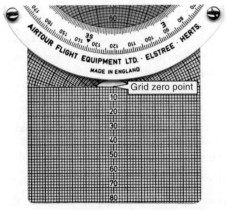

■ *Figure 9-64* **The square grid on the computer slide**

Finding Wind Components

What crosswind and headwind components exist on Runway 18 if the wind broadcast by the Tower is 120°M/30? (Runway 18 means that the runway direction is approx 180°M.)

STEP 1. SET UP THE W/V ON THE SQUARE GRID.

Set the zero point of the square grid under the centre-dot. Rotate the compass rose and set wind direction 120° under the index. Put a wind-mark 30 kt down from the centre-dot.

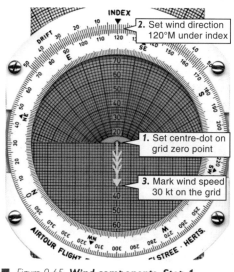

■ *Figure 9-65* **Wind components, Step 1**

STEP 2. SET RUNWAY DIRECTION.

Rotate the compass rose until the runway direction 180°M is under the index.

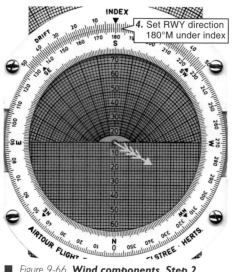

■ *Figure 9-66* **Wind components, Step 2**

STEP 3. READ OFF HEADWIND AND CROSSWIND COMPONENTS.
Drop a vertical line to the wind-mark. The length of this line is the headwind component, 15 kt.

The horizontal distance of this line from the centre-dot is the crosswind component, 26 kt.

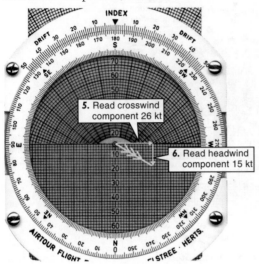

■ *Figure 9-67* **Wind components, Step 3**

ANSWER Headwind (H/W) 15 kt, crosswind (X/W) 26 kt

NOTE If, when the runway direction is set under the index, the end of the wind vector is above the horizontal line through the centre-dot, then there is a tailwind component and it is advisable to consider changing runways. The precise strength of the down-wind component can be found by placing the reciprocal to the runway direction under the index (360 in the above case), which allows you to find what is a headwind component for a take-off in that direction.

Now complete: **Practice Questions - Drift**

---

1. You are flying and maintaining a heading of 179°C with 11° right drift. From the compass card you know that the deviation is 4° W, the magnetic variation in the area is 9°W. What is the aircraft's true track?

(a) 177°T

(b) 166°T

(c) 192°T

(d) 190°T

2. You are flying and maintaining a true track of 255°T with 7° right drift. The magnetic variation in the area is 6°E and from the compass card you know that the deviation is 2°W. What is the aircraft's compass heading?

(a) 248°C

(b) 248°T

(c) 252°C

(d) 244°C

3. From the flight log below, what is the required magnetic heading?

Alt (ft) Temp (Celsius)	CAS (kt)	TAS (kt)	W/V	Track °T	Drift	Hdg °T	Var	Hdg °M	GS (kt)	Dist (nm)	Time (min)	ETA
5000 +10°	98		310/20	045			3°W					

(a) 037°

(b) 034°

(c) 031°

(d) 049°

4. From the flight log below, what is the required magnetic heading?

Alt (ft) Temp (Celsius)	CAS (kt)	TAS (kt)	W/V	Track °T	Drift	Hdg °T	Var	Hdg °M	GS (kt)	Dist (nm)	Time (min)	ETA
7000 +15°	120		160/25	300			3°W					

(a) 291°

(b) 296°

(c) 283°

(d) 310°

5. An aircraft is heading 116°T with a TAS of 130kt. If the groundspeed is 141kt, and the track made good is 120°T, what is the wind velocity?

(a) 360°T/20kt

(b) 340°T/15kt

(c) 290°T/15kt

(d) 310°T/25kt

6. An aircraft is heading 165°T with a TAS of 110kt. If the groundspeed is 96kt, and the track made good is 151°T, what is the wind velocity?

(a) 040°/20 kt

(b) 260°/30 kt

(c) 170°/35 kt

(d) 220°/30 kt

7. The maximum demonstrated cross wind component for the aircraft is 17 kt. Given a 22kt wind speed, by how many degrees can the wind direction differ from the runway direction before the crosswind component equals 17kt?

(a) 50°

(b) 60°

(c) 40°

(d) 80°

Timing and Fuel Management

The calculator side of the navigation computer is useful for solving quickly and accurately the numerous small calculations involved in air navigation.

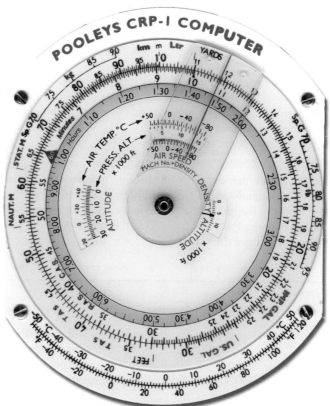

■ *Figure 10-1* **Calculator side of a navigation computer**

Various computer types differ in minor ways on the calculator side but the way they are used is the same. As you go through this chapter we suggest that you have your computer close by and follow our examples with it.

Use of the computer for solving the altitude and airspeed problems on the small scales in the mid-area of the calculator side is covered in Chapter 2, Speed and Chapter 7, Time. In this chapter we cover what can be done with the two outside scales, which form a circular slide rule.

The Circular Slide Rule

Simple multiplication and division can be done mentally, or, if more complicated, with electronic calculators, or with *logarithms*. A logarithm is one of a series of numbers, set out in tables, that make it possible to work out problems by adding and subtracting numbers, instead of multiplying and dividing. A slide rule is just a pictorial means of using logarithms.

To avoid the need for pilots to carry long, straight slide rules, a circular slide rule has been devised. It is fast, never has flat batteries, and is accurate enough for our purposes. The circular slide rule has two scales:

• an **inner** rotary scale; and
• an **outer** fixed scale.

Both scales are marked with logarithmic graduations, making it possible to multiply and divide simply by the physical addition or subtraction of lengths of the graduated scales. The numbers on the scales are marked in order from 10 all the way around the scale to 100, but the larger the number the closer it is to its neighbour.

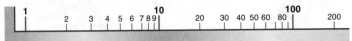

■ *Figure 10-2* **A simple logarithmic scale**

If you look at your circular slide rule you will see that the numbers 1, 10, 100, 1,000, 0.1, 0.001, etc., are completely interchangeable and are all labelled at the same point as 10. Similarly, 5, 50, 500, 0.5, 0.005 are interchangeable and are all labelled at the same point as 50.

Slide Rules are Accurate to Three Significant Figures

Slide rules and navigation computers are fairly small in size, so the accuracy to which you can read them depends on your eyesight. Most slide rule scales allow you to read to an accuracy of three digits.

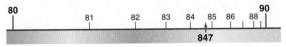

■ *Figure 10-3* **This scale reads 847**

Unfortunately the scale does not tell us where the decimal point belongs in relation to the three significant figures. For example, 847 could be written any of the following ways:

847.0
84.7
8.47
0.847
8,470.0

To know where to place the decimal point you must estimate the approximate answer to the question by quick mental arithmetic. The mental calculations give an approximate answer (allowing us to place the decimal point correctly); the slide rule manipulations give us that answer accurate to three significant figures.

Solving Speed, Distance, Time and Ratio Problems

Speed is the ratio of distance/time. As there are 60 minutes in 1 hour, a speed of 140 knots is the same as travelling a distance of 140 nautical miles over the ground in 60 minutes. We can set this up on the circular slide rule by placing the 60 minutes (sometimes written as 1:00 hour) on the inner TIME scale against the 140 on the outer DISTANCE scale.

On most computers the **inner scale** is marked TIME and the **outer scale** DISTANCE (usually somewhere near the 60 mark). This is important to keep in mind – that TIME is always on the inner scale and DISTANCE/SPEED on the outer.

■ Figure 10-4 **A typical distance-time problem**

The circular slide rule is now set up to answer many questions, such as:

EXAMPLE 1 At a groundspeed (GS) of 140 kt, how far will you travel in 30 minutes?

Step 1. Rough Check
30 minutes is half an hour which, at 140 kt, is 70 nm.

Step 2.
Find 30 minutes on the inner TIME scale and read off the answer 70 nm on the outer DISTANCE scale.

ANSWER 70 nm

EXAMPLE 2 At a groundspeed (GS) of 140 kt, how far will you travel in 15 minutes?

Step 1. Rough Check

15 minutes is ¼ hour which, at 140 kt, gives 140 ÷ 4 = 35 nm.

Step 2.

Find 15 minutes on the inner TIME scale and then read off the answer 35 nm on the outer DISTANCE scale.

ANSWER 35 nm

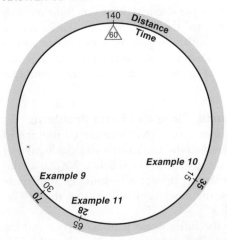

■ *Figure 10-5* **Speed, time and distance problems on the circular slide rule**

EXAMPLE 3 At a GS of 140 kt, how long will it take you to travel 65 nm?

Step 1. Rough Check

65 nm is slightly less than ½ of 140 nm which, at 140 kt, will take slightly less than 30 minutes to cover.

Step 2.

Find 65 nm on the outer DISTANCE scale and read off the answer 28 minutes (approximately) on the inner TIME scale.

ANSWER 28 minutes (approximately)

Further Problems

The computer can be used to help us solve many different types of problem involving multiplication, division or ratios. Another sort of calculation we can make is:

EXAMPLE 4 If we cover 16 nm over the ground in 10 minutes, what is our groundspeed?

Step 1. Rough check

10 minutes is ⅙ hour. We cover 16 nm in 10 minutes, so we will cover six times this distance in an hour, i.e. 6 × 16 = 96 nm. The speed is therefore 96 kt.

Step 2.

Set up 16 nm on the outer DISTANCE scale against 10 minutes on the inner TIME scale.

Step 3.

Against 60 minutes (1:00 hour) on the inner TIME scale read off on the outer DISTANCE scale the distance you would travel in that time, which of course is 96 nm; that is, the GS is 96 kt.

ANSWER 96 kt

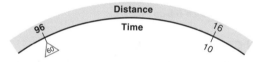

■ Figure 10-6 **Finding groundspeed**

The computer is now set up to answer other questions relevant to this situation, such as:

EXAMPLE 5 How far will the aeroplane then travel in a further 5 minutes?

ANSWER 8 nm

EXAMPLE 6 How long will it take to travel 24 nm?

ANSWER 15 minutes

In each case, a rough mental check will confirm that the answers are 8 nm (and not 80 or 0.8) and 15 minutes (and not 150 or 1.5).

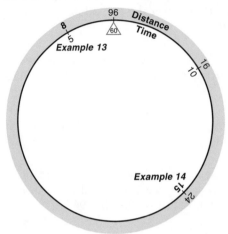

■ Figure 10-7 **Time-speed-distance set-up**

Example Prepared Chart and Flight Log

The flight log form can now be completed using the groundspeed and route segment (leg) distance information to calculate timing. This information is critically important for use, en-route, as it is the basis for:

- Timings associated with dead reckoning navigation
- The calculation of estimated times of arrival (ETA) at turning points and the destination. ETA information also forms part of situation reporting to en route air traffic control units.
- Fuel management. Knowing timings, useable fuel loads and fuel consumption information, assurance of available fuel is known.

Pilot: *A. Johnson*				Aircraft: *GABCD*				Date: *21 09 2015*				Depart' Time:		
From/To	Safety Alt.	Alt. Temp.	CAS	TAS	W/V	TRK °T	Drift	HDG °T	Var.	HDG °M	GS	Dist	Time	ETA
Shoreham	*2100*	*2400*	*98*	*102*	*270/30*	*082*	*-2*	*080*	*2°W*	*082*	*132*	*47*	*21*	
Lydd		*+10*												
Lydd	*1900*	*2400*	*98*	*102*	*270/30*	*346*	*-17*	*329*	*2°W*	*331*	*91*	*38*	*25*	
Southend		*+10*												
Southend	*2400*	*2400*	*98*	*102*	*270/30*	*212*	*+14*	*226*	*2°W*	*228*	*83*	*42*	*30*	
Uckfield		*+10*												
Uckfield	*1900*	*2400*	*98*	*102*	*270/30*	*241*	*+8*	*249*	*2°W*	*251*	*75*	*17*	*14*	
Shoreham		*+10*												
										Total		*144*	*90*	

■ Figure 10-8 **Example flight log form with timings.**

Fuel Consumption Problems

EXAMPLE 7 If an aeroplane is burning fuel at the rate of 30 litres per hour, what fuel burn-off can you expect in 8 minutes?

Step 1. Rough check
30 litres per hour is ½ litre per minute which, for 8 minutes, will give a burn-off of 4 litres.

Step 2.
Set 60 minutes (1:00 hour) on the inner TIME scale against 30 (litres) on the outer scale.

Step 3.
Against 8 minutes on the inner TIME scale read off 4 (litres) on the outer scale. (Our rough mental calculation indicates that the answer is 4 and not 40 or 400 or 0.4).

ANSWER 4 litres

■ *Figure 10-9* **Example 7, a typical fuel consumption problem**

EXAMPLE 8 If we have burned 4 litres in 10 minutes, how much will we burn in the next 25 minutes?

■ *Figure 10-10* **Example 8**

Step 1. Rough check
25 = 2.5 × 10, so expect to use 2.5 × 4 = 10 litres.

Step 2.
Set up 10 minutes on the inner TIME scale against 4 litres on the outer scale.

Step 3.
Against 25 minutes on the inner TIME scale read off 10 litres on the outer scale.

ANSWER 10 litres (not 1 or 100 or 1,000)

The circular slide rule is now set up to answer other problems relevant to this situation, such as:

1. What is the rate of fuel consumption in litres/hour?
   Answer: 24 litres/hour

2. How long would it take to burn 28 litres?
   Answer: 70 minutes

EXAMPLE 9 If your aeroplane has 26 US gallons of usable fuel in the tanks, and the average consumption rate is 5.5 USG/hour, what is the safe flight endurance if you wish to land with 1 hour's reserve unused?

Step 1. Rough check

Subtracting the reserve (5.5 USG in this case) leaves 20.5 USG as flight fuel. A rough mental check (20 USG at 6 USG/hour) = $3^1/_3$ hours.

Step 2.

By computer, with 60 minutes on the inner scale set against 5.5 USG on the outer, read against 20.5 USG on the outer scale the answer of 224 minutes on the inner.

ANSWER 3 hours 44 minutes (224 minutes)

CONSUMPTION RATE	7 USG/hr	
Stage	min	US gal
Route	90	
Reserve	45	
Fuel required		
Margin		
Total carried		

■ Figure 10-11 **Beginning of the fuel calculations**

CONSUMPTION RATE	7 USG/hr	
Stage	min	US gal
Route	90 → 10.5	
Reserve	45 → 5.3	
Fuel required		
Margin		
Total carried		

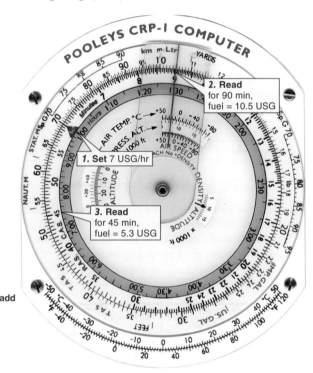

CONSUMPTION RATE	7 USG/hr	
Stage	min	US gal
Route	90	10.5
Reserve	45	5.3
Fuel required	135	15.8
Margin		
Total carried		

add

■ Figure 10-12 **Calculating fuel required**

Any fuel above the minimum required provides a **margin**. If, for instance 25 USG is loaded, a margin of 9.2 USG over and above the minimum fuel required (15.8 USG) is available. At the consumption rate of 7 USG/hr, this converts to a margin of 79 minutes, providing a total endurance of 214 minutes. This is useful information for the pilot.

1.

CONSUMPTION RATE 7 USG/hr

Stage	min	US gal
Route	90	10.5
Reserve	45	5.3
Fuel required	135	15.8
Margin		
Total carried		25.0 ←

3.

CONSUMPTION RATE 7 USG/hr

Stage	min	US gal
Route	90	10.5
Reserve	45	5.3
Fuel required	135	15.8
Margin	**79** ←	9.2 convert
Total carried		25.0

2.

CONSUMPTION RATE 7 USG/hr

Stage	min	US gal
Route	90	10.5
Reserve	45	5.3
Fuel required	135	15.8
Margin		9.2 subtract
Total carried		25.0

4.

CONSUMPTION RATE 7 USG/hr

Stage	min	US gal
Route	90	10.5
Reserve	45	5.3
Fuel required	135	15.8
Margin	79	9.2 add minutes
Total carried	**214**	25.0

■ Figure 10-13 **The main fuel calculations completed**

Sometimes you are required to plan for a flight to an alternate aerodrome if, for instance, poor weather does not allow you to land at the planned destination. For the flight from Shoreham to Lydd, with Southend as an alternate for Lydd, the calculations might appear as shown. The alternate fuel is sometimes called diversion fuel.

From/To	Safety ALT	ALT Temp	RAS	TAS	W/V	TR °T	Drift	HDG °T	Var	HDG °M	GS	Dist	Time	ETA	HDG °C
Shoreham	2080	2400 +10	98	102	270/30	082	−2	080	2W	082	132	47	21		
Lydd															
Lydd	1811	2400 +10	98	102	270/30	346	−16	330	2W	332	91	38	25		
Southend															

■ Figure 10-14 **Southend, as alternate for Lydd**

Stage	min	USG
Destination	21	2.4
Alternate	25	2.9
Flight Fuel	46	5.3
Reserve	45	5.3
Fuel Required	91	10.6

If you load a total of 17 USG, then the final fuel calculations will be:

Stage	min	USG
Destination	21	2.4
Alternate	25	2.9
Flight Fuel	46	5.3
Reserve	45	5.3
Fuel Required	91	10.6
Margin	55	6.4
Total Fuel	146	17.0

Sometimes an allowance for taxi fuel is made (say 1 USG with no time allowance), in which case the fuel table may look like:

Stage	min	USG
Destination	21	2.4
Alternate	25	2.9
Flight Fuel	46	5.3
Reserve	45	5.3
Taxi	–	**1.0**
Fuel Required	91	11.6
Margin	46	5.4
Total Fuel	137	17.0

Some operators like to carry an extra safety margin of 10%, and their fuel calculations may appear thus:

Stage	min	USG
Destination	21	2.4
Alternate	25	2.9
Flight Fuel	46	5.3
Reserve	45	5.3
Total	91	10.6
+10%	**10**	**1.1**
Taxi	–	1.0
Fuel Required	101	12.7
Margin	37	4.3
Total Fuel	138	17.0

This is becoming complicated, but, if you use the one procedure all the time, you soon get used to it.

Volume and Weight

In aviation we are faced with three different units for volume: the **imperial gallon,** the **US gallon** and the **litre.** In most general aviation aircraft the fuel gauges are marked in US gallons, yet you order fuel from the fuel agent in litres. There is great potential for confusion here, so you must become proficient in converting fuel quantities from one unit to another.

The weight of the fuel on board, as well as its volume, concerns the pilot for two main reasons:
- **weight and balance** (loading of the aircraft); and
- **energy content** of the fuel (which depends on weight, rather than volume).

So you must be able to convert fuel from a volume to a weight with accuracy.

100 octane (or higher) Avgas weighs only about 0.71 or 0.72 times the weight of an equal volume of water. We can describe this by saying that the **specific gravity (SG)** of Avgas = 0.71 or 0.72. The precise value depends to some extent on temperature and you should consult your instructor as to which value to use in your usual flying conditions.

Relative density is the modern term and it clearly describes its purpose, which is to compare the density of a particular fluid to the density of water. Most navigation computers, however, are marked with *Sp. G,* so we will continue to use the term *specific gravity.* It means the same thing.

The conversion from one unit of volume to another (imperial gallons, US gallons or litres), or to a weight (kg or lb) is easy on the *CRP-1* computer.

Weight Conversions

FOR QUICK MENTAL CHECKS, REMEMBER:		
1 kilogram (kg)	*=*	*2.2 pounds (lb)*

EXAMPLE 10 Convert 83 pounds (lb) to kilograms (kg).

Step 1. Rough calculation
   1 kg = approx. 2.2 lb
83 lb = approx. 83 ÷ 2.2 kg = approx. 40 kg

Step 2.
Set 83 on the inner scale against *lb* on the outer scale. Against *kg* on the outer scale read off 38 on the inner scale.

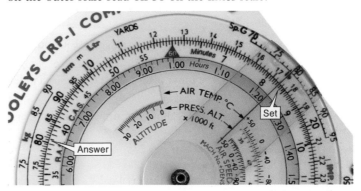

■ *Figure 10-15* **Example 10 answer: 36. Use the rotating arm to help align the numbers with the index.**

ANSWER 36 kg

EXAMPLE 11 Convert 293 kg to lb.

Step 1. Rough check
   1 kg = approx. 2.2 lb
293 kg = approx. 2.2 × 300 lb = 660 lb

Step 2.
Set 293 on the inner scale against *kg* on the outer scale. Against *lb* on the outer scale, read off 648.

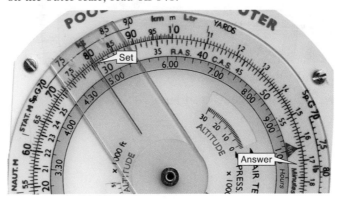

■ *Figure 10-16* **Example 11 answer: 648**

ANSWER 648 lb

Volume Conversions

FOR QUICK MENTAL CHECKS, REMEMBER:				
1 imperial gallon	=	1.2 US gallons	=	4.5 litres
0.8 imperial gallon	=	1 US gallon	=	4 litres
0.2 imperial gallon	=	0.25 US gallon	=	1 litre

For volume conversions, use the indices marked on the outer scale for *US gal, Imp gal* and *ltr*.

1. Set the known quantity on the inner scale against its index on the outer scale.

2. Read off the answer on the inner scale against the desired index on the outer scale.

EXAMPLE 12 Convert 24 US gallons to imperial gallons and litres.

Step 1. Rough check
  1 US gal = 0.8 imp gal
24 US gal = 0.8 × 24 = approx. 20 imperial gal
  1 US gal = 4 litres
24 US gal = 4 × 24 = approx. 96 litres

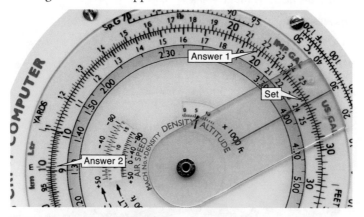

■ Figure 10-17 **Example 12, Step 2**

ANSWER 24 USG = 20 IG = 91 litres

Volume to Weight Conversions

We need to remember:

Specific gravity (SG) of Avgas = 0.71 or 0.72.

It is useful to know the relationship of volume to weight for water, since water is the standard for relative density (specific gravity). At normal temperatures and pressure:
- **1 litre** of water weighs 1 kg;
- **1 imperial gallon** of water weighs 10 lb;
- **1 US gallon** of water weighs 8.33 lb.

For a rough check on the volume/weight relationship for Avgas, use:

AVGAS: VOLUME/WEIGHT (APPROX.)	
Quantity	**Weight**
1 litre	1 × SG kg
1 imperial gallon	10 × SG lb
US gallons	first convert to imperial gallons (1 IG = 1.2 USG), then use 10 × SG to find weight in lb

Our navigation computer has two scales (one graduated in *kg* and one in *lb*) to cater for fluids of different specific gravity (SG). This is useful as the SG for Avgas (used in piston engines) is usually about 0.71 or 0.72, and the SG for Avtur (used in turbine engines) is usually about 0.79.

TO CONVERT A VOLUME TO WEIGHT:

1. Set the volume on the inner scale against its index on the outer scale.

2. Against the given SG (on the *kg* or *lb* scale) read off the weight on the inner scale.

EXAMPLE 13 What does 37 USG of Avgas (SG 0.71) weigh in lb and kg?

Step 1. Rough check

$$37 \text{ US gal} = 0.8 \times 37$$
$$= \text{approx. } 30 \text{ IG}$$
$$= 30 \times 10 \times 0.7 \text{ lb}$$
$$= 210 \text{ lb}$$
$$= \frac{210}{2.2}$$
$$= \text{approx. } 100 \text{ kg}$$

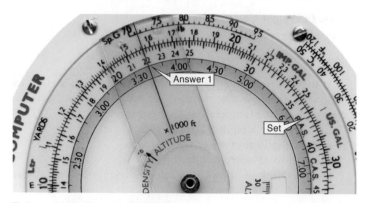

■ Figure 10-18 **Example 13, Step 2**

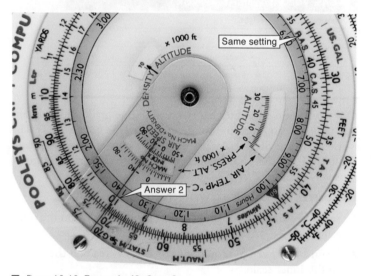

■ Figure 10-19 **Example 13, Step 3**

ANSWER 37 USG (SG 0.71) = 220 lb or 99.5 kg

Standard Specific Gravity Values

Remember:
Specific gravity of Avgas is 0.71 or 0.72.

The density of a fluid will vary with temperature; however, for our purposes in light aircraft where only relatively small quantities will be used, we can assume standard SG values for fuel and oil.

AVGAS SPECIFIC GRAVITIES	
Avgas 100 octane & higher	*SG = 0.71 or 0.72*
Avgas less than 100 octane	*SG = 0.72*

In round figures:

QUANTITY OF AVGAS	WEIGHT
1 litre	*0.7 kg*
1 imperial gallon	*7.2 lb*
1 US gallon	*2.69 kg*

You do not need to know the following specific gravity values at PPL level but they may be of interest. Jet engines burn Avtur (kerosene), which has a higher specific gravity than Avgas. Some aircraft load sheets require oil to be considered, so you need to know its specific gravity.

OTHER SPECIFIC GRAVITIES	
Avtur (for turbine engines)	*SG = 0.79*
Mineral oil	*SG = 0.90*
Synthetic oil	*SG = 0.96*
De-ice fluid	*SG = 1.1*

Now complete: **Practice Questions - Timing & Fuel Management**

1. From the flight log below, what is the required magnetic heading and leg time?

Alt (ft) Temp (Celsius)	CAS (kt)	TAS (kt)	W/V	Track °T	Hdg °T	Var	Hdg °M	GS (kt)	Dist (nm)	Time (min)
5000 -10°	110		360/30	210		5°E			79	

(a) *Magnetic Heading 215°; 34 min.*
(b) *Magnetic Heading 217°; 36 min.*
(c) *Magnetic Heading 222°; 34 min.*
(d) *Magnetic Heading 212°; 34 min.*

2. Complete the table below. From the completed table what is the magnetic heading and duration for the leg?

Alt (ft) Temp (Celsius)	CAS (kt)	TAS (kt)	W/V	Track °T	Hdg °T	Var	Hdg °M	GS (kt)	Dist (nm)	Time (min)
7000 +15°	120		160/25	300		3°W			83	

(a) *Magnetic Heading 291°; Duration 32 minutes*
(b) *Magnetic Heading 296°; Duration 42 minutes*
(c) *Magnetic Heading 296°; Duration 32 minutes*
(d) *Magnetic Heading 291°; Duration 42 minutes*

3. Your aircraft is maintaining a TAS of 94 kt and arrives overhead turning point A at 1450 UTC. Turning point B is 102 nm away using a track of 010°T. Calculate your ETA at B using a forecast wind of 220°/25 kt

(a) *1612 UTC*
(b) *1552 UTC*
(c) *1602 UTC*
(d) *1542 UTC*

4. If the fuel flow/hour was 9 US gallons and the total fuel on board the aircraft was 40 litres, what would be the endurance (to dry tanks) of the aircraft?

(a) *1 hour 52 min*
(b) *1 hour 10 min*
(c) *2 hour 16 min*
(d) *44 min*

5. Overhead point A the fuel contents are 17 USG. 19 minutes later, over point B, the fuel contents are 15 USG. Your destination, C. is 42 minutes away. Assuming the fuel flow remains constant and a Specific Gravity (Sp. G) of 0.72, how much fuel will remain, in lb, when overhead C?

(a) 27 lb

(b) 62.5 lb

(c) 10.5 lb

(d) 75 lb

6. Overhead point A the fuel contents are 22 USG. 27 minutes later, over point B, the fuel contents are 17 USG. Your destination is 55 minutes away. Assuming the fuel flow remains constant and a Specific Gravity (Sp.G) of 0.72, how much fuel will remain, in kg, when overhead C?

(a) 6.8 kg

(b) 10.2 kg

(c) 18.6 kg

(d) 4.1 kg

7. Overhead point A the fuel contents are 52 kg. 38 minutes later, over point B, the fuel contents are 45 kg. Your destination, C, is 1 hour and 14 minutes away. Assuming the fuel flow remains constant and a Specific Gravity (Sp.G) of 0.72, how much fuel will remain, in USG, when overhead C?

(a) 31.3 USG

(b) 13.7 USG

(c) 22.4 USG

(d) 11.5 USG

The Flight Plan Form

The flight plan is an ATC message, compiled by or on behalf of the pilot-in-command to a set CAA format and then transmitted by the appropriate ATC authority to organisations concerned with the flight. It is the basis on which ATC clearance is given for the flight to proceed.

Correct use of the flight plan form is most important. Incorrect completion may result in a delay to processing and subsequently to the flight. Full instructions for the completion of a flight plan form are detailed in an Aeronautical Information Circular (AIC).

Note that a pilot intending to make a flight must contact ATC (or other authority where there is no ATC) at the aerodrome of departure. This is known as **booking out** and is a separate and additional requirement to that of filing a flight plan.

PPL pilots may, if they wish, file a flight plan for any flight. They are advised to file a flight plan if intending to fly more than 10 nm from the coast or over sparsely populated or mountainous areas. Flight plans must be filed for all flights:
- **within Class A** airspace (IFR only);
- **within controlled airspace** in Instrument Meteorological Conditions (IMC) or at night, excluding Special VFR (SVFR);
- **within controlled airspace** in Visual Meteorological Conditions (VMC) if the flight is to be conducted under the Instrument Flight Rules (IFR);
- **within Scottish and London** Upper Flight Information Regions (UIRs, i.e. above FL245);
- **where the destination** is more than 40 km from departure and the maximum total weight authorised exceeds 5,700 kg;
- **to or from the UK** which will cross the UK Flight Information Region (FIR) boundary;
- **during which** it is intended to use the Air Traffic Advisory Service.

NOTE IFR flight in 'open FIR', by day or night, does not of itself require a flight plan.

A flight plan should be filed at least 30 minutes before requesting taxi or start-up clearance (60 minutes in certain cases where the controlling authority is London, Manchester or Scottish Control).

If a pilot who has filed a flight plan lands at an aerodrome other than the destination specified, the Air Traffic Service Unit (ATSU) at the specified destination must be told within 30 minutes of the estimated time of arrival there.

Completing the Flight Plan Form

The pilot should fill in the appropriate white space on the flight plan form using BLOCK LETTERS, or numerals for the time in UTC and the number of persons on board. A typical flight plan could be as follows:

ITEM 7: Insert the aircraft registration, **GMEGS**, five letters with no hyphens.

ITEM 8: Insert V for **Visual Flight Rules**. Insert G for a **general aviation** type of flight.

ITEM 9: Insert, in this case, **P28A** for **type of aircraft** using four characters only, and **L** for **light**-aircraft wake-turbulence category. The first box (two spaces), labelled *number,* is left blank unless there is more than one aircraft in your group.

ITEM 10: Insert V to signify that you have **VHF** communications radio, and **C** for that category **transponder** for secondary surveillance radar (SSR). The letter S is used to signify **standard** radio equipment, which is considered to be VHF, ADF, VOR and ILS.

ITEM 13: Insert **EGBB** for **Birmingham** (ICAO codes for all aerodromes are listed in the UK AIP and *Pooley's Flight Guide*), and the estimated **off-block** taxiing time of 1210 UTC.

ITEM 15 AND 16: Insert **N0105** to indicate the cruising TAS in **nautical** miles per hour (kt) to the value of 0105 (i.e. TAS is 105 kt), and **A025** to indicate a **cruising altitude** of 2,500 ft amsl, and **DCT** to indicate the **direct** route with no turning points to the destination **Northampton** (EGBK), which is inserted in item 16, and with the total **estimated elapsed time** of 0026 (00 hours and 26 minutes). The **alternate** aerodrome nominated for Northampton is **Leicester** (EGBG).

ITEM 18: Insert 0 to indicate no other information.
(continued on page 214)

FLIGHT PLAN **ATS COPY**

PRIORITY: << ≡ FF →

ADDRESSEE(S): << ≡

FILING TIME → ORIGINATOR << ≡

SPECIFIC IDENTIFICATION ADDRESSEE(S) AND/OR ORIGINATOR

3 MESSAGE TYPE: << ≡ (FPL

7 AIRCRAFT IDENTIFICATION: – GMEGS

8 FLIGHT RULES: – V

TYPE OF FLIGHT: G << ≡

9 NUMBER: –

TYPE OF AIRCRAFT: P28A

WAKE TURBULENCE CAT.: / L

10 EQUIPMENT: – V / C << ≡

13 DEPARTURE AERODROME: – EGBB

TIME: 1210 << ≡

15 CRUISING SPEED: – N0105

LEVEL: A025

ROUTE: → DCT

<< ≡

16 DESTINATION AERODROME: – EGBK

TOTAL EET HR MIN: 0026

ALTN AERODROME: → EGBG

2ND ALTN AERODROME: → << ≡

18 OTHER INFORMATION: –

) << ≡

SUPPLEMENTARY INFORMATION (NOT TO BE TRANSMITTED IN FPL MESSAGES)

19 ENDURANCE HR MIN: –E/ 0215

PERSONS ON BOARD: → P/ 003

EMERGENCY RADIO: → R/ UHF ~~U~~ VHF ~~V~~ ELBA ~~E~~

SURVIVAL EQUIPMENT: → ~~S~~ / POLAR ~~P~~ DESERT ~~D~~ MARITIME ~~M~~ JUNGLE ~~J~~

JACKETS: → ~~J~~ / LIGHT ~~L~~ FLUORES ~~F~~ UHF ~~U~~ VHF ~~V~~

DINGHIES: → ~~D~~ / NUMBER → CAPACITY → COVER ~~C~~ → COLOUR << ≡

AIRCRAFT COLOUR AND MARKINGS: A/ RED / WHITE WITH BLUE EAGLE

REMARKS: → ~~N~~ / << ≡

PILOT IN COMMAND: C/ KEMPFE) << ≡

FILED BY

SPACE RESERVED FOR ADDITIONAL REQUIREMENTS

■ *Figure 11-1* ***Completed flight plan form***

Supplementary Information

ITEM 19:

- **Insert endurance** of **0215** (02 hours 15 minutes), and **003** to indicate **three persons on board** (pilot plus two passengers).
- **No emergency radio** is carried, so each of these is struck out, as for the survival equipment, none of which is in this particular aeroplane.
- **The aircraft's colour and markings** are a distinctive red and white, with a blue eagle on the rear fuselage, so insert these details.
- **No further remarks** concerning survival equipment or matters of importance in a search and rescue situation, so strike out the N.
- Insert the pilot-in-command's **name.**

For rules to follow in filling in the flight plan correctly refer to the AICs (Aeronautical Information Circulars), AIP and General Aviation Safety Sense leaflet no. 20, *VFR Flight Plans*.

Flight plans are now generally filed electronically via the APEx system. See: www.flightplanningonline.co.uk or the NATS website: www.nats.co.uk/do-it-online/assisted-flight-plan-exchange-afpex which detail how to use this method.

Section **Three**

En-Route Navigation

En-Route Navigation Techniques

Deduced Reckoning

Deduced reckoning is the primary means of visual cross-country navigation. It is commonly known as dead reckoning (DR). It is based on:

- **starting** at a known position (called a fix);
- **measuring** the track and distance on a chart to the next point chosen along the desired track;
- **applying** the best estimate of wind velocity available to determine: the **heading** to steer to achieve the desired track; and the **groundspeed** to find estimated time of arrival over that next point.

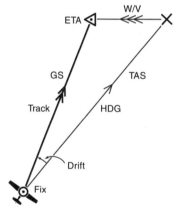

■ *Figure 12-1* **Dead reckoning is the fundamental method of navigating visually. The angle between heading (HDG) and track (TR) is the aircraft's drift.**

Dead reckoning navigation, where the pilot flies the estimated heading for the estimated time interval (both calculated when flight planning), should bring the aeroplane over the next checkpoint at the appointed time.

Map-reading is used as a backup to dead reckoning. This enables the pilot to pinpoint the aeroplane's position (obtain a fix) over some ground feature en route and evaluate the success of the dead reckoning navigation.

*A **fix** is the geographical position of an aircraft at a specific time, determined by visual reference to the surface of the earth, or by radio navigation equipment.*

A **pinpoint** is the ground position of an aircraft at a specific time determined by direct observation of the ground (not by radio navigation equipment).

Fixing the aircraft's position is not a continuous process second-by-second throughout the flight, but rather a regular process repeated every 10 or 15 minutes. (This may need to be reduced to 5 minutes or so in areas requiring precise tracking like Entry/Exit Lanes, see Chapter 16.) If you try to identify ground features to obtain a fix at shorter time intervals than this, then you may find yourself just flying from feature to feature without any time being available for the other important navigation tasks, such as planning ahead and monitoring the fuel situation.

For normal en route navigation you should:
- **fly accurate headings** (by reference to the direction indicator and the ground); and
- **periodically identify landmarks.**

Unfortunately it is generally the case that the actual track made good (TMG) is not precisely the desired track (or planned track). The difference between the desired track and the actual TMG is known as the **track error** (TE).

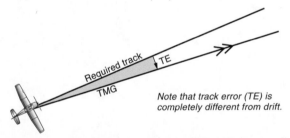

Note that track error (TE) is completely different from drift.

■ Figure 12-2 **Track error is the angular difference between required track and track made good**

Wind Effect

Most of the calculations in dead reckoning (DR) navigation are to compensate for wind effect, so if the wind differs in either speed or direction from the expected wind, then a track error will probably result.

Accurate tracking involves compensating for wind effect.

If we assume that there is no wind, then the aeroplane will end up at what we call its **air position** (symbolised by a cross), i.e. its position relative to the air mass.

The wind effect will blow the aeroplane to its **ground position** (symbolised by a small circle), i.e. its position relative to the ground – and this is what we are really interested in.

If we can actually fix or pinpoint the ground position of the aircraft by reference to features on the earth's surface, then we symbolise this on our chart with a small circle.

If this is not possible, we can determine a **DR position** by plotting the calculated track and distance flown since the last fix, and mark this point on our chart as a small triangle.

+	⊙	◬
Air position	Ground position	DR position

■ *Figure 12-3* **Navigation symbols**

At the flight planning stage, a *forecast* wind was used to calculate a heading for the aeroplane to make good a desired track. This wind will almost certainly not be precisely the same as the actual wind that is experienced in flight. This means that the actual drift in flight (the angle between heading and track made good) will most likely differ from that expected, to a greater or lesser extent.

Also, whether the track made good (TMG) is left or right of the desired track will depend on whether we have allowed too little, or too much, **drift** to counteract the crosswind effect.

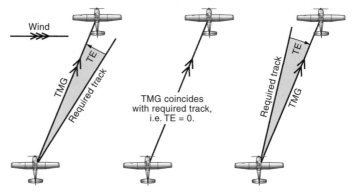

■ *Figure 12-4* **Track error results if we allow too little or too much drift**

En route we can counteract a track error by modifying the heading to achieve more accurate DR navigation for the remainder of the flight.

It is also usual to find that the actual in-flight groundspeed (GS) differs from that expected at the flight-planning stage, when all we had at hand was the forecast winds rather than the actual winds that we are experiencing in flight. This means that the original estimated time intervals (ETIs) to cover certain distances will be somewhat in error and will need to be modified once an accurate in-flight check of groundspeed (GS) is obtained. The estimated time of arrival at any point can then be revised.

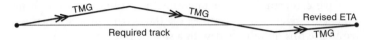

■ *Figure 12-5* **In-flight modification of HDGs and ETIs is usual in dead reckoning navigation**

The most important way to keep in-flight navigation workload to a minimum is to be thorough in your pre-flight preparation (flight planning). For in-flight navigation, concentrate on simple mental calculations.

Flight plan thoroughly.

This will allow you to modify the headings and estimated time intervals (ETIs) calculated at the flight-planning stage without too much 'head-down' work, and the methods that we discuss here will be adequate for most situations.

NOTE Remember that track error and drift are two different things and should never be confused.

Airmanship for the Pilot/Navigator

Airmanship is common sense. Do not become over-engrossed in navigation; as pilot of the aeroplane you are responsible for a safe flightpath.

FLY ACCURATELY. Try to fly the aeroplane reasonably accurately at all times (heading ±5°; altitude ±100 ft; indicated airspeed ±5 kt). Even though you are looking out of the cockpit most of the time to monitor the altitude and heading of the aircraft, and to check for other traffic, you should periodically check the flight instruments to achieve precise heading, airspeed and altitude.

Setting the correct power and holding the attitude will result in the required performance in general terms but, to fly precisely, you will need to refer to the flight instruments and make suitable minor adjustments to the attitude and the power. This means a quick look at the relevant flight instruments every 10 seconds or so throughout the flight.

Scanning the essential instruments in flight quickly and often is an important skill to develop. A good pilot has a fast scan rate, which is necessary for accurate flying.

LOOKOUT. Keep your paperwork in the cockpit neat and accessible – do not work 'head-down' for more than a few seconds at a time, and keep a good lookout!

Keep a good lookout!

TRIM. Ensure that the aeroplane is in trim, and can fly itself accurately 'hands-off'; not that you will actually fly it hands-off, but correct trimming will considerably lighten your task of maintaining height and heading. Check that the IAS used in your calculations is within 5 kt of that actually being flown, and that the altitude is within 100 ft; if not, do something about it by adjusting power and attitude.

CHECK WEATHER. Continually observe weather conditions, not only ahead of you, but also to either side and behind (just in case you have to beat a hasty retreat). You must assess any deterioration in weather and modify your flight accordingly. Ask Flight Information Service (FIS) or Air Traffic Control (ATC) for an update on the weather en route and at your destination aerodrome if necessary. Their function is to provide a service to pilots.

AVOID HAZARDOUS CONDITIONS. Take appropriate action to avoid hazardous conditions. For instance, it is good airmanship to divert around thunderstorms instead of flying near or under them, and to avoid areas of fog and reduced visibility. Also avoid dense smoke from fires because the visibility will be reduced and the air turbulent.

CHECK POSITION. Obtain a position fix every 10 or 15 minutes if possible and update your headings and ETAs (more frequently in poor visibility and/or congested airspace, e.g. every 5 minutes).

CHECK INSTRUMENTS. Carry out regular en route checks of the:
- **magnetic compass** and direction indicator alignment;
- **engine instruments;**
- **electrical and other systems.**

This en route check can be remembered by the mnemonic FREDA:

FREDA	
F	**Fuel:** on and sufficient; **Fuel tank:** usage monitored; **Mixture:** leaned as required for the cruise; **Fuel pump:** (if fitted), as required.
R	**Radio:** frequency correctly selected, volume and squelch satisfactory; any required calls made.
E	**Engine:** oil temperature and pressure within limits; carburettor heat if required; other systems checked, e.g. the electrical system, suction (if vacuum-driven gyroscopes are fitted);
D	**Direction indicator:** (direction indicator or directional gyro) aligned with the magnetic compass, and your position checked on the map.
A	**Altitude** checked and subscale setting correct (usually Regional Pressure Setting).

CHECK TIME. Maintain a time awareness, particularly with respect to fuel and latest time of arrival.

The Flight Sequence

Departure from an Aerodrome and the Initial Fix

The aim, at the start of the flight sequence, is to depart from the aerodrome safely whilst ensuring that an accurate heading from a convenient geographical point for the first leg of the flight is achieved. Dead reckoning navigation depends upon flying valid headings between two geographical points based on precise timings. If the initial set heading point is not targeted accurately at the start of the leg, errors will occur that will place extra demands on you to correct, en-route.

The actual method of departure from an aerodrome will depend upon factors such as: the circuit direction; VFR arrival and departure routes; IFR procedures; the proximity of controlled airspace and the need to route via access lanes. Other aerodromes may have local restrictions due to heavy traffic, high terrain or nearby built-up areas calling for special departure procedures.

Three methods of departure will be considered: the set heading point method; the overhead initial fix and the estimated initial fix. In each explanation, the pilot is trying to fly to a turning point on a bearing of 150°M from the aerodrome using runway 06 with a left hand circuit; the aerodrome elevation is 1,200 ft amsl.

Method 1: The Set Heading Point Method

Traditional navigation methods use the departure aerodrome as the default set heading point. This requires the pilot to take off, safely manoeuvre the aircraft to the aerodrome overhead, set heading and determine (and log) the actual time the leg commences. This imposes a very high workload on the pilot at a time when lookout and other airmanship factors are essential. Furthermore, overhead departures may not be permitted at certain aerodromes particularly those within the control zones and/or under the control areas of major airports. The use of Entry/Exit Access Lanes also prevents the use of overhead departures.

In this situation, you should consider selecting a familiar, neutral geographical point, with respect to VFR and IFR departure routes, approximately 4 nm from the aerodrome in the approximate direction of 150°M. This would be outside of the limit of any controlled airspace restrictions. This allows you to settle after the take-off, climb to the required cruising altitude, perform after take-off and top-of-climb (*FREDA*) checks and prepare the chart and flight log for use. You can also follow ATC instructions regarding exit from controlled airspace without distraction.

The flight to the set heading point would not be considered a formal leg with regard to the flight log: in this case the first leg starts at the set heading point and not the departure aerodrome. It is, however, important to build the route from the departure aerodrome to the set heading point into fuel plan.

Method 2. Establishing the initial DR fix overhead

After take-off, climb out to 500 ft aal (500 ft on QFE, or 1,700 ft on QNH) and turn left in the direction of the circuit. Continue left turns in the circuit direction and set course overhead the field at a height of at least 1,000 ft aal and climbing clear of the circuit (i.e. 2,200 ft on QNH in this case).

Log the actual time of departure (ATD) in the appropriate place on the flight log. The ATD will be your time of setting course overhead the aerodrome.

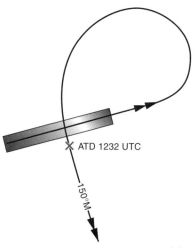

ATD 1232 UTC

150°M

■ *Figure 12-6* **Method 2. Setting course overhead**

Method 3. Estimating the initial DR fix

If methods 1 and 2 are not available to you, an estimate of the actual time of departure is necessary as if the track had been directly overhead. A groundspeed of 120 kt is equivalent to 2 nm per minute, so if you set course at say 4 nm from the aerodrome at time 1234 UTC and your estimated GS is about 120 kt, the ATD would be 2 minutes prior to this at 1232 UTC.

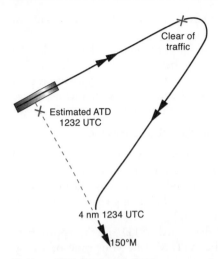

■ *Figure 12-7* **Method 2. Setting course en route
and calculating ATD**

This third method can be used whenever you intercept track
rather than setting course overhead the aerodrome.

Immediately after setting heading and becoming established on
track, you would:

- **log the actual time of departure** (ATD) and insert the
  estimate overhead the first checkpoint, based on the ATD and
  the flight-planned estimated time interval);
- **make a departure report** by radio if required (frequencies are
  shown on the aeronautical charts).

NOTE The terms estimate and estimated time of arrival (ETA) are
used loosely to mean the same thing, i.e. the time of arrival
overhead, although in a strict sense ETA applies only to the
aerodrome of intended landing.

Rough Check of Departure Track

On departure you should have in mind some ground feature en
route that is within 10 or 15 nm of the aerodrome, against which
you can check that you indeed are departing in approximately the
right direction.

EXAMPLE 1 After take-off from an aerodrome and taking up the
calculated heading to achieve your desired track of say 150°T, you
should pass slightly left of a large lake at about 8 nm from the

aerodrome. To confirm that it is the correct lake, your charts show a large hill and radio mast on its north-west side, so use these to confirm identification of it.

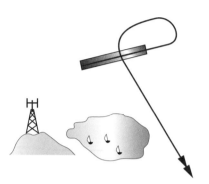

■ *Figure 12-8* **Check approximate tracking direction soon after departure**

You should ensure within the first few minutes that you are making good the correct track. If you are in any doubt, check the direction indicator against the magnetic compass. For accuracy, apply the deviation correction found on the card in the cockpit to amend °M to °C.

Cruise

On reaching the cruising altitude you should ensure that Regional Pressure Setting is set. If you are cruising above the usual UK transition altitude of 3,000 ft, it may be good airmanship to cruise at a flight level (based on 1013 hPa rather than QNH), the same as all the IFR traffic will be doing.

Establish cruise speed and cruise power and trim the aeroplane. Scan all the vital instruments and systems for correct operation. Verify that the gyroscopic DI is aligned with the magnetic compass. It may be a good time to do a full FREDA en route check.

It is good airmanship to check straight away that you are achieving the desired true airspeed (TAS) in the cruise. This may be completed quickly by:

- **approximation** (at 5,000 ft TAS is about 8% greater than IAS, and at 10,000 ft TAS is about 17% greater than IAS);
- **setting** the adjustable temp/TAS scale, if fitted on your ASI, so that, as well as reading IAS on one scale, the other scale indicates TAS. This is a feature found on some airspeed indicators in general aviation aeroplanes. It is a scale similar to that on your navigation computer where, by setting pressure altitude against true outside temperature, TAS can be read off against IAS, at least in the cruising range.

If the achieved TAS is significantly different from that expected then you should check:

- **correct power set;**
- **correct aircraft configuration** – flaps up, landing gear up (if appropriate), position of cowl flaps.

From two position fixes separated by about 20 to 30 nm, you should be able to establish an accurate groundspeed and determine if your heading is achieving the desired track or not. (Naturally, if you are about to fly over featureless terrain or water, where position fixing will be difficult, there is nothing to stop you using fixes obtained in the climb. Good airmanship is common sense.)

As soon as possible in the cruise obtain a groundspeed check.

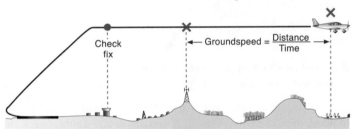

■ *Figure 12-9* **Check groundspeed and track early in the cruise**

If the actual GS is significantly different from that expected at the flight-planning stage, then you will have to revise your ETAs. If the track made good (TMG) differs significantly from the desired track, then you will have to make a HDG change. Make use of the best available information to estimate a suitable heading.

To obtain good fixes you need to select suitable check features and make use of your map-reading skills.

Map-Reading In Flight

The success of map-reading depends on:
- **Knowledge** of direction, distance and groundspeed.
- **Selection** and identification of landmarks and check features.

Select good checkpoint features

Landmarks and checkpoints that can be easily identified, which will be within your range of visibility when you pass by them, are best. Just how conspicuous a particular feature may be from the air depends on the:
- **flight visibility;**
- **dimensions** of the feature;
- **relationship** of your selected feature to other features;
- **angle** of observation;
- **plan outline** of the feature if you are flying high;
- **elevation** and side appearance of the feature if you are flying low.

Preferably the feature should be unique in that vicinity so that it cannot be confused with another nearby similar feature. A feature that is long in one dimension and quite sharply defined in another is often useful, because:

- **if a long feature** (such as a railway line, canal or road) runs parallel to track, it can assist in maintaining an accurate track; and
- **if a long feature** crosses the track it can be used as a position line to aid in determining an updated groundspeed (GS).

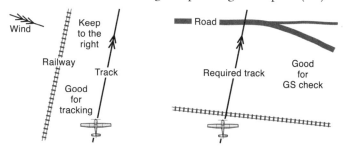

■ *Figure 12-10* **Long, narrow features are particularly useful**

NOTE It can be useful when tracking along line features, to stay to the right (i.e. keep the line feature on your left where you can best see it out of the captain's seat). Aircraft flying along the same line feature, but in the opposite direction, will normally be doing the same, thereby minimising collision risk.

The relationship between your selected feature and other nearby ground features is important for a positive confirmation of your position. For example, there may be two small towns near each other, but you have chosen as a feature the one that has a single-track railway line to the west of the town and with a road that crosses a river on the north side of the town, whereas the other town has none of these features. This should make positive identification fairly easy.

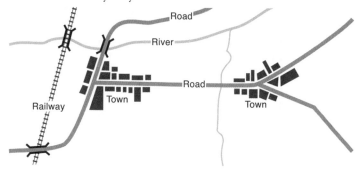

■ *Figure 12-11* **Confirm identification of your selected feature by its relationship with other features**

'Position Lines' Can Be Useful

A position fix is obtained when you can positively identify the position of the aeroplane relative to the ground. A position line is not as specific as a fix because you can only identify the position of the aeroplane as being somewhere along that line, and not actually fixed at a particular point.

> A **position line** is an extended straight line joining two points, some where along which the aeroplane was loated at a particular time.

You may see a position line referred to as a PL, LoP or a *line of position*. Position lines can be obtained:
- **from long narrow features** such as railway lines, roads, motorways, coastlines;
- **from two features** that line up as the aeroplane passes them (known as 'transit bearings');
- **from magnetic bearings** to (and from) a feature (this need not only be visual, it can also be a radio position line, i.e. a magnetic bearing from an NDB or VOR).

■ *Figure 12-12* **Each of these aeroplanes is on the same position line**

It is usual to show a position line on your map as a straight line with an arrow at either end, and with the time written in UTC at one end.

■ *Figure 12-13* **Marking a position line**

Of course, if you can obtain two position lines that cut at a reasonable angle, then you can obtain a good position fix. For the aeroplane to be on both position lines at the one time, it must be at the point of intersection.

■ *Figure 12-14* **Two position lines with a good cut can give you a fix**

Select Good Features 10 or 15 Minutes Apart

Do not choose a multitude of landmarks and checkpoints. Just one good checkpoint every 10 or 15 minutes is sufficient. At a groundspeed (GS) of 120 kt, this puts them 20 to 30 nm apart.

Look for a definite feature at a definite time. Choose a unique feature to avoid ambiguity.

Knowing direction, distance and groundspeed, you can think ahead, and anticipate the appearance of a landmark. This anticipation allows time for:

- **flying the aeroplane** (HDG, height, airspeed, engine, systems, checking DI against compass); and
- **navigation tasks** such as performing simple calculations (estimating new headings, revising ETAs, checking fuel) and then keeping an eye out for the next checkpoint; and then
- **looking ahead** at the appropriate time for the checkpoint which should be coming into view.

EXAMPLE 2 From the chart, you choose a small hill with a radio mast as a suitable checkpoint about 4 nm right of the desired track and about 20 nm ahead. The GS is 120 kt, so the 20 nm over the ground should be covered in 10 minutes.

If the present time is 1529 UTC, the estimated time interval (ETI) of 10 minutes gives an estimate at, or abeam, the checkpoint at 1539 UTC. You will, of course, be keeping an eye out for it for some minutes prior to this.

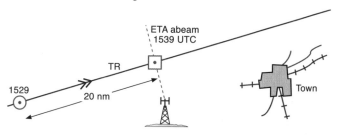

■ *Figure 12-15* **Look for a definite feature at a definite time**

If, instead of passing 4 nm abeam of the feature as expected, the aeroplane passes directly overhead, you recognise from the fix that you are off-track. Confirm that the feature is indeed the selected feature and not another nearby similar one. This can be done by checking the surrounding area for additional ground detail, say a small nearby town with a railway junction, and relating it to the whole picture.

Map-reading is used to assist dead reckoning navigation, not as a replacement for it.

Once certain that you have fixed the position of the aeroplane at a particular time, you can calculate very simply a new heading to achieve the desired track. Two easy ways to do this are by using track guides (or fan lines) already marked on the chart by you at the flight-planning stage, or by using the '1-in-60 rule' (to be discussed shortly).

Chart Orientation in the Cockpit

In flight, you must relate land features and their relative bearing from the aircraft to their representations on the chart. To do this it is best to fold the chart so that your desired track is 'up the chart'.

If, according to the chart, a landmark is 30° off the track to the right from the present position of the aeroplane, then you should be able to spot it by looking out of the aircraft window approximately 30° to the right of track. (Note that it may not be 30° to the right of the heading of the aeroplane because the heading may differ from the track, depending on wind velocity.)

■ *Figure 12-16* **Orientate the chart in the cockpit**

With the chart oriented correctly in the cockpit, the features shown to the right of the track drawn on the chart will appear on the right of the aircraft's track as you fly along (hopefully). The only disadvantage is that it may be difficult to read what is printed on the chart, unless you happen to be flying north.

In normal medium-level en route navigation, read from the chart to the ground. This means, from the chart select a suitable feature some 10 minutes or so ahead of your present position, calculate an ETA at, or abeam, it and then at the appropriate time (some two or three minutes before the ETA) start looking for the actual feature on the ground. Your chosen landmark need not be in view at the time you choose it, but you should anticipate it coming into view at the appropriate time.

Read from chart to ground.

Log Keeping

The purpose of keeping an in-flight log is to record sufficient data:
*   to enable you to **determine your position** at any time by DR;
*   to have readily at hand the **information required** for radio position reporting.

Logged data is invaluable if you are uncertain of the aircraft's position.

Keeping an in-flight log, however simple, helps the methodical navigation sequence:
*   **calculation of HDG** to achieve a desired TR;
*   **calculation of GS and ETI** to determine ETA at the next checkpoint;
*   **anticipation and recognition** of checkpoints;
*   **recalculation of HDG, GS and ETIs** if necessary (and the cycle repeats).

An in-flight log need only be very basic. On a normal cross-country flight you should log:
- **take-off time** on the flight log;
- **actual time of departure** (ATD) on the flight log;
- **fixes** (position and time) on the chart;
- **track made good** (TMG) on the chart;
- **changes of HDG** (and airspeed), and time of making them;
- **calculated GS;**
- **ETIs and revised ETAs** at the checkpoints;
- **altitudes.**

This sounds like a lot, but it isn't. Indicating TMG and fixes on the chart simplifies things for you, as these cover the two fundamentals of your progress towards your destination.

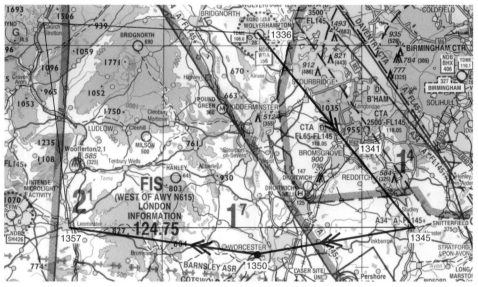

A.T. Dep **1336**

From/To	Safety ALT	ALT Temp	RAS	TAS	W/V	TR °T	Drift	HDG °T	Var	HDG °M	GS	Dist	Time	ETA	HDG °C
Halfpenny Green															
	2035	2500 −5	105	106	L&V	141	–	141	4W	145	96	23	13	1349	
Alcester															
	1904	FL45 −10	104	108	L&V	271	–	271	4W	275	97	32	18		
Leominster															
	2697	FL45 −10	104	108	L&V	352	–	352	4W	356	97	19	10		
Church Stretton															
	2697	2800 −5	105	106	L&V	099	–	093	4W	099	96	20	11		
Wolver-hampton															
										Total	94	52			

■ *Figure 12-17* **Keeping a log**

Using Position Lines for Groundspeed Checks

You should continually update your groundspeed (GS) as the opportunities arise. Time is of vital importance in navigation and your time of arrival anywhere will depend on the GS that you achieve.

Position lines that are approximately at right angles to your track can assist in updating your GS. Noting the amount of time it takes to cover the distance between the two position lines allows you to calculate the GS.

EXAMPLE 3

1351 UTC: Crossing a railway line perpendicular (at right angles) to track.

1359 UTC: Transit bearing of a radio mast and a bend in a river perpendicular to track 18 nm further on.

18 nm in 8 minutes = GS 135 kt.

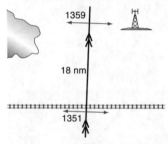

■ *Figure 12-18* **Groundspeed check using position lines perpendicular to track**

These position lines need not only be visual. You could also make use of radio position lines from an abeam NDB or VOR radio navigation station.

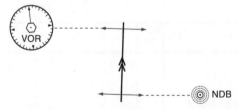

■ *Figure 12-19* **Groundspeed check using radio position lines from abeam radio navigation beacons (NDBs and VORs)**

NOTE As the use of radio beacons for navigation and position fixing is part of the 'Part-FCL PPL' syllabus, we have included some examples to show that basic navigation techniques are the same no matter where the information comes from. Experienced pilots always use a mix of information sources so as not to get caught out if one source suddenly ceases to be available during the flight. Radio navigation is covered in the final chapters of this book and in Vol. 5 of *The Air Pilot's Manual* series.

You can also carry out simple GS checks using *distance measuring equipment* (DME) radio navaid stations directly on track, either ahead or behind.

EXAMPLE 4

1325 UTC: DTY DME 67 nm and tracking directly towards Daventry DME.

1331 UTC: DTY DME 60 nm and tracking directly towards Daventry DME.

7 nm in 6 minutes = GS 70

■ *Figure 12-20* **GS check using DME**

Using Position Lines for Estimating Drift

If you have a position line roughly parallel to track you can use it to estimate the drift angle. Tracking directly overhead a long straight railway line makes a visual estimate of your drift angle quite easy, as does tracking along a radio position line to (or from) an NDB or VOR radio navaid station.

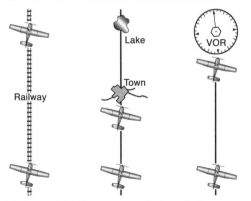

■ *Figure 12-21* **Determining drift angle from position lines parallel to track**

Uncertain of Position or Lost

Procedure When Uncertain of Position

If you have flown for some time without obtaining a fix (say 20 or 30 minutes), you may feel uncertain of your precise position. You will be able to calculate a DR position (using expected TR and GS), but you may feel anxious that you cannot back this up with a positive fix over or abeam some ground feature. This situation is a normal one and is no reason for immediate anxiety. It is far from being 'lost'.

It is impossible to give a set of rules that covers all possible situations, but the following are general rules that may assist you.

If a Checkpoint Does Not Appear at the Expected Time:

1. Log HDG (compass and direction indicator readings) and time.

2. If the direction indicator is incorrectly set, then you have the information needed to make a fair estimate of your actual position, then reset the DI and calculate a HDG and ETI to regain the desired track. Or:

If the DI is aligned correctly with the compass, then the non-appearance of a landmark, while it will perhaps cause you some concern, need not indicate that you are grossly off-track. You may not have seen the landmark for a perfectly legitimate reason, such as bright sunlight obscuring your vision, poor visibility, or a change in the ground features not reflected on the chart (e.g. removal of a transmission mast, or the emptying of a reservoir). Or if you are navigating above even a small amount of cloud, the inconvenient positioning of some of this cloud may have obscured your check feature.

3. If you consider the situation warrants it, make an **urgency call** (Pan-Pan) on 121.5 MHz. This should enable ATC to fix your position by 'auto-triangulation'.

4. If you obtain a fix, or if the next checkpoint comes up on time, the flight can continue and normal navigation procedures apply once again.

5. If still unable to fix your position, follow the procedure below.

Procedure When Lost

Becoming lost is usually the result of human error. Being lost is totally different from being temporarily uncertain of your position, where you can determine a reasonably accurate DR position.

Once again, it is impossible to lay down a set of hard and fast rules on what to do if you do become lost, but there are some general guidelines you can follow. Remember that careful pre-flight planning and in-flight attention to the normal, simple en route navigation tasks will ensure that the situation of being lost will never arise.

If you are lost, formulate a positive plan of action.

If you are lost, you must formulate a plan of action because it is futile to fly around aimlessly in the hope of finding a pinpoint.

If you change your thinking from one of being *uncertain of position* to one of being *lost,* then make use of the Radar Advisory Service, if available (see point **3** above). If still lost:

1. It is important initially to maintain HDG (if terrain, visibility and what you know of the proximity of controlled airspace permit) and carry out a sequence of positive actions.

2. If a vital checkpoint is not in view at ETA, then continue to fly for 10% of the time since your last positive fix.

3. On deciding what your last positive fix was, check the headings flown since that last fix, ensuring that:

– the magnetic compass is not being affected by outside influences such as a headset, portable radio, mobile telephone, or other magnetic material placed near it;
– the gyroscopic direction indicator (DI) is aligned with the magnetic compass correctly;
– magnetic variation and drift have been correctly applied to obtain your HDGs flown;
– an estimate of track direction on the chart against that shown on the flight plan is correct;

Read from ground to chart when lost.

4. Read from ground to chart, i.e. look for significant ground features or combinations of features and try to determine their position on the chart.

5. Establish a 'most probable area' in which you think you are. There are several ways this can be done. Consult your flying instructor for his or her preferred method.

Finding the Most Probable Area

Estimate the distance flown since the last fix and apply this distance, plus or minus 10%, to an arc 30° either side of what you estimate the probable track made good (TMG) to be.

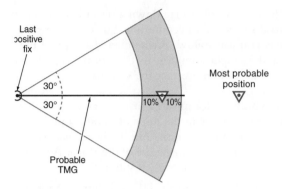

■ Figure 12-22 **Estimating the most probable area that you are in**

Finding the Most Probable Position

Estimate your 'most probable position' and draw a circle around it of radius equal to 10% of the distance flown since the last fix.

■ Figure 12-23 **Estimating most probable position**

Once the most probable area has been plotted, you should:

- **Establish a safety altitude** at which to fly in order to ensure adequate clearance of all obstacles in what you consider the general area to be. Be especially careful in conditions of poor visibility or low cloud.
- **Check large features** within this area of the chart with what can be seen on the ground. Try and relate features seen on the ground with those shown on the chart, i.e. read from ground to chart. Confirm the identification of any feature by closely observing secondary details around the feature, e.g. a small irregular lake is confirmed by the position of a small town on a bend in the railway line as it turns from west to south. Double check any fix.

When you do positively establish a fix, re-check your direction indicator (DI) and recommence normal navigation. Calculate the HDG, GS and ETI for the next check feature and set course for it.

At all times continue to fly the aircraft safely, maintaining an awareness of time, especially with respect to the beginning of official night (SS+30) and fuel state.

If you are still unable to fix your position, you should consider taking one of the following actions:

- **Increase the 'most probable area'** by 10, 15 or even 20% of the distance flown from the last fix.
- **Climb to a higher altitude** to increase your range of vision.
- **Turn towards** a known prominent line feature, such as a coastline, large river, railway line or road, and then follow along it to the next town where you should be able to obtain a fix. (Don't forget that it may also lead you into a control zone.)
- **Steer a reciprocal heading** and attempt to return to your last fix.
- **Seek navigational assistance** from an Air Traffic Services Unit.

Tell someone if you are hopelessly lost – share the problem!

Airmanship

Note the following important points of airmanship:

RANGE. If you want to cover as much ground as possible with the fuel available, you should fly the aeroplane for best range.

LOG. Keep a navigation log going.

TIME. Remain positively aware of time. Keep your eye on the fuel and on the time remaining until the end of daylight. If darkness is approaching, remember that it will be darker at ground level than at altitude, and that it becomes dark very quickly in the tropics.

LANDING. If you decide to carry out a precautionary search and landing (i.e. a forced landing with the use of power), allow sufficient time and fuel to do this on the assumption that two or three inspections might have to be made before finding a suitable landing area.

Why Did You Become Lost?

If at any stage you became lost, you should systematically try to determine the reason (either in flight or post-flight) so that you can learn from the experience. Common reasons for becoming lost include:

- **incorrectly calculated HDGs, GSs and ETIs** (hence the need for you always to make mental estimates of approximate answers to these items);
- **incorrectly synchronised direction indicator** i.e. gyroscopic DI not aligned correctly with the magnetic compass (this should be done every 10 or 15 minutes);
- **a faulty compass reading** (due to mobile phones, radios, cameras and other metal objects placed near the compass);
- **incorrectly applied variation** (variation west, magnetic best; variation east, magnetic least);

- **incorrectly applied drift** (compared to TR, the HDG should be pointing into wind, i.e. flying north with a westerly wind blowing would mean that the HDG should be to the left of track and into-wind);
- **a wind velocity** significantly different from that forecast, and not allowed for in flight;
- **a deterioration in weather,** reduced visibility, increased cockpit workload;
- **an incorrect fix,** i.e. mis-identification of a check feature;
- **a poorly planned diversion** from the original desired track;
- **not paying attention** to carrying out normal navigation tasks throughout the flight.

With regular checks of direction indicator alignment with the magnetic compass, reasonably accurate flying of heading, and position fixes every 10 or 15 minutes, none of these errors should put you far off-track. It is only when you are careless and let things go a bit too far that you become lost.

Off-Track Heading Corrections

I t is usual to find that the actual track made good (TMG) over the ground differs from the desired track that you plotted on the chart at the flight-planning stage. If this is the case, then you will have to make some precise corrections to the HDG so that you can return to track at some point further on.

Since the in-flight workload for the pilot/navigator can be quite high, we will concentrate on quick methods of mentally calculating track corrections.

1. The angle between the track made good (TMG) and the required track is called **track error** (TE).

2. The angle at which you want to close on your required track is known as the **closing angle** (CA). The size of the CA will depend on how much further down the track you wish to rejoin it – obviously the sooner you want to rejoin the desired track the greater the CA will have to be.

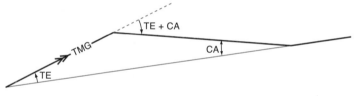

■ *Figure 13-1* **Track error and closing angle**

Figure 13-1 shows that to rejoin the desired track at the chosen position, a track change equal to TE + CA is required. (This makes use of a theorem of geometry you may remember from school which says that 'the external angle of a triangle equals the sum of the two interior opposite angles'.)

It is at the point that we make an approximation that simplifies our in-flight calculations. We assume that a track change of, say, 15° can be achieved by a heading change of the same 15°. This is not perfectly accurate because the effect of the wind may cause a different drift angle after making a significant heading change, but within limits it is accurate enough for visual navigation.

The main advantage in doing this is that it allows us to make track corrections without having to calculate the actual wind velocity.

For angles up to about 15°, assume that a track change can be achieved by an equal heading change.

Methods of Estimating Track Error

Using Track Guides to Estimate Track Error

With track guides (or fan lines) already drawn on the chart at the flight planning stage and emanating from certain checkpoints along the route, the estimation of track error (TE) and closing angle (CA) to regain track at that next checkpoint is made easy. After obtaining a fix, you can estimate TE and CA, which, when added together, will give you the required track change (and the required heading change) to close track at the next checkpoint.

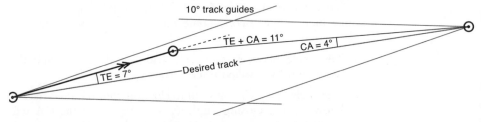

■ *Figure 13-2* **Track correction using 'track guides' (or 'fan lines')**

An advantage is that you do not have to measure distance off-track, although this is in fact quite simple to do. A disadvantage is that you must have passed over the point from which the track guides emanate behind and you will rejoin track at the point ahead to which the track guides close. Sometimes this is not the situation and other methods need to be employed.

If 5° and 10° track guides (just 10° adequate if short stage) are drawn either side of your desired track on your map, then estimation of track error in flight becomes easy.

Using the 1-in-60 Rule to Estimate Track Error

The 1-in-60 rule can be used to estimate correction angle. This is the most useful method of regaining track for VFR pilots. Time spent understanding this method now will make your en route navigation tasks much easier in future. The 1-in-60 rule is based on the fact that:

> *1 nm subtends an angle of 1° at a distance of 60 nm.*

This statement can be extended to say that:

> *5 nm subtends an angle of 5° at 60 nm.*
> *10 nm subtends an angle of 10° at 60 nm.*
> *15 nm subtends an angle of 15° at 60 nm.*

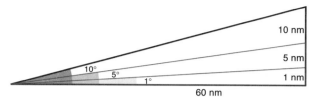

■ *Figure 13-3* **The 1-in-60 rule**

We cannot always wait until we have flown 60 nm to find our distance off-track, but that is of no concern because it is *ratios* in which we are interested.

EXAMPLE 1 4 nm off-track in 30 nm distance run is the same as:

8 nm off-track in 60 nm, i.e. a track error of 8°.

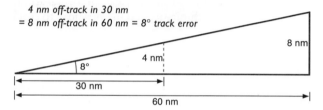

■ *Figure 13-4* **Example**

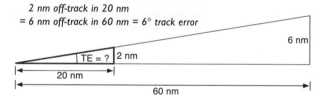

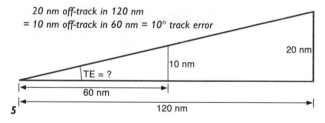

■ *Figure 13-5* **Determining track error using the 1-in-60 rule – solve mentally or by flight computer**

In addition to the track line on the chart, the careful selection of chart markings can facilitate your preferred method of en-route navigation. Use of 5° and 10° fan lines can provide a ready means of determining track error and closing angle for short route segments. This may not be practical for longer route segments where the fan lines become excessively divergent. In this case, the planner may wish to use two guidelines that are parallel to the track line at a distance of 5 nm either side. This allows distance off track to be estimated without the need to use a plotter to measure (hopefully) small deviations. To facilitate 1-in-60 rule calculations, marking the track line at factors of 60, e.g. at 10 or 15 nm, can make the determination of track error, using mental arithmetic, very easy.

Careful selection of chart markings can facilitate your preferred method of en-route navigation.

It is important to strike the balance between additional markings, used to facilitate en-route navigation mental arithmetic, and chart clarity. Over enthusiastic marking may lead to confusion and could potentially obliterate small but essential ground features.

Regaining Track

Having established the track error, using either fan lines or the 1 in 60 rule processes, the next stage is to alter heading either to regain the planned track or to intercept the next waypoint (turning point or destination). This section will consider methods for regaining track without the need for calculation and those requiring calculation based on triangular geometry.

Calculating Closing Angle using the 1-in-60 Rule

If we change our TR by the amount of the calculated track error, we will *parallel track.* (We can do this approximately by changing our HDG by this number of degrees – accurate enough for angles up to 15°.)

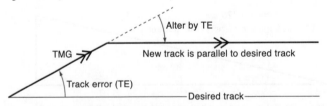

■ *Figure 13-6 Paralleling track by altering HDG by the angle of TE*

The same 1-in-60 rule can be applied to the closing angle (CA) once we have chosen the point at which we wish to rejoin track.

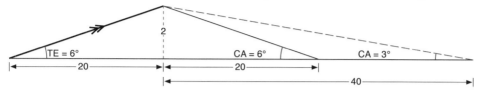

■ Figure 13-7 **Calculating closing angle by the 1-in-60 rule**

Now, knowing both track error (TE) and closing angle (CA) allows you to make a **heading change** (TE + CA) that should change your track by the same amount.

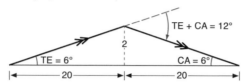

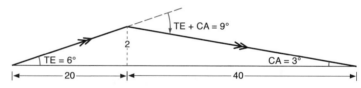

■ Figure 13-8 **Changing HDG (and TR) by 'TE + CA' to rejoin desired track**

This is an extremely important means of DR navigation and sample problems are given below

EXAMPLE 2 After flying 30 nm on a heading of 085°M, you find yourself 5 nm left of track. What should your new heading be to regain track 30 nm further on?

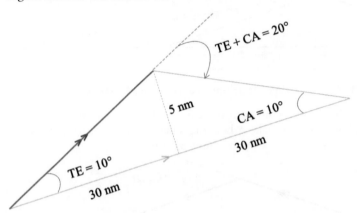

■ Figure 13-9 **Example 2**

5 nm left of track in 30 nm = TE 10° left

To close 5 nm in a further 30 nm requires a CA = 10°

Thus a heading change of 20° to starboard, that is 105°M, is required.

EXAMPLE 3 After 60 nm on a heading of 320°M, you find yourself 6 nm right of track. What heading has to be steered to regain track in a further 30 nm?

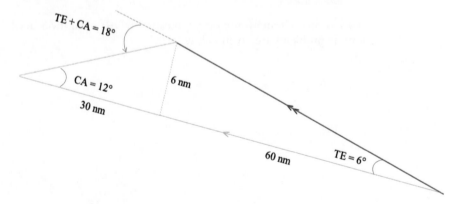

■ Figure 13-10 **Example 3**

6 nm left of track in 60 nm = TE 6° right

To close 6 nm in a further 30 nm requires a CA = 12°

Thus a heading change of 18° to port, that is 302°M, is required.

It can be seen, from Examples 2 and 3, that marking the track with factors of 60 simplifies the mental arithmetic. A further simplification is possible using the Ratio Method for estimating track corrections.

The Ratio Method for Estimating Track Corrections

The following rules of thumb, based on the 1-in-60 rule, can help in rapidly estimating closing angles.

- **To regain track in the same distance** (or time) since you were last on-track, change heading by double the track error (because the CA will be equal to the TE).
- **To regain track in double the distance** that it took you to get off-track, then the CA will be equal to only one-half the TE.
- **To regain track in only half the distance** that it took you to get off-track, then the CA will be double the TE.

Figure 13-11 illustrates the **ratio method** of using the 1-in-60 rule.

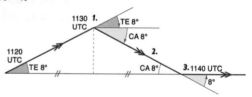

To regain track after running an equal distance:
1. Alter HDG by TE + CA, i.e. 2 × 8° = 16°
2. Fly for the same time.
3. Alter HDG by the 8°.

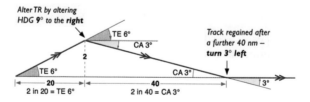

To regain track at a point further along the intended route:
1. Alter HDG by the TE approximately to parallel the flight-planned TR..
2. Alter HDG further by the CA (closing angle) to close on the TR at the chosen point.
3. When TR is regained, alter HDG back by the CA.

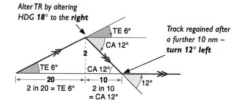

■ Figure 13-11 **Track corrections using the ratio method of 1-in-60 rule**
– a summary

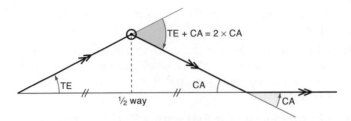

■ *Figure 13-12* **If 'distance-to-go' equals 'distance-gone', then alter heading by '2 × CA'**

The Inverse-Ratio Method

In the UK, it is seldom possible to fly direct visual routes over long distances because of the presence of controlled airspace, Restricted Areas and Danger Areas. Normally we have to fly a series of shorter tracks with a number of turning points to avoid such areas. It is sound planning to select turning points that can be easily identified, say over a prominent landmark.

With short legs, the 1–in-60 rule can be simplified even further by concentrating on the closing angle (CA) to the next turning point and using what is known as the 'inverse-ratio' method.

Using the Inverse Ratio Method at the Half-Way Point

Previously we saw that, to close track in a distance equal to that already travelled since we were last on track, TE = CA. We would then alter heading by this amount which (since TE = CA) is equal to 2 × CA. This is the situation if we fix the position of the aeroplane at the half-way point along a straight track leg.

Using the Inverse-Ratio Method at Other Points En Route

At any common fraction of the track gone then, to regain track, alter heading by 'CA × the inverse of the fraction of the distance gone'.

- At the ½-way point, alter heading by 'CA × 2', as we have just seen.
- At the ⅓-way point, alter heading by 'CA × 3'.
- At the ¼-way point, alter heading by 'CA × 4'.
- At the ⅕-way point, alter heading by 'CA × 5'.

EXAMPLE 4 A track leg is 45 nm. After travelling 15 nm, you are 2 nm left of track. Aim to regain track at the next turning point.

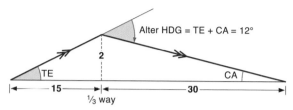

Alter HDG = TE + CA = 12°

■ *Figure 13-13* **Example 4**

Previous method:

TE is 2 nm in 15 nm = 8 nm in 60 nm = 8° TE.
CA is 2 nm in 30 nm = 4 nm in 60 nm = 4° CA.
Alter heading by TE + CA = 12°.

Inverse-ratio method:

⅓ of track gone.
Alter heading by CA × 3 = 4° × 3 = 12°.

Application of Inverse-Ratio Method

Proper preparation of charts makes in-flight track corrections easy.

1. Mark 5° and 10° track guides either side of the desired track from the end of that track;

2. Divide the track into quarters and mark these points.

It is now easy to estimate both closing angle and fraction of track gone for any fix that we obtain.

EXAMPLE 5

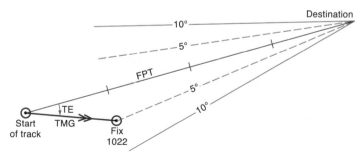

■ *Figure 13-14* **Example 5**

By estimation, CA = 5° and fraction gone is ¼.
Alter heading by 5° × 4 = 20° to the left.

NOTE The same 'inverse-ratio' method can be used to revise the estimated time interval (ETI). Time gone from start to fix is 7 minutes, therefore total time for leg = 7 × 4 = 28 minutes.

A limitation of the inverse-ratio method is that it only allows for one alteration of heading per stage, and it only regains track at the next turning point. For short legs this is not a significant disadvantage and the method is more than adequate. Its simplicity greatly reduces the workload in the cockpit for just a little extra effort at the flight-planning stage.

The methods described to regain track, thus far, require some degree of mental arithmetic to calculate the closing angle. Albeit, calculations can be simplified by careful selection of chart marking and approximations such as the ratio method. The standard closing angle method is an approximation that does not require mental arithmetic.

The Standard Closing Angle Method

This procedure provides a basis for calculating the change in heading needed to regain the planned track in the number of minutes corresponding to the number of nautical miles off track. As before, it is necessary to establish the number of nautical miles off track, to the left or right, using preferred chart markings, e.g. fan lines or 1-in-60 Rule markings, etc.

The principle of the standard closing angle method is shown below.

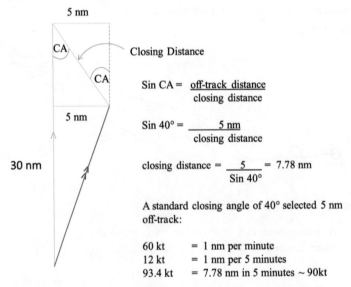

■ Figure 13-15 **The principle of the standard closing angle method**

In this example, an aircraft is off track by 5 nm after 30 nm along its planned track. An aircraft flying with a TAS of 90kt will regain track in approximately 5 minutes, i.e. the distance off track at the start of the manoeuvre, by turning through 40°. This method actually does not need a knowledge of the track error, indeed it can be applied at any point along the track where a deviation is detected.

Mental algebra is not required as a table can be drawn up based on the construction in Figure 13.15 and referred to en-route.

TAS kt	1 Minute Standard Closing Angle	2 Minute Standard Closing Angle
60	60	30
70	50	26
80	45	23
90	40	20
100	36	18
110	33	16
120	30	15

The table shows the 1 minute standard closing angle for common general aviation airspeeds, e.g. if you are flying at a TAS of 100 kt and are 3 nm right of track, turn left 36° and fly for 3 minutes (the number of minutes equal to the number of degrees off-track). Some pilots are concerned with the use of 1 minute standard closing angles that require a turn of greater than 30°. The 2 minute standard closing angle provides an option whereby a less acute closing angle can be selected but where the time to regain track is now double the off-track distance. It can be seen that halving the 1 minute standard closing angle whilst doubling the off-track distance allows track to be regained.

EXAMPLE 6 You are flying at a TAS of 90 kt on a heading of 085°M. After 13 nm of a 37 nm route segment you notice that you are 4 nm right of track. What action can you take to regain your original track?

From the table above, the 1 minute standard closing angle for 90kt TAS is 40°. You therefore alter heading 40° to the left; in this case onto a heading of 045°M. This heading is flown for 4 minutes, corresponding to the off-track distance. During this time, the reason for the deviation can be analysed, e.g. incorrect DI alignment or different wind effects than planned. At the end of 4 minutes a heading of 085°M can be re-established and the aircraft should be back on the planned track.

If there is concern that a 40° heading change is too acute, the 2 minute standard closing angle can be used instead. In this case the standard closing angle is 20°, requiring a change of heading onto 065°M but this time for 8 minutes.

This technique has the advantage that it is simple to apply, the course correction strategy can be developed quickly at any stage on the route segment and does not require extensive calculation. The method does rely on approximations that become progressively less accurate as off-track distances become greater.

Once the desired track is regained, if you do not alter the heading you used to regain track, you will fly straight through the desired track.

Maintaining a Desired Track (Having Regained It)

From Figure 13-11 it is clear that to remain on track you will have to alter your latest TMG (i.e. the TMG flown as you returned to the desired track) by an amount equal to the chosen closing angle (CA).

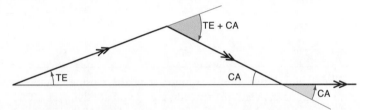

■ *Figure 13-16* **When back on-track, change heading by the chosen closing angle**

Diversions

En Route Diversions

Occasionally you will have to divert around such things as thunderstorms, heavy rain showers, and towns. If there are suitable landmarks you can use these to assist you to divert around the 'obstacle' and then to return to track.

If there are no suitable landmarks, then it is a good idea to follow a simple procedure such as:

1. Divert 60° to the desired side of track for a suitable time (and note the HDG and time flown).

2. Parallel track for a suitable time (and note the time flown).

3. Return at 60° for the same time to return to track.

4. Take up a suitable HDG to maintain track.

NOTE A 60° diversion is very convenient because an *equilateral* (equal-sided) triangle's three angles are each 60°.

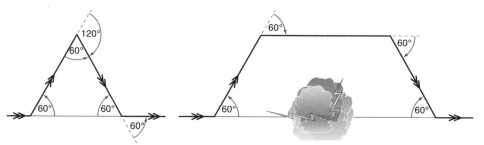

■ *Figure 13-17* **The angles of an equilateral triangle are each 60°**

With a 60° diversion followed immediately by a 60° return to track, the actual distance flown on the diversion is double the on-track distance. In nil-wind conditions this will take double the time.

If the initial 60° diversion HDG is flown for 2 minutes, and the 'return to track leg' is flown for 2 minutes, i.e. a total of 4 minutes, this will then exceed the direct on-track time interval by 2 minutes. The ETA at the next checkpoint will therefore be 2 minutes later than previously estimated. If we had flown 5 minute diversion legs, then it would add 5 minutes to our ETA.

The length of the leg flown parallel to track will not affect the ETA.

NOTE We have assumed nil-wind conditions in this discussion. If a significant wind is blowing, then you have to make appropriate allowances for it.

Diversions to Alternate Aerodromes

Occasionally it may be necessary to divert from your planned destination. Reasons for diverting include deteriorating weather at the destination, the possibility of running out of daylight if you continue to your planned destination, or a suspected mechanical problem that suggests an early landing would be prudent.

If the diversion only entails a small change in HDG (say up to 15°), then using the 1-in-60 rule is adequate.

NOTE An unplanned diversion is part of the PPL Skill Test.

EXAMPLE 7 You are tracking 320°T to your destination aerodrome which is 135 nm further on when you receive a met report to say that a large thunderstorm is approaching it. Your HDG is 315°M and your GS 133 kt.

You decide to divert and land at a small aerodrome which, from your present position, is located 10 nm to the right of track and 42 nm distant. Calculate an approximate HDG to steer and an approximate ETI.

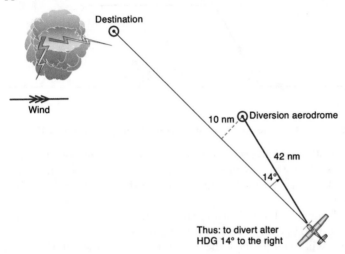

■ *Figure 13-18* **Example of a diversion slightly off the desired track using the 1-in-60 Rule**

10 nm in 42 nm = 14° to the right of your present track.

Because the change in direction is only 14°, a track change of 14° will be achieved reasonably accurately by a HDG change of 14°. (This is because the wind effect will not differ greatly between the two tracks.) Similarly, we can assume the GS to be unaltered due to the similar wind effect on the two reasonably similar tracks.

ANSWER Steer a HDG of (315 + 14) = 329°T to achieve a TR of (320 + 14) = 334°M. 42 nm at a GS of 133 kt = ETI 19 minutes. If a diversion requires a *significant* change of heading (and this is usually the case), then the wind effect on the new track may differ significantly from that on the original track. The drift experienced may be quite different on the two different headings. In this case it will be necessary to use your computer to calculate the HDG and GS on the new TR using the latest and most accurate W/V that you have.

EXAMPLE 8 En route from Alpha to Bravo. Approaching Charlie, you decide to divert to Delta.

The best technique to use is to maintain HDG and original TR to the next checkpoint (say Charlie) and carry out calculations to enable you to divert from that known position. (5 minutes should be adequate to get yourself organised for an accurate diversion.)

Measure track and distance from your diversion point to the diversion aerodrome, and, using the known TAS and the most accurate wind velocity (W/V) to hand, calculate (on the wind side of your flight computer) the heading (HDG) to steer, and the expected groundspeed (GS), from which you can find an estimated time interval (ETI) and estimated time of arrival (ETA) overhead the aerodrome.

Check your answers with quick mental approximations.

Calculations:
Charlie to Delta, TR 352°T, 27 nm VAR 5°W.
TAS 105, W/V 240°T/30.

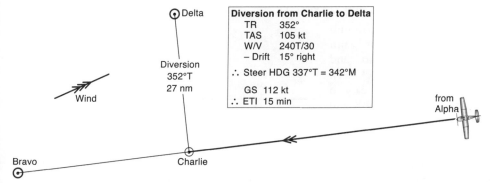

■ *Figure 13-19* **A diversion involving a significant change of heading**

Some Practical Hints on Diversions

Diversions sometimes become necessary at the most inopportune moments, possibly when you have other problems on your hands. It therefore pays to have a few tricks up your sleeve to allow you to make quick and practical diversions without having to use your computer and go 'head-down' in the cockpit.

If you can estimate direction and distance by eye, then your diversion will be made considerably easier. Direction is most important and, once you have taken up an approximate diversion heading and settled into the diversion track, you can calculate an accurate heading, distance to go, groundspeed, and ETI in a more relaxed atmosphere.

Estimating Track

Estimation of track is surprisingly easy and, with a bit of practice, you can achieve a ±5° accuracy. In fact, you should always estimate track before measuring it with a plotter – this will avoid making 180° or 90° errors as has happened from time to time.

Estimating before measuring will also develop faith in your ability to estimate to a practical degree of accuracy.

'Halving known angles' is the simplest means of estimating angles. Halving the angle between a quadrantal point and a cardinal point will give you an angle of 22.5°, say 22°, and halving this again will give you 11°. An accuracy of ±5° will be achieved with practice.

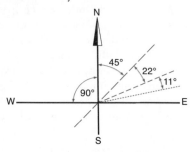

■ *Figure 13-20* **Halving angles as a means of estimating track**

Estimating Distance – Rule of Thumb!

The average adult 'top thumb joint' will cover about 10 nm on a 1:500,000 chart (and 5 nm on a 1:250,000). Check yours! This makes it easy to estimate short distances and times.

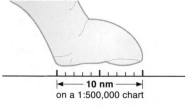

■ *Figure 13-21* **The top thumb-joint covers approx. 10 nm 1:500,000**

A '10-mile thumb' at a groundspeed of 120 kt = 5 min, 100 kt = 6 min, 85 kt = 7½ min, 70 kt = 8½ min, 60 kt = 10 min. For example, an unplanned diversion of 30 nm at groundspeed 100 kt = (3 × 6) 18 minutes.

A full hand span might measure 60 nm on a 1:500,000 chart. Check yours!

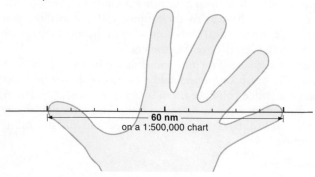

■ *Figure 13-22* **A full hand span is approximately 60 nm on a 1:500,000 chart**

If you have a 60 nm span and a 10 nm top thumb-joint, then you have an in-built 1:60 measuring device, ideally designed to measure 10°.

10 nm in 60 nm = 10°, by the 1-in-60 rule.

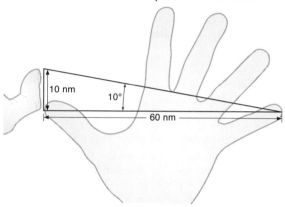

■ *Figure 13-23* **The personal 1-in-60 measuring device for 10°**

As part of your Skill test (en route techniques) or Navigation Flight Test (NPPL) you will be asked to carry out a diversion. Should you decide to use radio navigation fixes then these will also be examined. Radio navaids need to be thoroughly understood before being used for navigation. (See Chapter 17-23 of this book and Vol. 5 of *The Air Pilot's Manual*).

Now complete: **Practice Questions - Off-Track Heading Correction**

1. An aircraft plans to fly a direct route from A to B; a distance of 120nm. 60nm down track from A, a visual fix shows the aircraft to be 5nm left of track. What alteration of heading is required to arrive overhead B?

   (a) 10° right
   (b) 12° right
   (c) 10° left
   (d) 15° right

2. An aircraft is flying between two points 90 nm apart, after 30 nm the aircraft is found to be 5 nm to the right of track. In order to route directly to the destination what heading correction is necessary?

   (a) 15° left
   (b) 12° right
   (c) 10° left
   (d) 15° right

3. An aircraft is flying between two points 80 nm apart, after 20 nm the aircraft is found to be 3 nm to the right of track. In order to route directly to the destination what heading correction is necessary?

   (a) 14° right
   (b) 3° right
   (c) 9° left
   (d) 12° left

4. An aircraft is flying between two points 90 nm apart, after 50 nm the aircraft is found to be 7 nm to the left of track. In order to route directly to the destination what heading correction is necessary?

   (a) 11° right
   (b) 8° left
   (c) 20° left
   (d) 19° right

5. An aircraft is flying between two points 120 nm apart, after 40 nm the aircraft is found to be 5 nm to the right of track. In order to route directly to the destination what heading correction is necessary?

(a) *8° left*
(b) *4° right*
(c) *11° left*
(d) *14° right*

Navigation in Bad Weather and Degraded Visual Environments

This topic is considered here because flights into adverse weather conditions represent a significant safety hazard to PPL holders. Whilst accidents associated with flights in degraded visual conditions represent a small proportion of general aviation accidents, they account for a significant percentage of fatalities. The following situations are the major causes of accidents:

- Loss of control of the aircraft when attempting to regain visual meteorological conditions
- Loss of control during the transition from flight using visual references to **control** of the aircraft by sole use of instruments
- Disorientation, resulting in a controlled flight into terrain, the sea, obstacles or other aircraft.

The threat and error management framework can be used as a guide for pre-flight weather planning, and in-flight decision-making, should the visual environment degrade.

- Obtain - weather information as part of the pre-flight planning exercise and use it to identify weather hazards that could impact flight safety. Thought should also be given to how you will gain information en-route, particularly if weather conditions start to deteriorate.
- Analyse – weather information to determine risks to safety.
- Act – take positive steps to eliminate bad weather hazards by staying on the ground or reducing their impact, e.g. by a change of route.

Pre-flight Weather, Hazard and Risk Assessment
Careful analysis of forecast conditions is required to identify the following major hazards:

- **Low cloud ceiling** – this needs to be considered at all stages of the flight, i.e. departure, en route and at the destination, on the basis of reliable forecast information.
- **Poor visibility** – again, forecast visibility must be considered at all stages of the flight and whether it is sufficient to remain safe. A difference in the temperature and dew point of less than 4°C and/or a trend towards a decrease in the difference should alert the pilot to a potential degradation of the visual environment.

- **Sudden local changes to cloud ceiling or visibility** – flights over mountainous terrain or near the coast may be particularly susceptible to risks associated with rapid changes in weather conditions due to local heating/cooling effects.
- **Strong wind** – the wind conditions at the departure and destination airfields must be within the gust and crosswind limits of the aircraft and within the limitations of the pilot's skill level.
- **Windshear** – is to be expected in the vicinity of thunderstorms, when sea or land breezes exist and when there is a large disparity between surface wind and upper level wind strength.

As part of the pre-flight planning process, it is important to consider whether to commit to the flight in the first instance. Sadly, many pilots commit to flights in inappropriate conditions because of: economic pressures, e.g. the loss of time and money or wasted effort; poor situation appraisal due to inexperience in gathering or interpreting weather data; inadequate risk assessment of weather hazards due to a lack of understanding of risk or over-confidence in limited flying ability; social pressures connected with demands from passengers to complete the flight or the desire to keep social or business appointments. One of the most effective threat and error management tools (risk avoidance) is to wait for bad weather to pass. You should ask for assistance from your instructors or more experienced pilots with the analysis of weather information to understand hazards that exist. It is important to recognise and work within your skill limitations and experience. The PPL is primarily a recreational qualification and steps should be taken to resist economic and social pressures to fly when it is not safe to do so.

Contingency options must be built into your VFR navigation pre-flight planning. It is important to identify the direction from which bad weather is coming and to know in which direction to turn to avoid it in search of a safe place to land. An acceptable alternative airport should be identified for each 25-30 nm segment of the route. Steps should also be taken to avoid flying near the limit of fuel exhaustion so that diversion options do not become limited if the weather deteriorates.

In-flight Navigation in Bad Weather and Degraded Visual Environments

Once the flight is underway, it is necessary to monitor the weather and the state of the visual environment. For practical purposes, this is mainly achieved by a visual assessment of the weather conditions along the route and whether they match the expectations of your pre-flight planning. Sometimes, there can be local deviations in weather conditions, e.g. isolated thunderstorm cells, fog and low cloud, that were not forecast which may present a hazard to navigation. You can also obtain weather information from ATIS broadcasts, en route, or from air traffic control units as a component of the Basic Service.

Changes in the weather can occur at the limits of human visual perception. The eye responds best to rapid change and degradation of the visual environment can occur quite gradually. Lighting conditions are also very important. Strong, direct sunlight provides a lot of information about terrain, obstacles and other aircraft through reflections and the formation of shadows. This aids the detection of reflective objects, e.g. water and other aircraft and textural information enabling judgment of distance and depth. "Flat light" occurs when sunlight becomes highly diffused, e.g. through thin sheets of cloud. In flat light, the reflective and textural information available in direct sunlight is not present.

In-flight hazards include the following:

* A low level of ambient or flat light
* No visual horizon
* Poorly visible ground features
* An inability to detect changes in attitude and height above terrain by visual reference alone
* A degraded visual environment that cannot be escaped by a reduction in altitude
* A cockpit view obscured by rain or other precipitation
* A lowering cloud base that requires a sustained descent to maintain VMC
* Cloud, mist or fog forming underneath your current cruising altitude.

In this situation, serious consideration should be given to abandoning the flight and returning along the reciprocal flight path in search of improved conditions, with the aim of returning to the departure aerodrome or seeking an alternate aerodrome in good weather. As a last resort, a precautionary landing must be considered as a viable alternative to flying in bad weather.

Entering a non-VMC Degraded Visual Environment

A PPL without an instrument rating should never knowingly enter instrument meteorological conditions. If licensed for VFR flying, you should consider yourself to be in a degraded visual environment if:

• You are unable to maintain attitude control by reference to the natural horizon (regardless of the prevailing weather conditions)

• You are unable to navigate, or establish your current geographical position, by visual reference to surface landmarks

THIS MUST BE CONSIDERED AN EMERGENCY PROMPTING IMMEDIATE APPROPRIATE ACTION TO REGAIN VMC.

Your primary goal in this situation is to maintain control of the aircraft, seeking to maintain straight, level and trimmed flight. At this stage, you have three options:

• If substantially above the safety altitude, a descent is possible to fly clear of cloud.

• If below the safety altitude, a climb must be initiated until it is exceeded.

• A 180° turn onto a reciprocal heading should be executed assuming that, as VMC existed before flying into degraded conditions, this is the quickest known path back to VMC.

Combined manoeuvres, e.g. climbing turns and descents, must be avoided.

• **Climbs** – with wings level, can be achieved by a simple increase in power whilst accepting any rate of climb that results. Attainment of a specific, accurate climb speed is unnecessary in these circumstances.

• **Descents** – again with wings level, can be achieved with small, incremental power reductions (e.g. 100 RPM or 1" of manifold air pressure) enabling a descent at not more than 500 feet per minute.

• **Turns** – should be made with the smallest practicable bank angle and in any case not more than 10°.

You should not hesitate to inform air traffic control that you are flying in conditions where the visual environment is degrading. The controller must be informed if you are uncertain of your position, particularly if there is a risk that you will infringe controlled airspace with a potential loss of separation from IFR traffic. Your primary responsibility in this situation is to regain and maintain control of the aircraft. Any urgent instruction from a controller, requiring a manoeuvre that could result in loss of control, should be complied with only within the limitation of your ability to control the aircraft.

Low Level Navigation

A flight can continue, under VFR, at an altitude lower than the planned cruising altitude provided that safe terrain clearance can be maintained, and the low flying rules one observed. In principle, navigation could proceed as low as 500 ft provided that large urban areas are avoided, although this is highly questionable in practice. Low level navigation is conducted in the same way as navigation at higher levels with a few special considerations. Before attempting to navigate at low level by a modified dead reckoning approach, consideration should be given to alternative means of navigation, e.g. the identification and tracking of clear line features (especially the coastline), or use of radio navigation aids, e.g. VOR/DME.

At low level, it is not possible to see far into the distance and extra vigilance is necessary to avoid terrain and other obstacles. It is important to select check points and turning points based on prominence at lower levels, e.g. large lakes and reservoirs, coastal features and features with prominent side elevations, e.g. bridges, radio masts and power stations. The ground features, relied upon at higher altitudes, are of little use at low level, e.g. roads, small rivers and railway lines. The presence of unusually high obstructions that may be difficult to see, e.g. fine, high radio masts, must be anticipated and avoided. Being close to the ground, your limited field of vision may lead to ground features appearing suddenly and to becoming lost by being overflown at low level. It is therefore important to use accurate timing information to anticipate the appearance and identifying features of landmarks so that they can be identified quickly and assuredly. Your selection of checkpoints for standard navigation may not take into consideration these special requirements for low level navigation. For this reason, a switch from standard to low level navigation, in degrading visual environments, may not be successful unless some familiarity with the geography exists.

Navigation In Remote Areas

One day, you may fly into one of the world's remote and featureless areas, such as North Africa, the Middle East, India or even the Australian outback. The transition from cross-country flying in the more heavily populated areas of the UK to flying in the featureless areas should not be taken lightly. Navigation in remote areas is not necessarily more difficult, but the lack of landmarks requires more disciplined flight planning and flying.

A number of accidents have occurred when inexperienced pilots encountered navigation difficulties in remote areas of the world. A common theme has been:
• lack of experience; coupled with
• inadequate flight preparation; and
• poor in-flight navigation technique.

EXPERIENCE. Where does one gain experience? Pilots are faced with 'lack of experience' many times in their flying careers. How do we gain experience, except by reading and studying and then finally 'doing'? First solo and first cross-country flight as a single pilot/navigator are stages in extending ourselves to new limits, and in the process gaining experience.

Often we learn some lessons that have been learned many times before by other pilots. Listen to them! But make your own operational judgements. *Biggles* stories may contain lessons for you. Read reports of trips where things did not go as planned (and learn from other pilots' experiences rather than your own).

The term 'lack of experience' is used here in reference to navigation experience. We assume that, as a responsible pilot, you would only venture forth into a remote area in an aeroplane in which you had recent flying experience and with whose systems (fuel system, electrical system, etc.) you were fully conversant.

FLIGHT PREPARATION. There is no excuse for inadequate flight preparation, even for the most inexperienced pilot. You must do your homework properly for a particular route, so that you can make reasonably correct in-flight decisions when the unexpected occurs. Of course, with proper pre-flight preparation, the unexpected seems to occur less often.

IN-FLIGHT NAVIGATION TECHNIQUE. Flying in remote and featureless areas requires some good DR flying. Following dirt tracks that meander through the desert and then peter out is a poor navigation technique for remote areas.

This is not to say that following the only railway line up to Alice Springs or the one-and-only sealed road across to Perth in Australia shouldn't be done – this is an area for your own operational judgement – but we are referring here particularly to areas where such features are not available.

What can you, a pilot-in-command, do to avoid the pitfalls that can occur in remote area flying?

Flight Plan Carefully

'Day-Before' Pre-Flight Planning

- Allow plenty of time to flight plan carefully without any pressure of time being placed on you.
- Ensure that your charts are current and adequate for your intended route, plus or minus any reasonable planned or unplanned diversions.
- Examine your charts carefully for landmarks and distinguishing features along your proposed route, and to either side of track.
- Ensure that you are up to speed on your computer usage, especially in calculating headings, groundspeeds and times.
- Ensure that you carry the required radio and survival equipment and that it is in good condition and you know how to operate it.
- Make use of the local knowledge of other pilots and briefing officers who know the area you intend flying over. Determine suitable fix points and obtain as much information as possible on suitable landing areas along the route. Ensure that the information is reliable and up to date, because it is not unknown for landing grounds in remote areas to be abandoned and possibly unusable.
- If practicable, plan your route over suitable landing areas.

Obtain a Thorough Met Briefing

- Ensure that you are briefed thoroughly on the route and for your destination and alternate aerodromes.
- Do not be embarrassed if you do not understand all aspects of the Area Forecasts or Aerodrome Forecasts, or some of the abbreviations. Ask for clarification!
- Be wary of areas where visibility may be reduced in dust or haze.
- Do not plan on flying above a low layer of cloud for long periods where your visual navigation could be impeded.
- In hot, desert areas, try and determine an appropriate altitude above which you will be out of the convective turbulence layer and its associated 'bumpy ride' for the time at which your flight will occur.

Obtain a Thorough Operational Briefing

- ATSU personnel are aviation professionals. They are trained to a high standard and it is their job (and usually their pleasure) to assist you in any way possible. It is up to you to request their assistance.
- Pay particular attention to landing area and aerodrome service-ability along your proposed route, especially following rain.
- Determine availability of the correct fuel at appropriate landing points.
- Determine if any military activity is planned in the area. Military jet low-level navigation exercises do occur at high speed in remote areas – some of these aircraft are camouflaged fighters that are hard to see, and some of them large bombers. It is nice to know if they are around.
- Verify the time of last light for your destination.

Submit a Flight Plan

- Check tracks and distances mentally following your computer calculations to ensure that there are no gross errors, e.g. tracks wrong by 90° or 180°. Apply magnetic variation correctly (variation east – magnetic least).
- Check that drift has been allowed for in the correct direction and that ETIs are approximately correct.
- Plan on flying as high as is practicable because:
  - a better picture of the country can be obtained;
  - on hot days, the flight should be smoother;
  - VHF radio coverage is better.
- Allow adequate fuel, plus reserves – not only for the planned flight, but for any possible alternative action, including what procedures you will follow in case selected fix-points are not located as expected.
- Allow sufficient time for the planned flight plus any possible alternative action, especially if flying in the latter part of the day when last light is a consideration. Only a foolishly over-confident visual pilot would allow a mere 10-minute buffer prior to last light for arrival over the destination.
- Early departure times in the desert areas generally produce better flights. Cooler air gives better take-off performance and a smoother ride. Visibility may be better and the pressure of impending last light removed. The benefit of the early start can be lost if you dawdle along, though, wasting time with inefficient flight planning, refuelling, etc.
- Allow for proper food and rest at appropriate intervals. It is not only the aeroplane that needs fuel.

In-Flight Navigation Technique

• Fly estimated headings accurately. Do not allow the aircraft to wander off-track simply through inattention. Have in your mind an awareness of approximate direction – and check that drift is applied in the correct direction for your desired track and the wind experienced. Check for drift soon after departure and adjust your heading as necessary.

• Map-read carefully as the flight progresses, but do not let this distract you from flying an accurate heading. Be aware that, following heavy rains in remote areas, large uncharted rivers and lakes may appear and disappear within a few days. Even if you cannot pinpoint yourself visually at all times due to the lack of landmarks, at least know your dead reckoning (DR) position at all times based on estimated TR and GS since your last fix.

• Maintain an in-flight log, recording all HDGs flown and the time of any significant changes. It takes a few seconds to complete and may prove invaluable.

• Maintain a general sense of direction and ensure that the direction indicator is re-aligned with the magnetic compass at regular intervals (every 10 or 15 minutes).

• Do not deviate from your flight plan without any real justification. A flight plan should be adhered to unless a positive fix indicates that you are off-track, or unless you change your intentions in flight and prepare a new flight plan. With a positive fix, you have data that will enable you to make a reasoned correction to your heading.

• Anticipate your fix points some minutes ahead of your estimate for them and commence a good lookout, not just ahead but also to each side of track. Do not just wait for planned fix points to show up – anticipate them. Continually study the surrounding countryside, but not to the extent that it disturbs your accurate heading keeping.

• Positively establish your position in relation to a selected fix point before continuing to the next fix point.

• If you are unable to locate your selected fix point and you are uncertain of your position, commence your planned alternative action, being aware of fuel and time in particular. This alternative action could be to return to the last positive fix or to divert to some prominent landmark, even if some distance away. In these circumstances you may have to abandon your original plan for proceeding to your original destination, in favour of a destination that is easier to locate and in a more accessible area. Maintain an accurate log in this procedure.

• If you depart from your original flight plan, notify your new intentions to the appropriate ATSU, but do this after you have planned on your new course of action and flying the aeroplane is well in hand.

If Things Do Not Work Out As Planned ...

- Do not become flustered. With reasonable planning, you should have allowed fuel and time to sort out this sort of problem. Establish the fuel state and time remaining to last light.
- Do not assume that you are in a particular place simply because that is where you want to be. Keep an open mind and study the surrounding countryside carefully. Log all significant changes of heading, and the times they are made.
- Follow the procedures suggested in the previous chapter on what to do if you are uncertain of your precise position or if you become lost.
- Advise the ATSU of the headings and times flown since your last positive fix; the SAR (search and rescue) organisation can plot your flight using the latest wind data and assist in establishing your position.
- If, despite your precautions, things go unexpectedly wrong and you are caught with insufficient fuel or daylight to reach your destination or a suitable alternate, be intelligent in the use of your resources.
- Carry out a precautionary search and landing while you still have adequate fuel and daylight available. Stay with the aircraft and activate the emergency locator transmitter.

The Emergency Locator Transmitter (ELT)

In remote areas visual searches can be difficult. The emergency locator transmitter (ELT), if properly used, can allow the search area to be reduced quickly so that the visual search can be concentrated in a small area.

ELT is a generic (family) term covering devices known as crash locator beacons, emergency locator beacons, etc. They all operate on both 121.5 and 243 megahertz.

A few common sense points on the use of the ELT are:

- Know how to use the ELT. Revise the operating instructions for your particular transmitter prior to flight.
- Ensure that the battery is fully charged.
- Ensure that the ELT is capable of operating properly (tests are restricted, so seek the advice of the authorities before activating a test, as it may result in the commencement of unnecessary SAR action, such as scrambling of aircraft, etc.).
- If you are forced down, however, do not be reluctant to activate the ELT at an appropriate time.

Personal Locator Beacon

These small lightweight beacons are now a compulsory requirement for flights crossing the English Channel. The beacons transmit on 406Mhz and also on 121.5, although the latter frequency is no longer monitored by satellite. It is necessary to register your details at the EPIRB Registry at the Maritime and Coastguard Agency in Falmouth

Entry/Exit Lanes and
Low-Level Routes

Special Entry/Exit Access Lanes and Low-Level Routes are provided for light aircraft to allow exit from and entry to some aerodromes that lie within Control Zones (CTRs) or under controlled airspace. They are established to allow easier access for training aircraft, for example.

There may be other routes legitimately usable which do not infringe Restricted Areas or controlled airspace, but the established Access Lanes provide a readily identifiable channel through complex sections of airspace.

Entry/Exit Lanes and Low-Level Routes are designed to simplify navigation and operational procedures for non-IMC-rated pilots flying near or into busy Control Zones.

Basic Rules
You should refer to the relevant aerodrome listing in AIP AD and/ or *Pooley's Flight Guide* for instructions.
- **Follow the published instructions.**
- **Adhere to the published tracks** and entry/exit points (labelled 'E/E').
- **Conform with the general flight rules** regarding terrain clearance, flight over populous areas, danger areas, etc.
- **Operate no higher than the altitude specified** as the upper limit in the section being flown.
- **Keep to the right** (traffic separation may not be provided by ATC).

Navigating an Access Lane or Low-Level Route is based on the normal visual navigation procedure of flying accurate headings and backing up with frequent visual fixes.

Flight Plan Accurately
Entry/Exit Access Lanes and Low-Level Routes are very confined areas. Control Zones (CTRs) that you must avoid entering are adjacent. The traffic in the area may be concentrated in the lane or route. For these (and other) reasons, extra attention must be paid to keeping a good lookout outside the cockpit compared to normal cross-country flying, and to map-reading with more than the usual number of fixes.

The easiest way to achieve this is to flight plan accurately and thoroughly.

- Study the weather forecasts and actual reports thoroughly. Note any significant weather, visibility, cloud ceiling and wind. Relate the weather conditions to the terrain or built-up areas that you will have to fly over, ensuring that adequate terrain clearance and clearance from cloud is available. Be aware that strong winds may give rise to turbulence in the low levels where you will be flying.
- Request an operational briefing from your instructor, checking to see if any special considerations need to be made for your flight.
- Select the best route. Sometimes there are several Access Lanes to choose from, and sometimes you may choose to avoid one and fly a completely different route. Prevailing conditions may make a more circuitous route, offering easier navigation, flatter terrain, better visibility, higher cloud base, more separation from controlled airspace, etc., more suitable than the published Access Lanes, although generally they are perfectly suitable.
- Study the chart carefully for suitable landmarks and specified points in or near the lane. Read all relevant operational comments in the AIP AD or *Pooley's Flight Guide*.
- Identify a landmark on the approach to the lane over which you can accurately position the aeroplane to commence the transit of the lane; this point is best chosen to be, say, 5 nm prior to the commencement of the lane to allow you room to manoeuvre without penetrating controlled airspace.
- Check all computer work for accuracy, and do mental checks of all HDGs, GSs and ETIs.
- Have an alternative plan of action ready in case poor weather or some other reason makes a transit of the lane undesirable.
- Aim to reduce the in-flight workload to a minimum.

Navigate Accurately

- You need to keep on track in an Access Lane, because of the proximity of Control Zones in most cases, where both large and small aircraft may be operating.
- Accurately position your aeroplane (over a landmark if possible) prior to entering the lane. This is your starting point for accurate track-keeping through the lane.
- Aim to have all other tasks (such as after-take-off checks, a departure or position report, copying the landing information off the ATIS, aligning the direction indicator with the magnetic compass) completed prior to entering the lane.

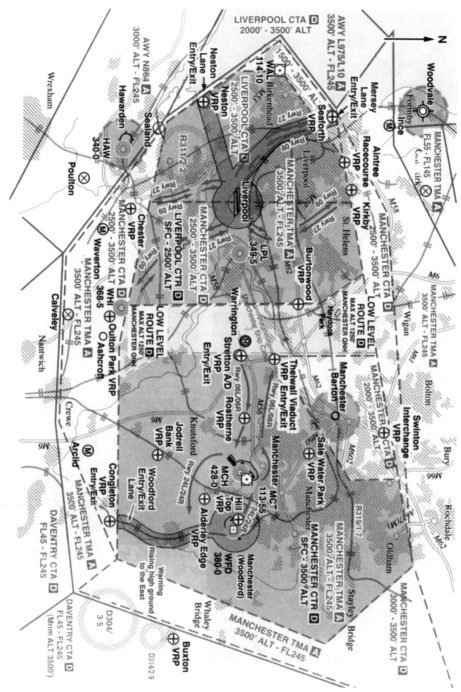

■ Figure 16-1 **Manchester Low-Level Route, as shown in the UK AIP**

Coming up to VRP Junc. M6/M58 (at left)

Haydock Racetrack and M6 junction

Passing the canal at Warrington

Approaching Warrington

VRP Stretton (airfield at right)

Lake north of Northwich

Entering the Low-Level Route by Winsford

Navigating the Manchester Low-Level Route (views when tracking northbound)
Copyright 2013 Infoterra Ltd, Bluesky and Google.

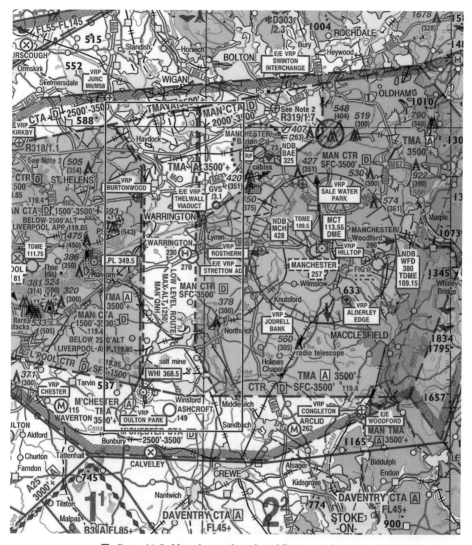

■ *Figure 16-2* **Manchester Low Level Route as shown on 1:500,000 chart**

- Check the weather ahead to see if it is clear enough for a safe transit of the lane. If not, adopt your alternative course of action, which might be to return to the aerodrome of departure, or to try another track.
- Ensure that your direction indicator is aligned with the magnetic compass in straight and level unaccelerated flight.
- From your commencement point, steer your calculated or estimated HDG and continue with steady map–reading. Adjust your HDG to maintain the desired track and to avoid straying into controlled airspace.

- Be suspicious of any HDG that differs more than 10° from what you calculated was necessary at the flight-planning stage. Many pilots have tracked visually along wrong railway lines, when a quick HDG check would have alerted them to an incorrect track.
- Look ahead for navigation features. If you miss one, look ahead for the next one, flying your best estimate of HDG. This is essential if visibility deteriorates.
- You should aim to stay on-track and within the confines of the lane by identifying the various features and either tracking over them or tracking abeam them on the correct side. Check that your HDG approximates to the HDG that you calculated.
- Concentrate on navigation, but keep a sharp lookout for other aircraft and for landmarks.
- Don't forget an occasional en route check of other items such as engine settings, fuel state, etc. (the FREDA check).
- Listen on the radio for other traffic, and broadcast your own intentions if you consider it necessary.
- If you feel uncertain of your position, do not be reluctant to request assistance. You will often be in radar environments, and if you are experiencing navigation difficulties because unexpected poor visibility is making visual fixes difficult to obtain, call for help! A request for a radar vector (HDG) to steer to remain in the lane or route may prevent an inadvertent penetration of a Control Zone.

These remarks have been directed at a pilot who is not familiar with a particular Entry/Exit Lane. An experienced pilot in good weather may feel quite happy tracking visually through a familiar lane with little planning, but if visibility decreases unexpectedly or some other unforeseen situation arises, these procedures give him something to fall back on. Local experience can count for a lot, but not always.

We all know very calm and proficient pilots who always seem to be on top of the task at hand, no matter what situation arises. These pilots are usually the ones who have done their homework and have done as much preparation on the ground as possible to minimise their in-flight workload. Having cards up your sleeve and alternative plans of action ready allow you to look calm.

Entry/Exit Lanes and Low-Level Routes require extra vigilance, and it is good to plan on a minimum in-flight workload so that your extra capacity is available to cope with any unforeseen distractions, which do occasionally occur.

Section **Four**

En-Route Navigation with Radio Navigation Aids "Navaids"

NOTE

1   The material in this section is intended only for PPL candidates. IMC and Instrument Rating candidates should refer to Vol. 5 of *The Air Pilot's Manual* for full details on instrument flying techniques, let-downs and the instrument landing system etc.

2   For the PPL Skill Test, you are not required to be fully conversant with all the radio navigation facilities described in this section – the requirements will vary depending on the geographic location of your flying school. Your flying instructor will advise you on which sections to study.

Introduction to Radio Navigation Aids

NB. NPPL and LAPL candidates are **not** required to demonstrate the airborne skills of radio navigation but will be examined on Radionav Theory.

Having achieved a high standard in visual attitude flying, it is now time to apply this ability to cross-country navigation with reference to radio navigation instruments.

It is, in fact, possible to fly cross-country using attitude flying only, without referring to any radio navigation instrument in the cockpit, simply by following instructions passed to you by a radar controller.

Instructions such as "Turn onto heading three four zero, and descend now to eight hundred feet," can be followed, even to the point of a cloudbreak for a straight-in landing on a particular runway.

Radar is the first of the radio navigation aids, or *radio navaids*, that we consider in this section, since it does not involve a great deal of understanding before you can benefit from it. As well as explaining how radar can be of use to you, we also discuss the basic theory of its operation, together with the transponder in the aircraft.

It is possible that your instructor may follow an order of study different from that presented here. If so, simply bypass the other chapters and proceed to the one desired. Each chapter is self-contained, and reading earlier chapters is not necessary to understand the content of a later one.

VHF direction finding (VDF), which, like radar, does not require additional instrumentation in the cockpit, may also be used for cross-country flying. By requesting ATC to provide you with a magnetic bearing to the station, known as a QDM, which can be determined at some aerodromes by detecting the direction from which your VHF radio communications are received, a track to or from the station can be flown. The procedure used is a little more complicated than simply steering radar headings, so we have left it until the end of this section.

Radio navigation aids covered that do require cockpit instruments include:

- **GPS (GNSS)**;
- **the VHF omni range (VOR)**;
- **distance-measuring equipment (DME)**;
- **the non-directional beacon (NDB)** and **automatic direction finder (ADF)** combination. The ADF has various cockpit presentations, such as the relative bearing indicator (RBI) and radio magnetic indicator (RMI).

It may sound a little complicated at this stage, but careful consideration of each of these radio navigation aids one at a time will make it easy for you. There is a certain amount of jargon, but it will not take long before you are familiar with all the terms.

The main function of this section of the manual is for you to understand how the aids work, and how to use them, especially for tracking to or from a ground station.

Radar

Most air traffic control in busy airspace occurs in a *radar environment*. This means that the air traffic controller has a radar map of the area showing the position of the various aircraft within it, bringing enormous advantages, such as:

- A significant reduction in the amount of air–ground communication. For instance, there is no need for pilots to transmit regular position reports.
- The ability to handle an increased number of aeroplanes in the same airspace, with reduced, but still safe, separation distances.
- The ability to 'fix' an aircraft's geographic position.
- The ability to *radar vector* an aeroplane along various tracks by passing headings to steer to the pilot.
- The ability to feed aeroplanes onto final approach to land, either to the commencement of an instrument approach such as an ILS (instrument landing system) or until the pilot becomes 'visual', without the need for excessive manoeuvring, and with more than one aeroplane on the approach at any one time.

This use of radar is known as **surveillance radar.** Surveillance radar, although extensively used in air traffic control, is not confined to controlled airspace. Wide areas of the UK have radar coverage, and you may, even if operating in uncontrolled airspace, take advantage of services such as the Lower Airspace Radar Advisory Service (LARS).

Most aeroplanes are now fitted with a secondary surveillance radar **transponder,** which transmits a unique signal in response to a radar signal from the ground, thereby allowing the radar controller to identify a particular aeroplane on a radar screen. You are probably familiar with the operation of the transponder – if not, it is considered in detail towards the end of this chapter. The name *transponder* is derived from *transmitter/responder*.

■ *Figure 18-1* **A typical SSR transponder**

At certain aerodromes, the surveillance radar controller can provide tracking guidance and height information down final approach in what is called a surveillance radar approach (SRA). This is a common approach for an IMC-rated or Instrument Rating (Restricted) pilot.

Radar Vectoring

Radar vectoring is when a radar controller passes a heading to steer to a pilot with an instruction such as:

> Charlie Delta
> Steer heading two five zero

Bear in mind that the radar controller is trying to get you to achieve a particular track over the ground and, because he does not know precisely what the wind at your level is and the amount of drift that it is causing, he will occasionally request a modification to your heading while radar vectoring your aeroplane.

No radio navigation instruments are required in the aeroplane for it to be radar vectored, but radio communication is necessary. The pilot concentrates on attitude flying (maintaining the desired heading, altitude and airspeed), while the radar controller concentrates on the aeroplane achieving the desired track over the ground. This is not to say that you should not be very aware of where your track is taking you, especially if high terrain is in the vicinity, and you should always maintain a picture of where the aeroplane is with respect to the aerodrome. This is essential in case of radio communication failure.

The termination of radar vectoring is indicated by the phrase:

> Resume own navigation

How Radar Works

> The remainder of this chapter discusses the theory of radio waves and of radar. It is not essential knowledge but it will help your understanding of radio, radar and radio navigation aids.

Radio uses the ability to transmit electromagnetic energy, in the form of radio waves, from one place to another. Radio has played a pivotal part in the development of aviation, and radar is an important type of radio system.

Waves of electromagnetic energy emanating from a radio transmitter can carry information, such as speech, music and Morse code, out into the surrounding environment. Radio receivers tuned to the *same* frequency can detect and use these signals, often at long distances from the transmitter.

Common uses for radio in aviation are:
- air–ground voice communication; and
- radio navigation (the ADF/NDB combination, VOR and ILS).

■ *Figure 18-2* **Radio is the transmission of electromagnetic energy
and the reception of it at a distant location**

The Reflection of Radio Waves

Electromagnetic radiation can be reflected from certain surfaces.
Light waves, for instance, will be reflected by the metallic coating
on a mirror. Similarly, radio waves of certain frequencies will be
reflected from metallic and other surfaces, with some of the radio
energy returning to the point from which it was transmitted as a
return echo. Other surfaces and objects, such as wood, may not
cause reflection of the radio waves, which will simply pass through
like X-rays pass through a body.

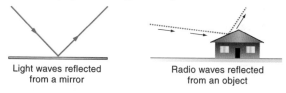

Light waves reflected   Radio waves reflected
from a mirror   from an object

■ *Figure 18-3* **Radio waves, like light waves, can be reflected**

Radar

Detection of the reflected radio waves at the point from where
they were originally transmitted is known as radar.

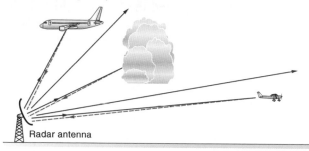

Radar antenna

■ *Figure 18-4* **Radar is the transmission of electromagnetic radio energy
and the detection of some of the reflected energy back at the point
of transmission**

The principle of radar has been known since the mid-1930s, and was used with devastating effect during World War II (1939–45) to detect objects such as aeroplanes and measure their range. Indeed, the name *radar* was devised from *radio detection and ranging.*

The combined transmitter-receiver used in radar is usually a parabolic dish that is very efficient both in transmitting radio energy in a particular direction and then receiving the reflected radio energy from the same direction. The best results are obtained with ultra-high frequency radio energy. The whole sky can be scanned systematically if desired, simply by slowly rotating the radar dish.

■ *Figure 18-5* **A typical radar antenna**

The Relationship of Time and Distance
All electromagnetic energy travels at the speed of light, 300,000 kilometres per second (162,000 nautical miles per second), the equivalent of almost eight journeys around the world in one second. Some common forms of electromagnetic energy are light, radio waves, X-rays, ultra-violet radiation and infra-red radiation.

By measuring the elapsed **time** between the transmission of a bundle or *pulse* of radio energy and the reception back at the source of its reflected echo, it is a simple mathematical calculation (knowing velocity) to determine the **distance** or *range* of the object causing the echo.

Radar converts an *elapsed time* to a *distance.*

$$\frac{distance}{time} = speed$$

Multiplying both sides of this equation by *time* gives an expression for *distance* in terms of the known speed of light and the measured elapsed time.

$$distance = speed \times time$$

During the elapsed time between transmission of the pulse and reception of its reflection (measured electronically at the radar site), the distance between the radar site and the object will of course have been travelled twice – once out and once back – so the elapsed time needs to be halved, and this is also done electronically.

The speed of light, being so great, means that the times involved are extremely short. This allows a stream of pulses to be transmitted, with only short time intervals between the pulses when no transmission occurs, to allow for reception of any echo. As a matter of interest, the time taken for a radar pulse to travel to and from a reflector 20 nm away (a total of 40 nm) is 0.000250 seconds, or 250 millionths of a second.

$$40 \text{ nm } (2 \times 20) \text{ at } \textit{speed of light } 162,000 \text{ nm/sec } = \frac{40}{162,000} \text{ sec}$$

$$= 0.000250 \text{ sec}$$

At what Range can Radar Detect Targets?

Radar uses ultra-high frequency (UHF) transmissions, which are basically *line of sight,* and so propagation will be interrupted by buildings, high terrain and the curvature of the earth. These will cause **radar shadows,** and objects in these shadow areas may not be detected.

Bearing in mind the curvature of the earth, the higher an aeroplane is flying, the greater the distance at which it can be detected by radar. An approximate maximum distance in nautical miles is given by the relationship:

$$\textit{Radar range } = \sqrt{1.5 \times \textit{height agl in feet (nm)}}$$

NOTE $\sqrt{1.5 \ \textit{height}}$ is the same as $1.22 \sqrt{\textit{height}}$, which some people prefer. It is a similar expression, since the square root of 1.5 is 1.22.

EXAMPLE 1 At 5,000 ft agl over flat terrain with no obstruction, an aeroplane will be detected up to approximately 87 nm away.

Radar range $= \sqrt{1.5 \text{ ht in feet}}$		*or*	$= 1.22 \sqrt{\text{ht in feet}}$
$= \sqrt{1.5 \times 5,000 \text{ ft}}$			$= 1.22 \sqrt{5,000 \text{ ft}}$
$= \sqrt{7,500 \text{ ft}}$			$= 1.22 \times 71 \text{ nm}$
$= 87 \text{ nm}$			$= 87 \text{ nm}$

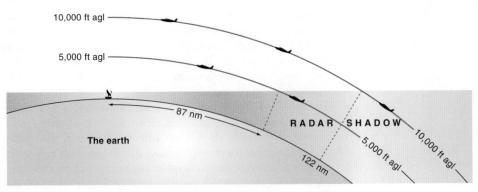

■ Figure 18-6 **Radar detection range for aircraft at 5,000 and 10,000 ft**

EXAMPLE 2 At 10,000 ft agl over flat terrain with no obstructions, an aeroplane will be detected up to approximately 120 nm.

$$Radar\ range = \sqrt{1.5\ ht\ in\ ft} \qquad \overset{or}{} \quad = 1.22\ \sqrt{ht\ in\ ft}$$
$$= \sqrt{1.5 \times 10{,}000\ ft} \qquad\qquad = 1.22\ \sqrt{10{,}000\ ft}$$
$$= \sqrt{15{,}000\ ft} \qquad\qquad\quad = 1.22 \times 100\ nm$$
$$= 122\ nm \qquad\qquad\qquad = 122\ nm$$

NOTE These are expected ranges under ideal conditions; in reality, the range of a radar may be significantly less than this, and it may experience *blind spots* and *radar shadows*.

Radar range may be increased if the radar antenna is sited at a high elevation, both to raise it above nearby obstacles that would cause shadows, and to allow it to 'see' further around the curvature of the earth. Hence radar dishes are to be seen on the tops of hills and buildings. The range at which an aeroplane can now be detected by a radar sited well above a uniform surface is given approximately by:

$$Radar\ range = \sqrt{1.5\ height\ of\ radar\ dish} + \sqrt{1.5\ height\ of\ aircraft}$$
or
$$Radar\ range = 1.22\ \sqrt{height\ of\ radar\ dish} + 1.22\ \sqrt{height\ of\ aircraft}$$

EXAMPLE 3 At 5,000 ft agl over flat terrain with no obstructions, an aeroplane will be detected up to approximately 99 nm if the radar dish is elevated 100 ft above a uniform surface.

$$Radar\ range = \sqrt{1.5 \times 100} + \sqrt{1.5 \times 5,000}\ \text{ft}$$
$$= (\sqrt{150} + \sqrt{7,500})$$
$$= (12 + 87)\ \text{nm}$$
$$= 99\ \text{nm}$$

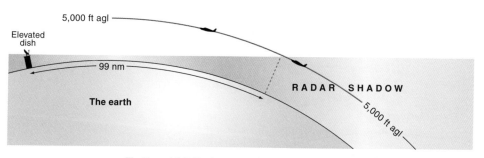

■ *Figure 18-7* **Radar range is increased if the radar dish is elevated**

Radar that makes use of reflected radio energy is known as **primary radar,** and it is used for a number of purposes in aviation, including:

- **surveillance radar** to provide an overview of a whole area, and used in surveillance radar approaches (SRA) for azimuth and height guidance on final approach to land; and
- **precision approach radar** (PAR) for extremely accurate azimuth and slope guidance on final approach to land.

Direction by Radar

If the direction from which the reflected signal comes can be determined, as well as its range, then the **position** of the object can be pinpointed. This is achieved by slowly rotating the radar dish, a typical rate being two revolutions per minute, during which time it will have fired out many millions of pulses in its radar beam and received almost instantaneously any reflected returns. The angle of the radar antenna compared to north at the time the return echo is received indicates the horizontal direction (or *azimuth*) of the object. These *returns* are displayed as *blips* on a screen.

Primary Surveillance Radar

Surveillance radar is designed to give a radar controller an overview of his area of responsibility. It does not transmit pulses in all directions simultaneously, but rather as a beam, which is slowly rotated. For an aeroplane to be detected, the beam must be directed roughly towards it. If the radar controller has his radar tilted up, then it may miss lower aircraft at a distance; conversely, nearby high aeroplanes may not be detected if the tilt is down.

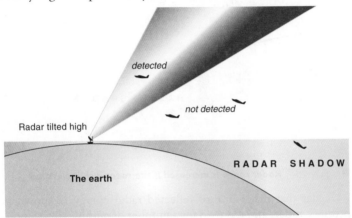

■ *Figure 18-8* **To be detected, aircraft must be within the radar transmitter's beam**

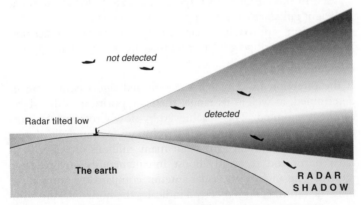

■ *Figure 18-9* **Radar tilted low cannot detect targets directly above**

The Radar Screen

Most radar screens are computer monitors.

Radar controllers generally have displays showing the position of the radar antenna in the centre, with range marks to aid in estimating distance. The radar screen is also known as a **plan position indicator (PPI)**.

The actual radar dish may be located away from the position of the radar controller, possibly on a nearby hill or tower.

In areas of high traffic density, the radar responsibility may be divided between various controllers, each with their own screen and radio communications frequency, and will go under such names as:

- **Approach Control;** and
- **Zone Control.**

Other markings besides the range circles may be superimposed on the screen as a video map to indicate the location of nearby controlled airspace, aerodromes, radio navigation aids such as VORs and NDBs, Restricted Areas, etc.

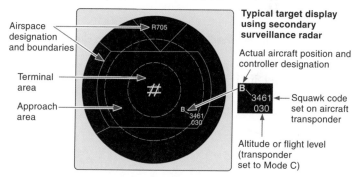

■ *Figure 18-10* **A typical ATC radar screen**

Some Disadvantages of Primary Radar

While a big advantage of primary radar is that no special equipment is required in an aeroplane, it does have some operational disadvantages, including:

- **clutter** from precipitation and high ground;
- **uneven returns** from different aircraft; and
- **blind spots.**

The radio energy in the reflected signal received at the radar dish may be quite small, depending on the strength of the original transmission, how good a reflector the target is, its distance from the radar antenna, and so on. A radar that is sensitive enough to pick up weak returns from targets may also pick up returns from terrain and precipitation, leading to *ground clutter* and *weather clutter* on the screen. During periods of heavy rain, primary radar may be significantly degraded.

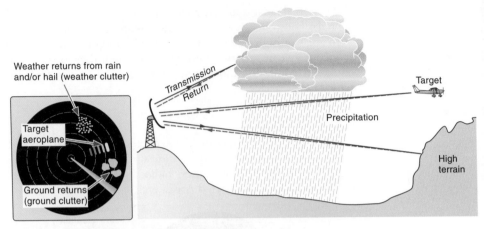

■ Figure 18-11 **Primary surveillance radar is subject to clutter**

Some radars incorporate an electronic sifting device known as a **moving target indicator** (MTI) that only allows signals from moving targets to be shown on the screen, in an attempt to eliminate clutter from stationary objects.

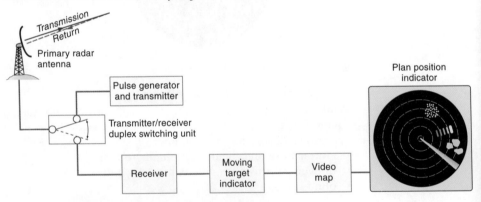

■ Figure 18-12 **Diagrammatic layout of a primary radar system**

With primary radar only, it is often difficult for the radar controller to distinguish between various signals, and he may have to request one aeroplane to carry out a manoeuvre such as a turn to distinguish its radar blip from that of another aeroplane. A typical request could be:

> *Golf Sierra Delta*
> *For identification*
> *Turn left thirty degrees*
> *Heading zero six zero*

Once the controller observes this turn on the screen:

> Golf Delta Sierra
> Identified one two miles northwest of Exeter

Secondary Surveillance Radar (SSR)

Secondary surveillance radar removes most of the limitations of primary radar simply by adding energy to the return pulse from the aeroplane, using a device carried on board the aeroplane known as a **transponder.**

Primary radar detects radar energy passively reflected from a target and displays it as a blip, or fading series of blips, on a screen; this is a similar process to a searchlight operator at night seeing an aeroplane in the beam of the searchlight.

Secondary radar is much more than this, and the target is far from passive. It is as if each time the searchlight strikes the target, the target is triggered to light itself up very brightly in response, and not just passively reflect some of the energy transmitted from the ground site. Secondary radar is really two radar sets talking to each other.

Because only a small amount of energy transmitted from the ground is required to act as a trigger for the airborne SSR transponder, the secondary radar ground transmitter and antenna system can be quite small (unlike the large primary radar dish and powerful transmitter in a system which depend on reflected echoes proportional to the original power of transmission). A long and narrow secondary surveillance radar antenna can often be seen above the large primary radar dish.

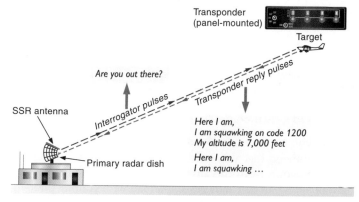

■ Figure 18-13 **SSR is two radars talking to each other**

The SSR ground equipment consists of:
- **an interrogator** that provides a coded signal asking a transponder to respond;
- a highly directional rotating radar **antenna** that transmits the coded interrogation signal, then receives any responding signals, and passes them back to the interrogator; and
- **a decoder,** which accepts the signals from the transponder, decodes them and displays them on the radar screen.

The SSR aircraft equipment consists of a transponder carried in the individual aeroplane.

The originating signal transmitted from the ground station triggers an automatic response from the aeroplane's transponder. It transmits a strong answering coded signal which is then received at the ground station. This response signal is much, much stronger than the simple reflected signal used in primary radar. Even a very weak signal received in the aircraft will trigger a strong response from the transponder.

The secondary responding pulse from the aeroplane's transponder can carry coding that distinguishes the aeroplane from all others on the radar screen. Depending on the code selected in the transponder by the pilot, it can also carry additional information, such as:
- the identity of the aeroplane;
- its altitude; and
- any abnormal situation such as radio failure, distress, emergency, etc.

A significant advantage is that SSR is not degraded to the same extent as primary radar by weather or ground clutter, it presents targets of the same size and intensity to the controller, it allows the controller to select specific displays, and the system has minimal blind spots.

Unfortunately, not all aircraft are fitted with transponders, yet they may be flying in the same airspace. For this reason, both primary and secondary surveillance radar information will be presented to a radar controller on the one screen.

SSR Symbols on the Radar Screen

We recommend that you visit a radar control centre to see the system in action from the air traffic controller's point of view. Understanding his task and how it interacts with yours as pilot-in-command will lead to greater professionalism.

Sometimes ATC need to distinguish a particular aeroplane from others in its vicinity. This situation may arise with a number of aircraft holding in the one area, or with a light aircraft that is having navigational difficulties and has requested assistance. ATC will then assign a code (such as 1700 or 4000) to this particular aircraft.

Technological advances have been made and many aeroplanes and SSRs are equipped for altitude reporting. For instance, some aircraft squawk specific codes, e.g. code 3916 applies to only one particular aeroplane, and on certain advanced SSR screens this will show up as that aeroplane, with a read-out of its altitude and groundspeed. Under less sophisticated radar coverage, the older SSR screens will show this only as belonging to the 3000 family, i.e. as a large circle.

All of these symbols are continually shown on the screen as a result of the coding selected on the aircraft transponder, except for the large *squawk* triangle which appears on the radar screen for 15 to 20 seconds only when a pilot presses the IDENT button.

"Squawk ident" is often requested by ATC when they want positive identification of an aeroplane on their screen. For this reason you should only press the IDENT button on your transponder when specifically requested to do so by ATC.

Using the Transponder in the Cockpit

Usually the transponder is warmed up in the STANDBY position during the taxi, the code to be used (a four-figure number) selected, and then switched ON just prior to take-off.

Even though transponders produced by various manufacturers vary slightly in design, they are operated in basically the same manner. As a responsible pilot, you will become familiar with your particular transponder.

■ *Figure 18-14* **Transponders from various manufacturers**

The Function Selector Knob

The function selector knob enables you to select the transponder to one of its various operation modes, e.g. OFF, ON, STANDBY, ALT. Typical transponder modes include:

OFF: switches the transponder off.

STANDBY: warmed up, and ready for immediate use. This is the normal position until you are ready for take-off, when you would select ALT or ON (if transponder is to be used in flight).

ON: transmits the selected code in Mode A (aircraft identification mode) at the normal power level.

ALT: (altitude) may be used if the altitude-reporting capability (known as mode C) is installed in your aircraft. This is a special **encoding altimeter** which feeds your altitude to the transponder for transmission on to the ATC radar screen.

(If an encoding altimeter is not installed, the transponder still transmits in Mode A, i.e. aircraft identification without altitude reporting.)

TST: tests that the transponder is operating correctly and if so, illuminates the reply monitor light. It causes the transponder to generate a self-interrogating signal to check its operation.

Code Selection

Knobs are provided for you to select the appropriate squawk code for your transponder, and the selected code is prominently displayed in digital form.

An important procedure to follow when selecting and altering codes is to avoid passing through vital codes (such as 7700 for emergencies, 7600 for radio failure) when the transponder is switched ON. This can be avoided by selecting STANDBY while the code is being changed. Your flying instructor will explain further.

The Reply-Monitor Light

The reply light will flash to indicate that the transponder is replying to an interrogation pulse from a ground station.

The reply-monitor light will glow steadily when you:

- press the TEST button or move the function switch to the TEST position (depending on the design of your particular transponder) to indicate correct functioning; or
- transmit an IDENT pulse.

The IDENT Switch or Button

When the IDENT button is pressed by the pilot on request from the radar controller to SQUAWK IDENT, a special pulse is transmitted with your transponder's reply to the interrogating ground station. This causes a special symbol to appear for a few seconds on the radar screen around the return from your aircraft's transponder, thus allowing positive identification by the radar controller.

NOTE Your particular transponder may have minor variations from that described above, but will certainly be fundamentally the same. It may for instance have a separate mode selector to select Mode A (position reporting) or Mode C (position and altitude reporting). These variations are easily understood.

Squawk

The term *squawk* that you will often hear is confined to transponder usage, and the instruction following squawk is usually quite clear, for instance: "Squawk ident"; "Squawk code 4000"; "Squawk Mayday" (7700), etc.

Mode S Secondary Surveillance Radar

Mode S is a Secondary Surveillance Radar system which interrogates aircraft by means of a unique 24-bit aircraft address. It uses ground-based interrogators and airborne transponders that operate in the same UHF radio frequencies as current SSR systems.

Current SSR systems are unsustainable: in busy airspace, the maximum number of targets is readily exceeded; a wide range of interference modes can lead to the loss of targets or misidentification; there is a shortage of Mode A squawk codes. Mode S SSR addresses these problems and provides the basis for enhanced radar surveillance.

Mode S SSR is being implemented in two stages: **Mode S Elementary Surveillance (ELS)** and **Mode S Enhanced Surveillance (EHS)**.

Mode S Elementary Surveillance

Aircraft with Mode S ELS equipment will be able to report as follows:

- The aircraft identity is automatically presented to the radar controller
- Altitude reporting to within 25ft intervals
- Transponder capability signalling allowing ground stations to determine the type of data link achievable
- Whether the aircraft is on the ground or in the air
- Whether the transponder can operate within a lower complexity **Surveillance Identifier (SI)** code ground environment.

Mode S Elementary Surveillance with SI code functionality is the minimum specification for use in European airspace. Mode S Elementary Surveillance is also referred to as 'basic functionality'.

The **Mode S ELS system** will provide a more accurate picture of airspace occupation, both horizontally and vertically, due to the improved quality of air to ground data transmissions. Furthermore, the improved quality, data integrity and resolution of the system will improve the quality of airborne collision avoidance systems. The system has a greater capacity than current SSR systems, being able to process a higher number of aircraft tracks. Most importantly, the 24-bit data resolution will have a capacity for 224, approximately 16.7 million unique aircraft identification codes. This will address both the shortage in Mode A SSR squawk codes and, in conjunction with automatic flight identity reporting, provide a means of identifying an aircraft in flight, unambiguously, independently of an assigned squawk.

Mode S Enhanced Surveillance

Aircraft with Mode S EHS equipment builds advanced features on the Mode S Elementary Surveillance functionality features. Advanced aircraft reporting features include:

- The selected altitude entered into the **Flight Management System**. This allows the controller to verify that the correct altitude is programmed into the flight computer to identify pilot error that may lead to reduced separation or mid-air collision
- Roll and track angle information used to allow the modelling of horizontal manoevres ensuring that changes in heading can be seen more accurately and quickly in real-time.

- Groundspeed
- Magnetic heading
- Indicated airspeed (IAS) and Mach-number.
- Airborne collision avoidance system resolution advisory information.

Mode S Secondary Surveillance Radar systems are a necessary evolution to enhance radar-based flight safety both in controlled and non-controlled airspace. This new system will help controllers to track aircraft with a more precise and rapid recognition of airspace developments. With a greater level of information provided on radar displays, fewer radio situation reports will be necessary reducing both controller and pilot workload. Finally, features such as the enhanced reporting of selected altitude will allow controllers to validate compliance with their instructions thus improving safety.

Automatic Dependent Surveillance - Broadcast (ADS-B)
Aircraft can broadcast information, derived from onboard GPS receivers via the ADS-B surveillance system. Unlike normal SSR operation, the data is broadcast and does not require interrogation from ground stations. ADS-B is enabled by the interfacing of suitably equipped GPS receivers and Mode S SSR transponders.

Cockpit Operation
The Mode S transponder, looks, and is operated in the same way as current transponders with Mode A and C capability. The 4,096 active squawk codes can be selected in the usual way and Mode C can be selected as required.

The main difference relates to the selection of the 'aircraft identification' also referred to as the Flight Identification of FLT ID. The Mode S transponder can be configured by the installer to allow the flight crew to enter a Flight Identification or this may be fixed. After the transponder is switched on, those configured to allow entry of the Flight Identification require the flight crew to type the appropriate code before normal operation can commence. It is essential that Flight Identification information transmitted by the transponder is the same as the voice call sign and this is aligned with flight plan declarations.

In the case of general aviation, the aircraft registration is used as the call sign and this is programmed by the installer. In this situation, the Flight Identification crew entry function is disabled. In the situation where flight numbers or other operator-determined call signs are used, instead of the aircraft registration, Flight Identification must be entered by the crew before each flight.

Typical Transponder Radio Calls

ATC: "(CALLSIGN), SQUAWK IDENT". Pilot response is to press the transponder IDENT button, allowing the radar controller to identify you positively on his screen.

ATC: "(CALLSIGN), SQUAWK CODE 7340". Pilot response is a read-back of the assigned code: "(callsign), code 7340", and to select the transponder to that code.

ATC: "(CALLSIGN), SQUAWK STANDBY". Pilot response is to move the function switch to STANDBY from ON or ALT position, for a temporary suspension of transponder operation (maintaining present code).

ATC: "(CALLSIGN), RESET 7340". Pilot response is to readback "Reset 7340 (callsign)".

Further information on SSR operating procedures appears in UK AIP ENR 1-6-2-1.

1. What is the name of the aircraft equipment required for Secondary Surveillance Radar?

(a) Transponder
(b) Interrogator
(c) Antenna
(d) Decoder

2. The equipment associated with Secondary Surveillance Radar (SSR) are:

(a) A transponder on the ground and DME in the air.
(b) A transponder in the air and Plan Position Indicator on the ground.
(c) A transponder in the air and DME on the ground.
(d) A transponder on the ground and Secondary Radar Indicator on the ground.

3. How may the range of primary radar be increased?

(a) *By increasing the rate of rotation of the radar head.*
(b) *By increasing the width of the radar head antenna which will produce a long, narrow beam.*
(c) *By locating the head at an elevation above surrounding obstacles.*
(d) *By reducing the width of the radar head antenna which will produce a long and narrow beam.*

4. The transponder mode that provides the radar operator with both position and altitude reporting is:

(a) Mode A
(b) Mode S
(c) Mode C
(d) Mode Ident

5. The transponder mode that provides the radar operator with position reporting only is:

(a) Mode A
(b) Mode S
(c) Mode C
(d) Mode Ident

6. Transponder Mode A is selected at which position on the Function Selector:

(a) Standby
(b) ALT
(c) On
(d) TST

7. Transponder Mode C is selected at which position on the Function Selector

(a) Standby
(b) ALT
(c) On
(d) TST

Global Positioning System (GPS)

General Description

The global positioning system (GPS) is an extremely accurate area navigation aid for all classes of aviation as well as other modes of transport. GPS was developed for the United States Department of Defense, but has now been made available for civil use.

GPS should not be used as the primary navigation method.

VFR pilots may also use GPS as an aid to visual navigation, to provide information relating to aircraft speed and track over the ground, wind velocity and distance/time to waypoints or the destination. GPS is very accurate, but as satellites can become unserviceable etc., it should not be considered as such for more than 95% of the time. Therefore GPS should not be used as the primary navigation method, only as an aid to other methods.

Basically, GPS comprises three elements:

- a space element, consisting of a constellation of 21 active satellites orbiting the earth every 12 hours, in six orbital planes with four in each plane, at an altitude of 11,000 nm (21,300 km);
- a satellite control ground network (control station plus monitor stations), responsible for orbital accuracy and control; and
- navigation receiver/computers in aircraft capable of receiving and identifying signals from satellites in view at a particular time and place.

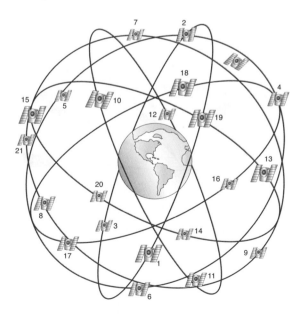

■ Figure 19-1 **The orbital configuration of the 21 GPS satellites**

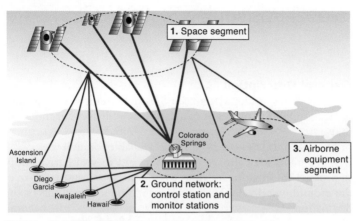

■ Figure 19-2 **The GPS consists of three basic segments**

Basic Operating Principle

Each satellite transmits its own computer code packet on frequency 1575.42 MHz (for civilian use), 1,000 times per second. The satellite continually broadcasts its position and the exact time UTC. By knowing the exact position of the satellite at the time of transmission, and then by measuring the time taken for the data packet to reach the receiver from the satellite, the distance between the satellite and the receiver can be determined. The satellite constellation configuration usually guarantees that at least four satellites are in view at any given time.

Each transmitted data packet contains a precise timing reference. GPS receivers use accurate clocks and appropriate software to ascertain position by receiving and computing data from at least three satellites for a two-dimensional fix, and four satellites for a three-dimensional fix, such as ground position and altitude.

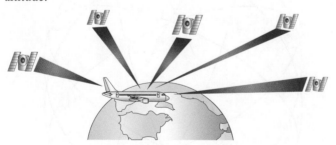

■ Figure 19-3 **Signals from satellites are received to establish position**

Cockpit Instruments

There are a range of GPS devices that can be used as an aid to VFR navigation, e.g. hand-held units, GPS-enabled tablet computers and permanently installed equipment. There are no installation standards for hand-held portable equipment not permanently installed in the aircraft, however equipment permanently installed must be fitted in a manner approved by the CAA. Care should be taken to ensure that hand-held equipment does not interfere with the normal operation of the aircraft's controls or equipment. Furthermore, the movement of the pilot or their vision must not be obstructed.

System Familiarisation

The diversity of equipment requires that you should learn about the function of your particular GPS receiver, in detail, before attempting to use it in the air. Full information can be obtained from the manufacturer's instruction manual, together with general operational information from CAA publications Safety Sense Leaflet 25: Use of GPS, and CAP773. Recommended topics for training include:

- Principles of GPS
- Pre-flight preparation, e.g. loading routes, waypoints, alternate routes and cross-checking data entry
- Database integrity and contents
- Confirmation of accuracy
- System installation, initialisation and status checking of the receiver, satellites, battery and databases
- Use of RAIM functionality if applicable
- Use of the system in flight including: route selection, 'direct' or 'Go-To' functions and screen selection/recovery
- Human error and system errors and malfunctions

Flight Planning and GPS

It is important that you create a comprehensive route plan that involves the preparation of a fully marked-up aeronautical chart and VFR flight log using techniques described in Section 2. Vertical navigation is best considered by conventional means as some databases do not contain valid information that can be relied upon for terrain and obstacle clearance. The programming of the GPS system can then be checked against other forms of flight planning, e.g. dead reckoning or VFR navigation supported by conventional radio navigation aids, e.g. VOR.

The following two threat and error management considerations must be addressed:

- With respect to system accuracy, does the GPS system agree with at least one other independent source of navigation information?
- If the GPS system fails, permanently (battery failure) or temporarily (loss of satellite feed), can the flight continue safely using other navigation modes?

Waypoint management is critical. User Waypoints should be labelled clearly and a separate record kept of all loaded waypoints. If a communal receiver is used, e.g. one jointly owned by flying club members, there must be clear procedures for the labelling and manipulation of waypoints in the system. It is essential to ensure that the latitude and longitude reference of a waypoint agrees with its true position on an aeronautical chart or AIP reference, as errors can occur if an incorrect datum is programmed.

Prior to use in flight, the route should be validated by running it in 'simulation' or 'demo' mode. This ensures that programming has been completed correctly and waypoint information is present and correct. Each individual route segment should be cross-checked with the flight log for accuracy and consistency.

If an aviation database is used, ensure that it is valid for the geo-graphical area in which the route resides and that it is current.

Errors in positioning may exist and can be checked by comparing the actual initial position of the aircraft, at the aerodrome, with the corresponding database reference point.

Use in Flight

The importance of a continuous assessment of positional precision and accuracy, when compared to other navigation modes, has already been stressed. The re-programming of the GPS receiver in flight is problematic for a number of important reasons: it distracts from in-flight tasks, e.g. lookout, and control of the aircraft; re-programming in the air is complicated and human errors may be made. You should consider programming diversions to alternate aerodrome and routes to bypass controlled airspace, on the ground pre-flight.

System and Signal Errors

The GPS system is generally reliable, however regular users will be familiar with itnerruption in the availability of information. The following technical issues can impact the reliability of GPS information:

- Satellites positioning – and operating GPS receiver requires line of sight to several satellites with sufficient angular separation. At times, insufficient satellites may be visible or small angular separations will degrade accuracy.
- Satellite interference is available via NOTAMs. Details about the general system status is available on the US Coastguard website. Satellites experience technical failure which may affect navigation.
- External interference and masking – at low level, line of sight can be blocked by high terrain. A familar problem with hand-held receivers with integral aerials is dynamic masking where screening by part of the aircraft's structure interrupts signal reception. If possible, remote aerial extensions should be positioned in an open area of the aircraft, e.g. the windscreen, to prevent loss of signal. Signal may be reflected from surrounding terrain or obstacles leading to anomalous error messaging and/or flickering of the aircraft's icon position in 'moving map' modes. Finally, the system is vulnerable to errors created by sunspot and solar flare activity.

In the fullness of time, the use of GPS will grow, at the expense of other forms of radio navigation, to dominate the performance navigation area. It is a generally reliable, intuitive system that is easy to use and an important support to VFR navigation. For the time being, it is important that you thoroughly understand how to use your GPS receiver and the general system limitations, to avoid becoming over reliant on the technology, and using it without other navigational contingencies in place.

Now complete: **Practice Questions - GPS**

1. When using GPS, what is the minimum number of satellites required to provide three dimensional position fixing?

   (a) 4
   (b) 1
   (c) 2
   (d) 3

2. You are making a flight with sole reference to a hand-held GPS receiver mounted on the aircraft's control wheel. Whilst turning over a waypoint, the signal is lost. After several seconds of navigation by dead reckoning, the signal is regained. The most likely cause is:

   (a) Interference from UHF or microwave television signals.
   (b) Multi-path reflections from the surrounding terrain.
   (c) Dynamic masking by part of the aircraft's structure.
   (d) Terrain shielding.

3. You are making a flight with sole reference to a GPS receiver in the vicinity of hills. Whilst using the map page, you note that there are several sudden shifts in the aircraft's position. The most likely cause is:

   (a) Interference from UHF or microwave television signals.
   (b) Multi-path reflections from the surrounding terrain.
   (c) Dynamic masking by part of the aircraft's structure.
   (d) Terrain shielding.

4. During a flight with sole reference to a GPS receiver, you encounter a degrading visual environment and elect to divert using the 'Direct' (or Go to) function. Having obtained clearance to transit the MATZ of a nearby military airfield, the GPS system alerts you to the proximity of the airfield's ATZ. What following action do you take?

   (a) You ignore the alert as you have clearance to penetrate the MATZ.
   (b) You assume that the alert is the result of an error in the database.
   (c) The information is correct: you remain clear of or seek permission to enter the ATZ.
   (d) Resume navigation by other means as the GPS receiver has malfunctioned.

5. You are conducting a flight with reference to a GPS receiver when you are required to make an unplanned diversion. You turn onto the GPS track and after 10 minutes become lost. The most likely cause is:

(a) *Position errors due to multi-path reflections from the surrounding terrain.*

(b) *Signal consistency errors due to dynamic masking by part of the aircraft's structure.*

(c) *An out of date database.*

(d) *Human error and failure to validate the re-programming with other independent sources of navigation information.*

The VOR

The VOR (pronounced *"vee-oh-are"*) is a very high frequency radio navigation aid that is extensively used in instrument flying. Its full name is the **very high frequency omni-directional radio range,** commonly abbreviated to the VHF omni range, VOR, or omni.

A VOR ground station can be selected on the VHF-NAV radio set.

Each VOR ground station transmits on a specific VHF frequency between 108.00 and 117.95 megahertz (MHz), which is a lower-frequency band than that used for VHF communications. A separate VHF-NAV radio is required for navigation purposes, but is usually combined with the VHF-COM in a NAV-COM set.

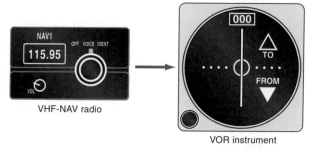

VHF-NAV radio

VOR instrument

■ *Figure 20-1* **Cockpit VOR equipment**

The VOR was developed in the United States during the late 1940s, and was adopted by the International Civil Aviation Organisation (ICAO) as the standard short-range radio navigation aid in 1960. When introduced, it offered an immediate improvement over existing aids such as the ADF/NDB combination, most of which operated in lower frequency bands than the VOR and suffered significant limitations, such as night effect, mountain reflections, interference from electrical storms, etc.

Principal advantages of the VOR include:

*   **reduced susceptibility** to electrical and atmospheric interference (including thunderstorms);
*   **the elimination of night effect,** since VHF signals are line-of-sight and not reflected by the ionosphere (as are NDB signals in the LF/MF band).

The reliability and accuracy of VOR signals allows the VOR to be used with confidence in any weather conditions, by day or by night, for purposes such as:

*   **orientation** and position fixing (Where am I?);
*   **tracking** to or from a VOR ground station;

- **holding** (for delaying or manoeuvring action); and
- **instrument approaches** to land.

Many VORs are coupled with a DME (distance-measuring equipment providing a measure of distance from the station in nautical miles), so that selection of the VOR on the VHF-NAV set in the cockpit also selects the DME, thereby providing both tracking and distance information.

VORs are often paired with a DME.

How the VOR Works

The VOR ground station transmits two VHF radio signals:

1. **the reference phase,** which is omni-directional (the same in all directions); and

2. **the variable phase,** which rotates uniformly at a rate of 1,800 revolutions per minute, with its phase varying at a constant rate throughout the 360°.

The aerial of the VOR aircraft receiver picks up the signals, whose **phase difference** (the difference between the wave peaks) is measured, this difference depending on the bearing of the aeroplane from the ground station. In this manner, the VOR can determine the **magnetic bearing** of the aeroplane from the VOR ground station.

■ Figure 20-2 **Typical VOR aerial**

■ Figure 20-3 **A VOR ground station (Brookmans Park, near London)**

The two signals transmitted by the VOR ground station are:
- in phase on magnetic north, which is the reference for VOR signals;
- 90° out of phase at magnetic east 090°M;
- 180° out of phase at magnetic south 180°M;
- 270° out of phase at magnetic west 270°M; and
- 360° out of phase (back *in* phase) at magnetic north 360°M, or 000°M.

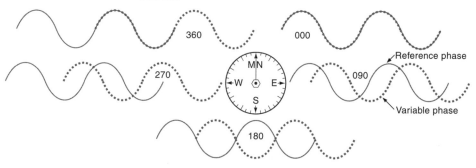

■ *Figure 20-4* **The VOR transmits two VHF signals with a phase difference between them**

Check the Morse code ident before using a VOR.

Every 10 seconds or so a Morse code **ident** signal is transmitted, allowing you to identify the VOR positively . Some VORs may also carry voice transmissions with a relevant automatic terminal information service (ATIS).

The VOR is a very high frequency aid operating in the frequency band 108.0 MHz to 117.95 MHz. It allows high-quality *line-of-sight* reception as there is relatively little interference from atmospheric noise in this band. Reception may be affected by the terrain surrounding the ground station, the height of the VOR beacon, the altitude of the aeroplane and its distance from the station.

VOR Range

The VOR signal is line-of-sight.

The approximate maximum range of a VHF signal is given by the formula (which you do not need to remember):

$$VHF\ range\ in\ nm = \sqrt{1.5 \times altitude\ in\ feet}$$

EXAMPLE 1 At 7,000 ft amsl, approximate VHF range:

$$= \sqrt{1.5 \times 7,000}$$
$$= \sqrt{10,000}$$
$$= 100\ nm$$

Different VOR stations may operate on the same frequency, but they should be well separated geographically so that there is no interference between their VHF line-of-sight signals. The higher the aeroplane's altitude, however, the greater the possibility of interference. The AIP specifies a designated operational coverage (DOC) for each VOR above which interference is possible. Within the DOC coverage, VOR reception should be reliable. *Detling VOR,* for instance, has a DOC of 60 nm/50,000 ft (see AIP ENR 4-1-1).

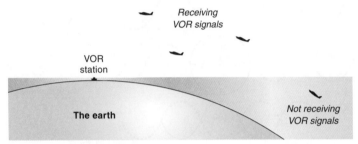

■ *Figure 20-5* **VHF line-of-sight signals**

Tracking with a VOR

The VOR can be used to indicate the **desired track** and the aeroplane's **angular deviation** from that track. For a desired track of 015°M, expect to steer a heading of approximately 015°M, plus or minus a wind correction angle (WCA). By selecting an omni bearing of 015 under the course index of the VOR cockpit display, you can obtain tracking information, as illustrated in Figures 20-6 and 20-7.

The VOR cockpit display is not heading sensitive, which means that the display will not change as a result of the aeroplane changing heading. Figure 20-7 shows the same aeroplane as Figure 20-6, except that a wind correction angle of 10° right is being used by the pilot to counteract a wind from the right, and so the aeroplane's magnetic heading is now MH 025 (rather than MH 015 previously).

Note that:
• the VOR indication depends on the **angular deviation** of the aeroplane relative to the selected track;
• the VOR indication will *not* change with any heading change of the aeroplane.

It is usual, when tracking en route from one VOR to another, to select the next VOR when the aeroplane is approximately half-way between them, as in Figure 20-8. This allows the use of the stronger signal, although intervening mountains which might shield the signal of a VOR may affect your decision in this regard.

Change VORs at the approximate mid-point between them.

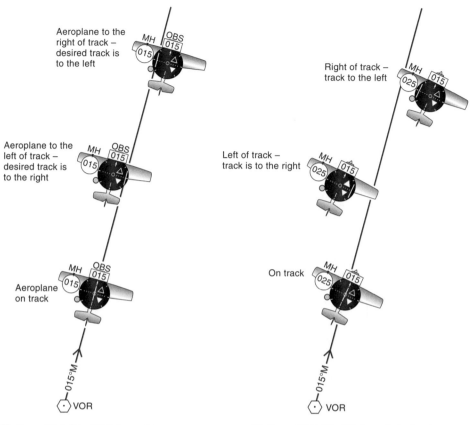

■ Figure 20-6 **The VOR is used to indicate track**

■ Figure 20-7 **The VOR cockpit display is not heading sensitive**

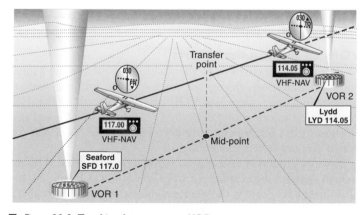

■ Figure 20-8 **Tracking between two VORs**

VOR Radials

As its name *omni* suggests, a VOR ground transmitter radiates signals in all directions. Its most important feature, however, is that the signal in any particular direction differs slightly from all the adjacent signals. These individual directional signals can be thought of as *tracks* or *position lines* radiating out from the VOR ground station, in much the same way as spokes from the hub of a wheel.

By convention, 360 different tracks away from the VOR are used, each separated from the next by 1°, and each with its direction related to magnetic north. Each of these 360 VOR tracks or position lines is called a radial.

> A *radial* is the magnetic bearing outbound FROM a VOR.

NOTE A specific VOR radial is the same as QDR. For instance, the 293 radial is QDR 293, which is a track of 293° magnetic away *from* the VOR ground station.

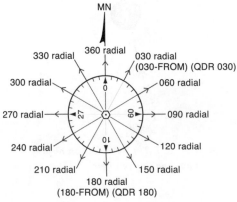

■ *Figure 20-9* **A radial is a magnetic bearing from the VOR ground station (QDR)**

VORs on Aeronautical Charts

Most aeronautical charts show the position, frequency and Morse code identification (ident) of each VOR ground station. Information on a particular VOR may be found in the UK Aeronautical Information Publication (AIP ENR 4-1-1), and any changes to this information will be referred to in NOTAM (to which you may refer prior to flight).

A VOR ground station may be represented in various ways on a chart – the common representations are shown in Figure 20-10. Since magnetic north is the reference direction for VOR radials, a magnetic north arrowhead usually emanates from the VOR symbol, with a compass rose heavily marked each 30°, and the

VOR radials are based on magnetic north.

radials shown in 10° intervals on the rose. This is generally adequate for in-flight estimation of track to an accuracy of ±2°; however, when flight planning, it is advisable to be more accurate.

At the flight planning stage, use a protractor or plotter for precise measurement of track, although in some cases this may not be necessary because some much-used tracks are published on Radio Navigation Charts (RNCs) in degrees magnetic. If you measure the track in degrees true (°T), then magnetic variation needs to be applied to convert to degrees magnetic (*variation west, magnetic best*).

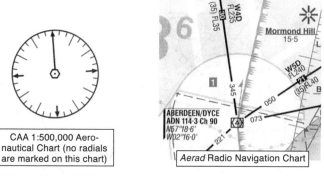

CAA 1:500,000 Aeronautical Chart (no radials are marked on this chart)

Aerad Radio Navigation Chart

■ *Figure 20-10* **A VOR and its radials represented on different charts**

It is usual for instrument-rated pilots to use the Radio Navigation Charts (published by *Aerad* and *Jeppesen*), and IMC-rated pilots to use the CAA 1:500,000 (half-million) ICAO Topographical Charts, already well known from visual navigation.

Further Information on VORs

The UK AIP carries information regarding radio navigation aids in its ENR 4-1-1 section. For example, the AIP extract for *Goodwood*, shown in Figure 20-11, includes:

- Frequency, 114.75 MHz (also found on the charts).
- Callsign, or identification, 'GWC' (also found on the charts) which, in Morse code, is *"dah-dah-dit dit-dah-dah dah-dit-dah-dit"*.
- Hours of service (24 hours a day, summer and winter).
- Location in latitude and longitude (if you cannot find it on the chart).
- Remarks that:
  - the VOR is an approach aid to Chichester/Goodwood aerodrome; and
  - it has a designated operational coverage (DOC) of 80 nm up to 50,000 ft amsl, above which there may be interference from distant VORs using the same frequency.

ENR 4.1 — RADIO NAVIGATION AIDS — EN-ROUTE						
Name of Station (VOR set Variation)	IDENT	Frequency (Channel)	Hours of Operation (Winter/Summer)	Co-ordinates	DME Aerial Elevation	Remarks
1	2	3	4	5	6	7
Goodwood VOR/DME Var 2.2°W - 2007 VOR 2.47°W - 2003	GWC	114.75 MHz (Ch 94Y)	H24	AD Purpose: 505118.78N 0004524.25W ENR Purpose: 505119N 0004524W	113 ft amsl	APCH Aid to Chichester/ Goodwood. On Chichester/Goodwood AD. VOR/DME DOC: 80 nm/50000 ft. Due to terrain, coverage at low level is reduced in Sector RDL 302°-047°.

■ Figure 20-11 **UK AIP ENR extract for Goodwood VOR**

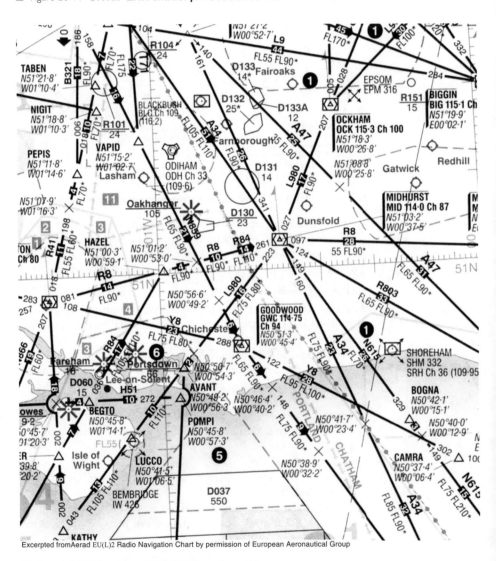

Excerpted from Aerad EU(L)2 Radio Navigation Chart by permission of European Aeronautical Group

■ Figure 20-12 **Goodwood VOR/DME on Aerad chart**

Also, the beginning pages of AIP ENR advise not to use any VOR if it cannot be identified by its Morse code ident. It may be that the VOR is radiating signals on test, in which case the ident is suppressed or the Morse letters 'TST' (for test) are transmitted, to indicate that the facility is not to be used for navigation.

VORs that have a DME (distance-measuring equipment) station associated with them may be described as VOR/DMEs. The DME is automatically tuned when you select the VOR frequency on the VHF-NAV radio. Goodwood has such a facility, see the AIP ENR and chart extract in Figure 20-12.

As the VOR is a VHF radio navigation aid, its line-of-sight signals can be stopped or distorted by high mountains in some locations. AIP ENR should contain a warning, as is the case in Figure 20-13, where Inverness VOR has reduced coverage in the sector between 154°M and 194°M from the VOR ground station.

ENR 4.1 — RADIO NAVIGATION AIDS — EN-ROUTE						
Name of Station (VOR set Variation)	IDENT	Frequency (Channel)	Hours of Operation (Winter/Summer)	Co-ordinates	DME Aerial Elevation	Remarks
1	2	3	4	5	6	7
Inverness VOR/DME (6.7°W - 1997)	INS	109.20 MHz (Ch 29X)	H24	AD Purpose: 573233.45N 0040229.55W ENR Purpose: 573233N 0040230W	58 ft amsl	APCH Aid to Inverness. On Inverness AD. DOC 60 nm/25000 ft. Reduced coverage in Sector RDL 154°-RDL 194°. Flag alarms may occur in this Sector when aircraft are 30 nm or more from the VOR and flying at or below 7000 ft. DME co-located and freq paired with VOR and unmonitored outside Inverness ATC hours of operation. Available for approach and landing purposes only during the hours of APP. Due to terrain effects the DME may unlock in Sector RDL 154° to RDL 194° when aircraft are at

■ *Figure 20-13* **AIP ENR extract for Inverness**

VOR Cockpit Instruments

There are various types of VOR cockpit display, but they are all reasonably similar in terms of operation. The VOR cockpit display is often referred to as the **omni bearing indicator,** or **OBI.** It displays the omni bearing selected by the pilot on the course card using the **omni bearing selector** (OBS), a small knob which is geared to the card.

If the aeroplane is on the selected radial, then the VOR needle, known as the **course deviation indicator** or **CDI,** will be centred. If the aeroplane is not on the selected track, then the CDI will not be centred.

Whether the selected track would take the aeroplane to or from the VOR ground station is indicated by the TO/FROM flags. The OBI is only to be used for navigation if:

- the red OFF warning flag is hidden from view;
- the correct Morse code ident is heard.

When a VOR is operating normally, the radials are transmitted to an accuracy of at least ±2°.

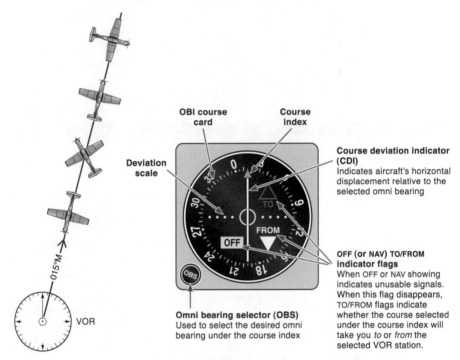

■ *Figure 20-14* **The VOR cockpit display (OBI) for aeroplanes on the 015 radial**

NOTE *Course* is an American term with the same meaning as *track*. Since most aviation radio equipment is manufactured by US companies, American terminology is used. In the UK, *course* sometimes refers to heading; however, it will not be used in this sense in *The Air Pilot's Manual*.

Course Deviation Indicator (CDI)

The course deviation indicator (CDI) in the VOR cockpit instrument indicates off-track deviation in terms of *angular deviation from the selected track*. At all times, the reference when using the VOR is the selected track under the course index. (This is a totally different principle from that of the ADF needle which simply points at an NDB ground station and indicates its relative bearing.)

The amount of *angular* deviation from the selected track is referred to in terms of *dots*; there are 5 dots either side of the central position. The inner dot on both sides is often represented by a circle passing through them. Each dot is equivalent to 2° track deviation.

- If the aeroplane is on the selected track, the CDI is centred.
- If the aeroplane is 2° off the selected track, the CDI is displaced 1 dot from the centre (i.e. on the circumference of the inner circle).
- If the aeroplane is 4° off the selected track, the CDI is displaced 2 dots.
- If the aeroplane is 10° or more off the selected track, the CDI is fully deflected at 5 dots.

A 1-dot deviation of the CDI on the VOR cockpit display represents 2°. Full-scale deflection at 5 dots represents 10° or more.

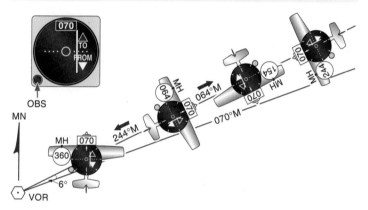

■ *Figure 20-15* **Each of these aeroplanes is displaced 6° from the 070 radial**

Since the CDI indicates *angular* deviation, the actual *distance* off track for a given CDI indication will be smaller the closer the aeroplane is to the ground station. In a manner of speaking, the aeroplane is 'funnelled' in towards the VOR ground station.

To or From

The 090 radial, which is QDR 090 (a magnetic bearing away *from* the station) of 090°M, is the same position line as QDM 270 *to* the station. If an aeroplane is on this position line, then the CDI will be centred when *either* 090 *or* 270 is selected with the OBS. Any ambiguity in your mind regarding the position of the aeroplane relative to the VOR ground station is resolved with the TO/FROM indicators.

The TO or FROM flags or arrows indicate whether the selected omni bearing will take you *to* the VOR ground station, or away *from* it.

In Figure 20-16, the pilot could centre the CDI by selecting either 090 or 270 (reciprocals) with the OBS. A track of 090°M would take the aeroplane *from* the VOR, whereas a track of 270°M would lead it *to* the VOR.

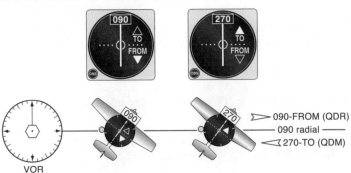

■ Figure 20-16 **Using the TO/FROM flag**

EXAMPLE 2 Illustrates two indications on the omni bearing indicator that would inform you that the aeroplane is on the 235 radial. The 235 radial is either:

- 235°M *from* the VOR; or
- 055°M *to* the VOR.

So, with the CDI centred, the VOR cockpit display could indicate either 235-FROM or 055-TO.

■ Figure 20-17 **Indications that the aeroplane is on the 235 radial**

At all times, the reference when using the OBI is the track selected under the course index. It determines:
- CDI deflection; and
- whether the TO or the FROM flag shows.

Different Presentations of the Omni Bearing

There are various presentations of VOR information. In all cases, full-scale deflection is 10° either side of the selected omni bearing (a total arc of 20°), with five dots either side of centre. In many VOR cockpit displays the two inner dots are joined by the circumference of a circle.

The course deviation indicator (CDI) may also differ between instruments. It may move laterally as a whole, or it may hinge at the top and swing laterally.

Similarly, the means of displaying the selected omni bearing may differ between instruments. It may be shown under a course index, or it may be shown in a window. In some equipment, the TO and the FROM flags may be displayed in the one window, in others they may have separate windows.

The VOR cockpit display usually doubles as the ILS (instrument landing system) display, with vertical dots marked to indicate glideslope (GS) deviation (using a second needle which lies or is hinged horizontally so that it can move up or down). When being used for the VOR (and not the ILS), the glideslope cross bar (or needle) may be biased out of view, and there may be a **red GS warning flag** showing.

Operational Use of the VOR

Preparing the VOR for Use

Always select, tune and identify a VOR before use.

A radio navigation aid is of little value if you do not use it correctly. Prior to using the VOR, you must:

• ensure electrical power is available, and switch the VHF–NAV ON;

• select the desired frequency (e.g. 114.3 MHz for Aberdeen VOR as found on navigation charts or in AIP ENR);

• identify the VOR (*dit-dah dah-dit-dit dah-dit*, which is ADN in Morse code as shown on the navigation charts for AberDeeN);

• check that the OFF flag is not showing (i.e. the signal is usable, otherwise the OFF flag would be visible).

Orientation

Using a Single VOR Position Line

Orientation means 'to determine one's approximate position'. The first step in orientation is to establish a position line (PL) along which the aircraft is known to be at a particular moment. To obtain a position line using the VOR display:

• rotate the OBS (omni bearing selector) until the CDI (course deviation indicator) is centred; and

• note whether the TO or the FROM flag is showing.

EXAMPLE 3 You rotate the OBS until the CDI is centred – this occurs with 334 under the course index and the TO flag showing. Illustrate the situation.

Could another OBI (omni bearing indicator) reading be obtained with the course deviation indicator centred?
In the aircraft's location, the CDI will be centred with either:
- 334–TO; or
- 154–FROM.

■ Figure 20-18 **On the 154 radial**

Using Two Position Lines to Fix Position
One position line alone does not allow you to fix positively the position of the aircraft overhead a particular point, it only provides a line somewhere along which the aircraft lies.

It requires two or more position lines to fix the position of an aircraft positively. Also, to be of any real value for position fixing, the two PLs need to intersect at an angle of at least 45°. Any 'cut' less than this decreases the accuracy of the fix.

Radio position lines can be provided by any convenient radio navigation aid, including VORs and DMEs.

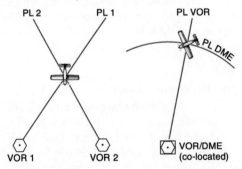

■ Figure 20-19 **Fixing position requires two position lines with a good 'cut' (angle of at least 45°)**

Two VORs

Some aeroplanes are fitted with two independent VHF-NAV systems, enabling two different VORs to be tuned at the same time, and thus two PLs from two different VOR ground stations can be obtained simultaneously. In an aeroplane fitted with only one VHF-NAV set, you can obtain two PLs using the one VHF-NAV by retuning it from one VOR to another.

EXAMPLE 4 An aeroplane fitted with two VHF-NAVs is tracking 134°M from Prestwick to Manchester via Dean Cross, and obtains the following indications:

- VOR 1. Dean Cross 115.2 is selected, and the CDI centres with 134-TO.
- VOR 2. Talla 113.8 is selected, and the CDI centres with 220-FROM.

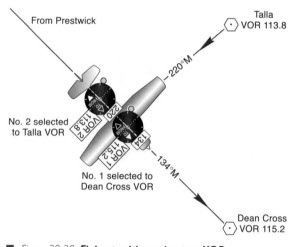

■ Figure 20-20 **Fixing position using two VORs**

Figure 20-20 shows that the aeroplane is on track (134°M between Prestwick and Dean Cross) and passing the Talla 220 radial. The two position lines cut at a good angle, and the pilot has a fairly positive indication of where the aeroplane is.

VOR and a DME

Probably the most common form of en route position fixing between aids is the VOR/DME fix, based on a ground station where the DME (distance-measuring equipment) is co-located with the VOR ground station. The VOR can provide a straight position line showing the radial that the aeroplane is on, and the DME can provide a circular position line showing the distance that the aeroplane is from the ground station. The intersection of the lines is the position of the aeroplane.

EXAMPLE 5 An aircraft tracking north from Brecon (ident BCN, frequency 117.45 MHz) has the cockpit indications of:

- BCN VOR 008-FROM; and
- BCN DME 31 nm.

   Where is the aircraft?

   As can be seen from Figure 20-21, the aircraft is at the RADNO position, an in-flight position determined purely by radio navaids.

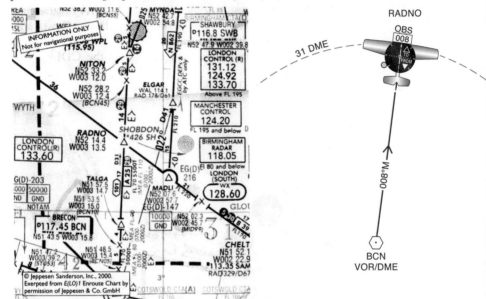

Figure 20-21 **Fixing position using a co-located VOR/DME**

Overhead a VOR

As an aircraft approaches overhead a VOR, the CDI will become more and more agitated as the ±10° funnel either side of track becomes narrower.

As the aircraft passes through the **'zone of confusion'** over the VOR ground station, the CDI may flick from side to side, before settling down again as the aircraft moves away from the station. The TO/FROM flag will also change from TO to FROM (or vice versa), and the red OFF flag may flicker in and out of view because of the temporarily unusable signal.

The zone of confusion can extend in an arc of 70° overhead the station, so it may take a minute or so for the aircraft to pass through it before the CDI and the FROM flag settle down, and the OFF flag totally disappears.

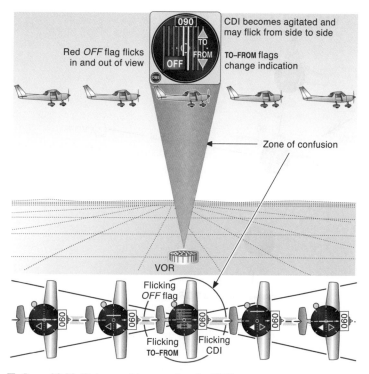

CDI becomes agitated and
may flick from side to side

Red *OFF* flag flicks
in and out of view

TO–FROM flags
change indication

Zone of confusion

VOR

Flicking
OFF flag

Flicking
TO–FROM

Flicking
CDI

■ *Figure 20-22* **Fixing position overhead a VOR**

Passing Abeam a VOR

A common means of checking flight progress is to note the time passing abeam (to one side of) a nearby VOR ground station. The most straightforward procedure is to:

- select and identify the VOR; and
- under the course index, set the radial perpendicular (at 90°) to your track.

EXAMPLE 6 An aircraft is tracking 350°M, and will pass approximately 20 nm abeam a VOR ground station out to its right. The VOR radial perpendicular to track is the 260 radial, and so 260 should be set with the OBS. The CDI will be fully deflected to one side if the aircraft is well away from the abeam position, and will gradually move from full deflection one side to full deflection on the other side as the aircraft passes through the ±10° arc either side of the selected radial. The aircraft is at the abeam position when the CDI is centralised.

The abeam position can also be identified by setting the QDM *to* the VOR under the course index (rather than the QDR or radial *from* the VOR), in which case the movement of the CDI will be from the opposite side.

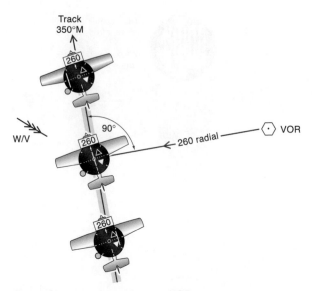

■ *Figure 20-23* **Passing abeam a VOR**

The 1-in-60 rule, frequently used in navigation, states that 1 nm off-track in 60 nm subtends an angle of 1°. In rough terms, this means that, as the aircraft flies at right angles through the 10° from when the CDI first starts to move to when it is centred, it will travel approximately 10 nm abeam the VOR when it is located 60 nm from the VOR ground station (or 5 nm at 30 nm, etc.). At say GS 120 kt (2 nm/min), passing through a 10° arc abeam the VOR will take 5 minutes at 60 nm, or 2.5 minutes at 30 nm.

Crossing a Known Radial from an Off-Track VOR

It is a simple procedure to identify passing a known radial from an off-track VOR and, indeed, some en route reporting points are based on this.

EXAMPLE 7 UPTON reporting point en route on the track between Ottringham and Wallasey VORs is specified by the 330 radial from Gamston VOR.

• With two VOR displays in the cockpit, it would be normal procedure to track using VOR 1 on Ottringham (and later Wallasey), and check UPTON using VOR 2 tuned to Gamston.
• With only one VOR set fitted in the aircraft, it would be normal procedure to leave it on the main tracking aid (Ottringham) until almost at UPTON (say two minutes before ETA), and then select Gamston and the 330 radial. Having crossed this radial, the VOR could be selected to a tracking aid (Ottringham or Wallasey).

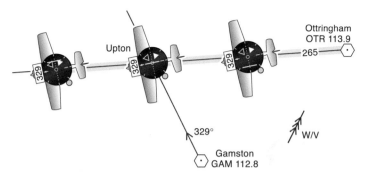

■ Figure 20-24 **Crossing a known radial**

If a 1:500,000 aeronautical chart is being used (rather than a Radio Navigation Chart), you can construct your own checkpoints along track using nearby off-track VORs. In Figure 20–25, the pilot has chosen to check position crossing the 105, 075 and 045 radials from an off-track VOR. By measuring the distance between these planned fixes en route and noting the time of reaching them, the pilot can calculate the groundspeed and revise estimates for positions further along track.

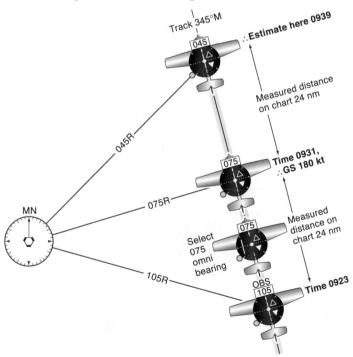

■ Figure 20-25 **Using an off-track VOR to monitor progress**

The VOR Display

The VOR indicates the position of the aeroplane with respect to the selected VOR track, and the VOR display in the cockpit will be the same irrespective of the aeroplane's heading. Each of the aeroplanes in Figure 20-26 will have the same VOR display, provided that the same track is set under the course index with the OBS.

> The CDI position will **not** change as the aeroplane changes heading.

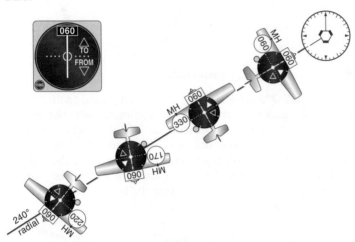

■ Figure 20-26 **The VOR cockpit display is not heading sensitive**

Orientation Without Altering the OBS

It is possible, without altering the omni bearing selector, to determine which quadrant the aeroplane is in with respect to the selected track. In Figure 20-27, the selected omni bearing is 340.

• The CDI is deflected left, which indicates that, when looking in direction 340, the aeroplane is out to the right (of the line 340–160); and

• The FROM flag indicates that tracking 340 would take the aeroplane *from* the VOR ground station, i.e. the aeroplane is ahead of the line 250–070 when looking in the direction 340.

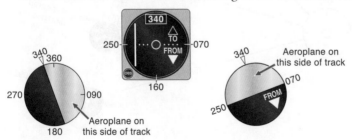

■ Figure 20-27 **Using the CDI and the TO/FROM flag for orientation without moving the omni bearing selector**

This puts the aeroplane in the quadrant away from the CDI, and away from the TO/FROM flag – between 340 and 070 radials (omni bearings from the VOR ground station).

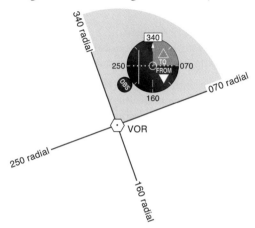

■ Figure 20-28 **The aeroplane is in the quadrant away from the CDI and TO/FROM flag**

NOTE No information is available from the VOR cockpit display regarding aeroplane heading. Heading information in °M must be obtained from the direction indicator.

EXAMPLE 8 With 085 under the course index, the OBI reads CDI deflected right with the TO flag showing. Position the aeroplane with respect to the VOR.

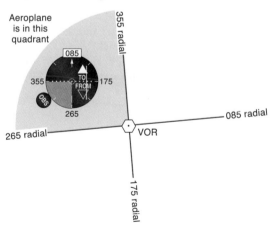

■ Figure 20-29 **The aeroplane is between the 355 and 265 radials**

This method is a quick way to determine the approximate position of the aeroplane in relation to the VOR ground station.

VOR Tracking

Tracking To a VOR

To track *to* a VOR:

- **select** the VOR frequency;
- **identify** the station (Morse code ident);
- **check** that the red OFF warning flag is not displayed; and
- **select the omni bearing** of the desired track with the OBS.

Orientate the aeroplane with respect to the desired track, and then take up a suitable intercept heading using the direction indicator (aligned with the magnetic compass). If the aeroplane is heading approximately in the direction of the desired track, the centre circle will represent the aeroplane, and the CDI the desired track. To intercept track in this case, turn towards the CDI.

This is using the OBI as a **command instrument.** This commands you to turn towards the CDI to regain track. Be aware, however, that this only applies when the aeroplane's heading is roughly in the same direction as the selected omni bearing.

On intercepting track, steer a suitable heading to maintain it, considering wind direction and strength. If the desired track is maintained, the CDI will remain centred.

EXAMPLE 9 In Figure 20-30, with the desired track 030 set in the OBI, the CDI is out to the right. Since the aeroplane's initial heading agrees approximately with the track of 030, the pilot concludes that the track is out to the right of the aeroplane. The CDI out to the right *commands* a right turn to regain track and centre the CDI.

The pilot has taken up a heading of 050°M to intercept a track of 030 *to* the VOR, which will give a 20° intercept. This is satisfactory if the aeroplane is close to the track.

If the aeroplane is well away from track, then a 60° or 90° intercept might be more appropriate. This would be MH 090 or MH 120.

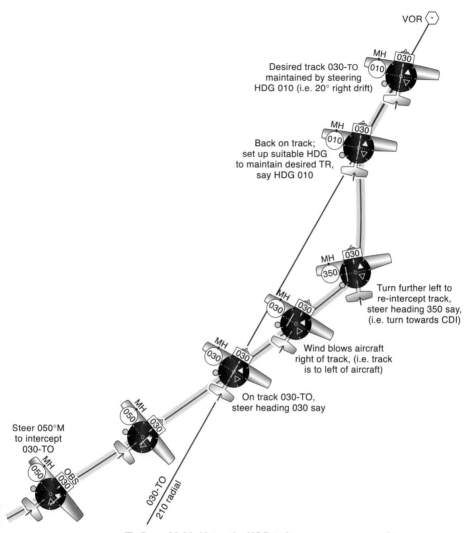

VOR

Desired track 030-TO
maintained by steering
HDG 010 (i.e. 20° right drift)

MH 030
010

Back on track;
set up suitable HDG
to maintain desired TR,
say HDG 010

MH 030
010

MH 030
350

Turn further left to
re-intercept track,
steer heading 350 say,
(i.e. turn towards CDI)

MH 030
030

MH 030
030

Wind blows aircraft
right of track, (i.e. track
is to left of aircraft)

On track 030-TO,
steer heading 030 say

Steer 050°M
to intercept
030-TO

MH 050   OBS 030

MH 050   030

030-TO
210 radial

■ Figure 20-30 **Using the VOR indicator as a command instrument**

Determining Drift Angle

When tracking inbound on 360 *to* a VOR with 360 set under the course index, MH 360 will allow the aeroplane to maintain track provided that there is no crosswind component.

If, however, there is a westerly wind blowing, then the aeroplane will be blown to the right of track unless a wind correction (WCA) is applied and the aeroplane steered on a heading slightly into wind. This is MH 352 in the centre diagram of Figure 20-31.

If, on the other hand, there is an easterly wind blowing, the aeroplane will be blown to the left of track, unless a wind correction angle (WCA) is applied and the aeroplane steered on a heading slightly into wind, such as MH 005 in the right-hand diagram of Figure 20-31.

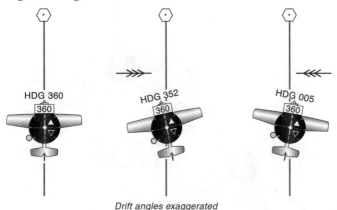

Drift angles exaggerated

■ Figure 20-31 **Tracking inbound and allowing for drift**

Just how great the WCA need be is determined in flight by trial and error (although any pre-flight calculations using the navigation computer when flight planning may suggest a starting figure for WCA). If the chosen WCA is not correct, and the aeroplane gradually departs from track, causing the CDI to move from its central position, then heading should be altered, the track regained (CDI centred), and then a new magnetic heading flown with an improved estimate of WCA. This process of achieving a suitable WCA is known as **bracketing**.

Of course, in the real world the wind frequently changes in both strength and direction, and so the magnetic heading required to maintain track will also change from time to time. This becomes obvious by gradual movements of the CDI away from its central position, which you will notice in your regular scan of the radio navigation instruments, and correct by changes in magnetic heading. See Figure 20-32.

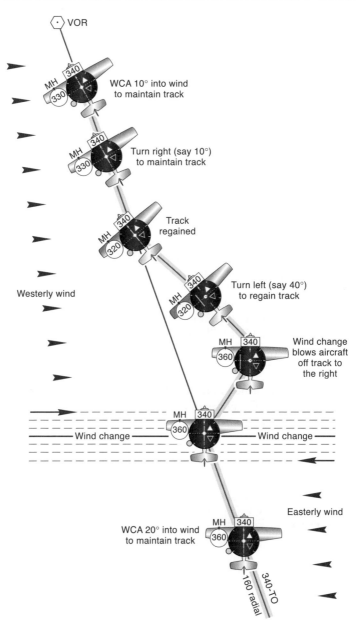

■ Figure 20-32 **Tracking inbound through a wind change**

Tracking From a VOR

To track *from* a VOR (assuming the VOR has not already been selected and identified):

- **select** the VOR frequency;
- **identify** the station (Morse code ident);
- **check** that the red OFF warning flag is not displayed; and
- **select the omni bearing** of the desired track with the OBS.

Orientate the aeroplane with respect to the desired track, and then take up a suitable intercept heading using the direction indicator (aligned with the magnetic compass). If the aeroplane is heading approximately in the direction of the desired track, the centre circle will represent the aeroplane, and the CDI the desired track.

To intercept track in this case, turn towards the CDI. This is using the OBI as a **command instrument.** This commands you to turn towards the CDI to regain track. Be aware, however, that this only applies when the heading is roughly in the same direction as the selected omni bearing.

On intercepting track, steer a suitable heading to maintain it, considering the wind direction and strength. If the desired track is maintained, the CDI will remain centred.

EXAMPLE 10 In Figure 20-33, with the desired track 140 set in the OBI, the CDI is out to the right.

Since the aeroplane's initial heading agrees approximately with the track of 140, the pilot concludes that the track is out to the right of the aeroplane (or, in this case, straight ahead and to the right).

The pilot has taken up a heading of 220°M to intercept a track of 140 *from* the VOR, which will give an 80° intercept. This is satisfactory if the aeroplane is well away from the track.

If the aeroplane is close to track, then a 60° or 30° intercept might be more applicable, which, in this case, would be MH 200 or MH 170.

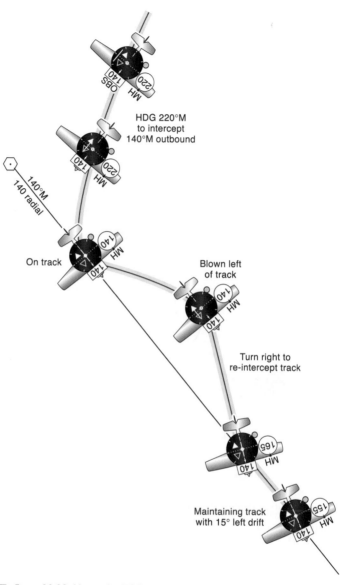

HDG 220°M
to intercept
140°M outbound

140°M
140 radial

On track

Blown left
of track

Turn right to
re-intercept track

Maintaining track
with 15° left drift

■ Figure 20-33 **Using the VOR indicator as a command instrument**

Use the OBI as a Command Instrument

Use the OBI as a **command instrument** whenever possible. With the desired track set in the OBI, and the aeroplane heading at least roughly in the same direction as the selected track, the omni bearing indicator will act as a command instrument. By flying *towards* the deflected CDI, you can centre it, and thereby regain track. For example:

- tracking 060 *to* the VOR, set 060 under the course index;
- tracking 030 *from* the VOR, set 030 under the course index.

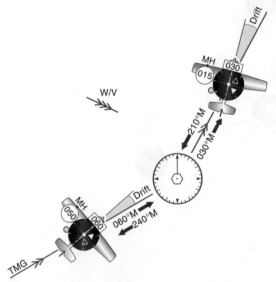

■ *Figure 20-34* **Use the OBI as a command instrument**

A minor complication can arise when the aeroplane is steered on a heading approximating the *reciprocal* of the omni bearing selected on the OBI. It causes the VOR cockpit display to be no longer a command instrument.

EXAMPLE 11 You have been tracking 140 *from* a VOR, with 140 selected in the OBI and by steering MH 140. The aeroplane has drifted left of track, and so the CDI will be deflected to the right of centre. To regain the 140-FROM track, you must turn towards the needle, in this case towards the right, i.e. heading and OBI selection are similar, so it is used as a command instrument.

The VOR indicator is not heading sensitive.

Now you want to return to the VOR ground station on the reciprocal track, which is 320 *to* the VOR, so turn through approximately 180° onto MH 320 without altering the 140 set under the course index. The omni bearing indicator, because it is not heading sensitive, indicates exactly as it did before the turn, with the CDI as seen by the pilot out to the right of centre.

A non-command VOR setup is difficult to interpret and use.

To regain track on this reciprocal heading, turn, not towards the CDI, but away from it. Turning towards the CDI on this reciprocal heading to the selected track would take you further away from the selected track, i.e. it is no longer a command instrument, which is a pity!

This inconvenience can be easily removed, and the OBI returned to being a command instrument, by selecting the new desired track under the course index, 320, which approximates the heading being flown. The immediate effect will be for:
• the TO flag to appear, replacing the FROM flag, and
• the CDI to swing across to the other side.

A command VOR setup is easy to interpret and use.

The CDI will now be out to the left, and a turn towards it will bring the aeroplane back towards the selected track. The OBI is once again a command instrument, easier to understand, and easier to fly.

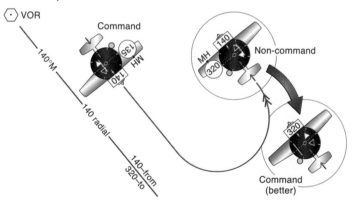

■ *Figure 20-35* **For ease of operation, use the OBI as a command instrument**

Intercepting a Track using the VOR

Orientation

You need to know:
* Where am I?;
* Where do I want to go?; and
* How do I get there?

The easiest method of orientating the aircraft using the VOR is to rotate the OBS until the CDI centres. This can occur on one of two headings (reciprocals of each other); choose the one with the omni bearing that most resembles the aircraft's magnetic heading. If the aircraft is heading towards the VOR ground station, then the TO flag will show; if it is heading away from the VOR, then the FROM flag will show.

Select the desired track in °M using the omni bearing selector (OBS). Determine which way to turn to intercept the desired track, and then take up a suitable intercept heading.

Intercepting an Outbound Track

The VOR is just as useful tracking away from a VOR ground station as tracking towards it, and it is much easier to use than the NDB/ADF combination. The next example illustrates the normal method of doing this.

EXAMPLE 12 You are tracking inbound on the 170 radial to a VOR (350-TO). ATC instructs you to take up a heading to intercept the 090 radial outbound (090-FROM).

Orientation is not a problem since you already know where you are (the usual situation). The best way to track inbound on the 170 radial (which is the same as QDR 170, making the inbound QDM 350), is to have 350 set in the OBI course index, since the aeroplane is tracking 350 *to* the VOR. This ensures that the indicator is a command instrument (fly towards the CDI needle to regain the selected track).

Visualise the situation:
* tracking northwards towards the VOR;
* the desired track, 090–FROM, lies ahead to the right.

To intercept the 090–FROM track:
* set 090 under the course index;
* take up a suitable intercept heading (MH 030 for a 60° intercept); and
* maintain MH 030 until the CDI moves from full-scale deflection towards the centre. To avoid overshooting the track, anticipate the interception, and 'lead-in' by commencing a turn just prior to intercepting track.

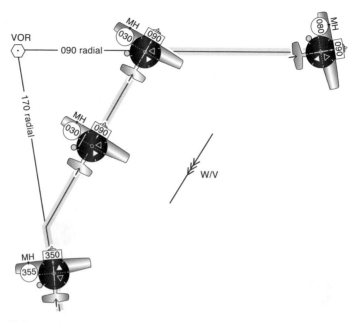

■ *Figure 20-36* **Intercepting a track outbound from a VOR**

Intercepting an Inbound Track

EXAMPLE 13 ATC instructs you to track inbound on the 010 radial to a particular VOR.

Select and identify the VOR; then
- Orientate yourself with respect to it (perhaps by centring the CDI suitably).
- Set the desired track under the course index – *inbound* on the 010 radial (QDR) is 190-TO (QDM) – and determine the position of this track.
- Take up a suitable intercepting heading, and wait for the CDI to centre.

In Figure 20-37:
- the CDI centres on 050-FROM (it would also centre on 230-TO);
- you have chosen a 90° intercept, steering MH 280 to intercept 190-TO; and
- as the CDI starts to move (within 10° of the selected track), lead in to join track smoothly, and allow a wind correction angle of 5°.

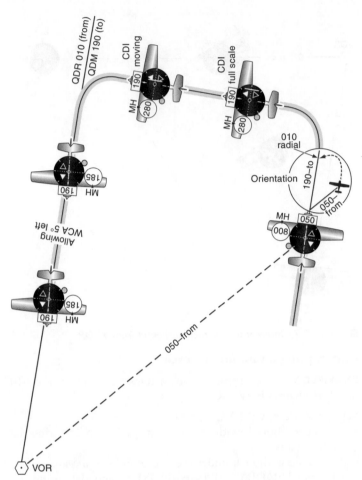

■ *Figure 20-37* **Intercepting an inbound track to a VOR**

Now complete: **Practice Questions - The VOR**

1. The VOR receiver displays:

(a) A true bearing to the VOR.

(b) A magnetic bearing relative to the VOR station.

(c) The slant distance to the VOR station.

(d) A compass bearing relative to the VOR station.

2. A VOR is a radio navigation aid that operates in which radio band?

(a) MF

(b) LF

(c) UHF

(d) VHF

3. The airborne VOR receiver:

(a) Measures the range from the ground station. It measures the time taken for the interrogation pulse to return to the aircraft.

(b) Measures the magnetic direction of the signal transmitted by the ground station.

(c) Measures the true direction of the signal transmitted by the ground station.

(d) Measures the phase difference between two signals transmitted by the VOR beacon.

4. A VOR radial is:

(a) The true bearing from the station.

(b) The magnetic bearing from the station.

(c) The true bearing to the station.

(d) The magnetic bearing to the station.

5. When flying towards a VOR on the 125 radial, in order to obtain CDI indications in the correct sense the OBS should be set to:

(a) 125° with a FROM indication.

(b) 125°with a TO indication.

(c) 305° with a TO indication.

(d) 305° with a FROM indication.

6. What should the pilot set on the OBS (omni bearing selector) to obtain CDI (course deviation indicator) indications in the correct sense when tracking towards a VOR on radial 255°?

(a) 075° with TO indicated.
(b) 255° with FROM indicated.
(c) 255° with TO indicated.
(d) 075° with FROM indicated.

7. What should the pilot set on the OBS (omni bearing selector) to obtain CDI (course deviation indicator) indications in the correct sense when tracking away from a VOR on radial 335°?

(a) 155° with TO indicated.
(b) 335° with TO indicated.
(c) 155° with FROM indicated.
(d) 335° with FROM indicated.

8. Which aircraft is on the 060° radial tracking towards a VOR beacon and receiving correct sense indications?

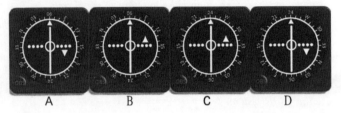

A   B   C   D

(a) A
(b) B
(c) C
(d) D

Answers: 1b, 2d, 3d, 4b, 5c, 6a, 7d, 8c.

DME

Slant Distance

Distance–measuring equipment (DME) can provide you with extremely useful information: the distance of your aircraft from a DME ground station. DME uses radar principles to measure this distance, which is the *slant distance* rather than the horizontal distance (or range). For most practical purposes, the DME distance can be considered as range, except when the aeroplane is within a few miles of the DME ground station.

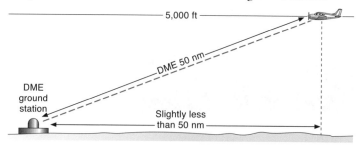

■ *Figure 21-1* **DME measures slant distance**

Passing directly over the DME ground station, the DME indicator in the cockpit will either show the height of the aeroplane in nautical miles (1 nm = 6,000 ft approximately), or the DME indication will drop out.

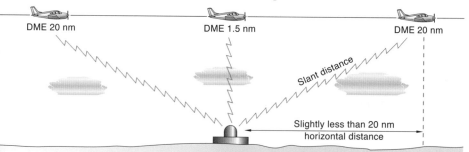

■ *Figure 21-2* **Passing overhead a DME ground station**

DME Cockpit Displays

DME distance is usually displayed in the cockpit as a digital read–out. The pilot generally selects the DME using the VHF–NAV radio (since most DMEs are paired with a VOR frequency or a localiser frequency). Once the DME is *locked on,* and a DME reading and *ident* obtained, the DME indications can be used for distance information irrespective of whether the VOR (or localiser) is used for tracking or orientation purposes.

Some airborne DME equipment is capable of computing the rate of change of DME distance (the *rate of closure* of the aeroplane with the DME ground station), and displaying this rate of closure on the DME cockpit instrument. If it is assumed that slant distance equals horizontal distance, and that the aeroplane is tracking either directly towards or directly away from the DME ground station, then the rate of closure read-out will represent **groundspeed (GS),** a very useful piece of information. Some DME indicators can also display **time to the station (TTS)** in minutes at the current rate of closure, by comparing the groundspeed with DME distance.

DME measures rate of closure to the ground station and displays your groundspeed and time to the station.

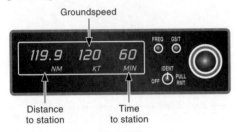

■ *Figure 21-3* **A digital DME panel**

If the DME equipment in the aeroplane does not give a groundspeed read-out, then simply note the DME distance at two particular times, and carry out a simple calculation of GS = distance/time either mentally or on your navigation computer.

EXAMPLE 1 You note DME distance and time as you track towards a DME ground station. Calculate groundspeed.

DME 35	Time 0215 UTC	
DME 25	Time 0220 UTC	
10 nm	5 min	= **GS 120 kt**

Circular Position Lines

The DME provides a circular position line. If the DME reads 35 nm, for instance, then you know that the aeroplane is somewhere on the circumference of a 35 nm circle centred on the DME ground station.

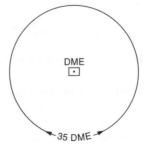

■ *Figure 21-4* **A circular position line from a DME**

Information from another radio aid may assist in positively fixing the position of the aeroplane, provided that the two position lines give a good 'cut' (angle of intercept).

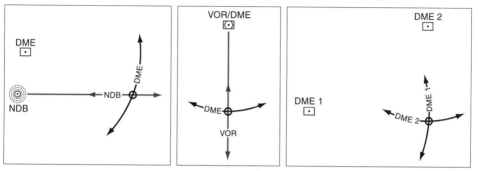

■ *Figure 21-5* **Using two radio navaids to fix position**

How DME Works

DME uses the principle of secondary radar. Radar is covered thoroughly in chapter 18, where both primary and secondary radar are discussed. **Primary radar** detects one of its own transmissions that is reflected from some object; **secondary radar** detects a *responding transmission* from a **transponder** activated by an *interrogation* signal.

Distance measuring equipment operates by the airborne transmitter (the *interrogator*) sending out a stream of radio pulses in all directions on the receiving frequency of the DME ground station transponder.

At the target DME ground beacon, these pulses are passed through an electronic *gate*. If the pulses and the gate match up, the DME ground beacon (or transponder) is triggered, and responds by transmitting a strong answering signal. The airborne DME equipment detects this answering signal and measures the time between the transmission of the interrogating pulse from the aircraft and the reception of the ranging reply pulse from the DME ground station. It converts this time to a *distance in nautical miles* and the DME indicator, when it displays this distance with the red OFF flag out of view, is said to have latched on or locked on.

NOTE Do not confuse the DME transponder at the DME ground station (and associated with the airborne DME equipment) with the SSR transponder carried in the aircraft (operated by the pilot and associated with the ground-based secondary surveillance radar).

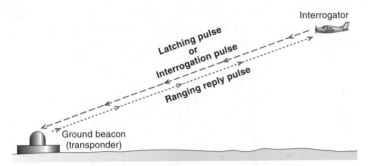

■ *Figure 21-6* **Operation of the DME**

Each DME ground transponder can cope with about 100 different aeroplanes at any one time before becoming saturated, and the system is designed so that there is no possibility of interrogation pulses from one aeroplane causing an incorrect range indication in another aeroplane. Also, because the frequencies are carefully chosen so that stations with like frequencies are situated far apart geographically, there is no likelihood of interference from the wrong DME ground station. DME signals are line–of–sight transmissions (like VHF radio communications, radar and VOR). The approximate usable range in nautical miles is the square root of (1.5 × height in ft).

> *You must positively identify a DME ground station before using it for navigation.*

DME Frequencies

DME operates in the UHF (ultra–high frequency) band from 962 MHz to 1,213 MHz which, with 1 MHz spacing, gives 252 possible frequencies. Each DME channel consists of two frequencies (an interrogation frequency from the aeroplane and a paired response frequency from the ground station).

There are 126 channels currently in use, numbered from 1 to 126, and with X or Y classification after them. You may see references such as DME CH 92Y or DME CH 111X in the AIP, but there is no need for you to know these details, since these numbers are not used by the pilot to select the DME – the DME is automatically selected on many types of VHF-NAV units when you select the VHF-NAV to an appropriate VOR or ILS frequency.

VOR/DME Pairing

Each VOR frequency has a specific DME channel paired with it. For instance, VOR frequency 112.00 MHz has DME channel 57X paired with it, so that the VOR's associated DME will automatically be interrogated when you select the VOR frequency 112.00 on the VHF-NAV. The purpose of this pairing is to reduce your workload in the cockpit, with only one selection instead of two required, and to reduce the risk selecting the right VOR but the wrong DME station. It is normal for only **co-located** VORs and DMEs to be frequency paired. Co-located VORs and DMEs are situated within 800 metres of each other, and each will have the same Morse code ident.

A paired VOR and DME give a very good position fix:
- the radial from the VOR; and
- the distance from the DME.

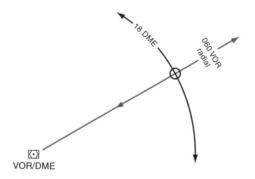

■ *Figure 21-7* **Fixing position with VOR and DME**

DME Station Information

Further information on individual DME ground stations appears in the ENR 4-1-1 section of the UK AIP.

ENR 4.1 – RADIO NAVIGATION AIDS – EN-ROUTE						
Manchester VOR/DME Var 3.2°W - 2007 VOR 2.8°W - 2007	MCT	113.55 MHz (Ch 82Y)	H24	AD Purpose: 532125.29N 0021544.24W ENR Purpose: 532125N 0021544W	282 ft amsl	APCH Aid to Manchester. On Manchester AD. VOR/DME DOC: 90 nm/50000 ft.

SAMPLE ONLY
Not to be used for flight
operations or flight planning

■ *Figure 21-8* **Information from AIP ENR 4-1-1 for the Manchester VOR/DME**

Now complete: **Practice Questions - DME**

1. DME operates in which frequency band?

(a) MF

(b) VHF

(c) UHF

(d) LF

2. When using a DME what range is displayed on the cockpit display?

(a) Slant range

(b) Horizontal range

(c) Corrected slant range

(d) Arc range

3. Approximately what is the maximum number of aircraft that are able to use a DME station at any one time?

(a) 50

(b) 75

(c) 100

(d) 150

4. Whilst inbound to an aerodrome, you are asked, by ATC, to report at a range of 4 nautical miles. You are flying with reference to a GPS receiver and radio navigation aids as an independent source of navigation information. Your altitude is 2,700 ft when your GPS receiver indicates that you are 4 nm from the airfield. Which is the correct statement?

(a) The DME indicates a distance greater than the GPS receiver.

(b) The DME indicates a lesser distance than the GPS receiver.

(c) A discrepancy exists between the two instruments: the GPS receiver is malfunctioning.

(d) A discrepancy exists between the two instruments: the DME is malfunctioning.

5. You are directly overhead a coupled VOR/DME beacon cluster at a height of 2,700 ft agl. The distance reading on the DME only reduces to 0.4 before starting to increase, never reaching zero. What is the possible reason?

(a) *You have made a small navigation error missing the beacon by 0.4nm.*

(b) *The DME reading is in error due to the VOR zone of confusion.*

(c) *The VHF signal from the VOR beacon is interfering with the VHF signal of the DME equipment.*

(d) *You have actually flown overhead the beacon where the slant range of 0.4nm equals your height of 2,700 ft above the equipment.*

6. Having selected and identified and operational DME associated with a VOR, the DME display does not provide distance, groundspeed and time-to-run information. After 30 seconds, information is displayed as expected by supporting information on your VFR flight log. The most probable reason for this is:

(a) *There is an intermittent fault with the DME instrument in the aircraft.*

(b) *The ground-based DME is oversubscribed and the delay in the display of information is due to queuing.*

(c) *There is a fault with the ground-based DME equipment.*

(d) *The VHF signal from the VOR beacon is interfering with the VHF signal of the DME equipment.*

Answers: 1c, 2a, 3c, 4a, 5d, 6b.

The NDB and the ADF

General Description

The non-directional beacon (NDB) is the simplest form of radio navigation aid used by aircraft. It is a ground-based transmitter that transmits radio energy in all directions, hence its name – the **non-directional beacon.**

The **automatic direction finder** (ADF), fitted in an aeroplane has a needle that indicates the direction from which the signals of the selected NDB ground station are being received. This is extremely useful information for pilots flying in instrument conditions and/or at night. In days past, the combined ADF/NDB system was referred to as the **radio compass.**

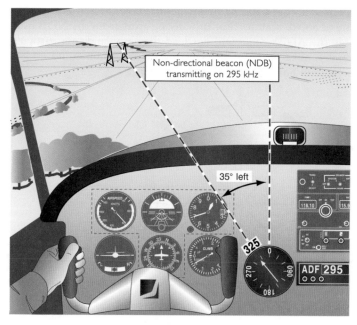

Non-directional beacon (NDB) transmitting on 295 kHz

35° left

ADF 295

■ *Figure 22-1* ***A correctly tuned ADF indicates the direction of the selected NDB from the aircraft***

Flying to an NDB in an aeroplane is similar to following a compass needle to the North Pole – fly the aeroplane towards where the needle points and eventually you will arrive overhead.

■ *Figure 22-2* **Flying to a station is straightforward**

Flying away from the North Pole, however, with the magnetic compass needle pointing behind, could take the aeroplane in any one of 360 directions. Similarly, flying away from the NDB using only the ADF needle will not lead the aeroplane to a particular point (unlike flying *to* an NDB). The aeroplane could end up anywhere! Further information is required.

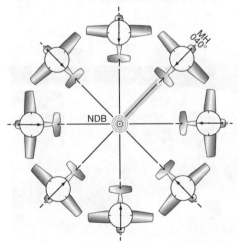

■ *Figure 22-3* **Flying away from a station requires more information than just the needle on the tail**

The ADF and the Direction Indicator

The extra information required by the pilot, in addition to that supplied by the ADF needle, comes from the magnetic compass, or more commonly, from the direction indicator. Accurate navigation can be carried out using the aircraft **ADF needle** which points at an NDB ground station, and a **direction** indicator which indicates the aeroplane's magnetic heading (MH).

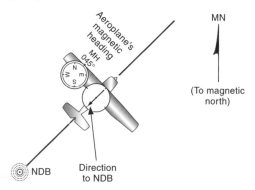

■ *Figure 22-4* **The ADF/NDB combination needs support from a magnetic compass (or from a direction indicator)**

NOTE Since a direction indicator will most probably drift slowly out of alignment, it is essential that you realign it periodically with the magnetic compass in straight flight at a steady speed, say every 10 or 15 minutes.

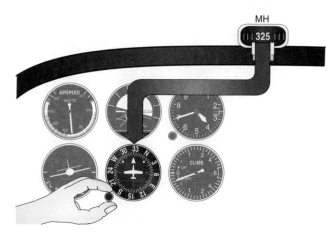

■ *Figure 22-5* **Periodically realign the DI with the magnetic compass in steady flight**

The NDB/ADF Combination

Before using an ADF's indications of the bearing to a particular NDB, the aeroplane must be within the promulgated range of the NDB and you must have:

- **correctly selected** the NDB frequency;
- **identified** its Morse code ident; and
- **tested** the ADF needle to ensure that it is indeed 'ADFing'.

If the NDB is 40° to the left of the aeroplane's magnetic heading, say MH 070°M, then the situation can be illustrated as shown in Figure 22-6. The NDB, since it is 40° left of the nose, will have a magnetic bearing (MB) of 030°M from the aeroplane.

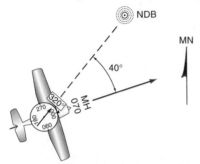

■ *Figure 22-6* **A diagrammatic representation**

The ADF/NDB combination, in conjunction with the direction indicator, can be used:
- **to track** to the NDB on any desired track, pass overhead the NDB, and track outbound on whatever track is desired; or
- **to fix** the aeroplane's position.

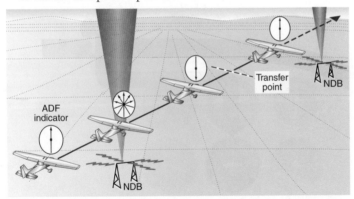

■ *Figure 22-7* **Flying towards, over, and past an NDB, and on to the next one**

The ADF in the aeroplane should, whenever possible, be selected to an NDB relevant to the desired path of the aeroplane. If tracking en route between two NDBs, the point of transfer from one NDB to the next would reasonably be the half-way point, depending of course on their relative ranges.

If the ADF needle points up, the NDB is ahead. If the ADF needle points down, the NDB is behind.

If the NDB is ahead, the ADF needle will point up the dial; if the NDB is behind, the ADF needle will point down the dial. As the aeroplane passes overhead the NDB, the ADF needle will become very sensitive and will swing from ahead to behind.

The NDB/ADF combination is the simplest form of radio navigation in theory, yet it takes a good instrument-trained pilot to use it accurately. Other more advanced systems, such as the VOR, are more complicated in principle but easier to use.

The NDB

The NDB is a ground-based transmitter.

The non-directional beacon (NDB) is the ground-based part of the combination. It is called *non-directional* because no particular direction is favoured or differentiated in its transmissions; the NDB radiates identical electromagnetic energy in all directions. Each NDB transmits on a given frequency in the low-frequency or medium-frequency LF/MF bands (somewhere between 200 to 1,750 kHz). The transmission aerial is either a single mast or a large 'T-aerial' slung between two masts.

■ *Figure 22-8* **NDB transmission aerials**

Identify an NDB before using it for navigation.

To avoid confusion between various NDBs, and to ensure that the pilot is using the correct beacon, each NDB transmits its own particular identification signal (or **ident**) in the form of a two- or three-letter Morse code signal, which you should monitor periodically in the cockpit.

EXAMPLE 1 The Plymouth NDB has a frequency of 396.5 kHz and is identified by listening to, and identifying the Morse code symbols for PY, which are: *"dit-dah-dah-dit dah-dit-dah-dah"* or:
. _ _ .   _ . _ _

NDB Range

For long-range en route navigation where no other aids are available, a fairly strong NDB with a range of 100 nm or more is usually required. Some NDBs used for long-distance overwater

tracking, for instance in the Pacific area, may have a range of
400 nm. In the UK most of NDBs formerly used for navigation
have now been decommissioned, however there are still a small
number at airfields, such as Shoreham, Lydd and Southend. The
range of each non-directional beacon (NDB) is listed in AIP
ENR 4-1-1, and within this promulgated range the NDB should
provide bearings accurate to within ±5°. The promulgated range
also provides guidance as to when you should shift your attention
to the next aid.

UK AIP   **(28 Jul 11) ENR 4-1-1-3**

ENR 4.1 — RADIO NAVIGATION AIDS — EN-ROUTE						
Name of Station MAG Var VOR Declination	IDENT	Frequency (Channel)	Hours of Operation (Winter/Summer)	Co-ordinates	DME Aerial Elevation	Remarks
1	2	3	4	5	6	7
Henton NDB Var 2.08°W - 2009	HEN	433.5 kHz	H24	514535N 0004725W	—	Range 30 nm.

■ *Figure 22-9* **Many NDBs have only a short range**

For manoeuvring in the vicinity of aerodromes, only lower-
powered NDBs are required. NDBs used for approaches are
referred to as locators. Such low-powered beacons are listed in
AIP Aerodrome Section (AD 2) and seldom have a range greater
than 20 nm.

The range of an NDB depends on:
- **transmission power** (10–2,000 watts);
- **transmission frequency;** and
- **atmospheric conditions** existing at the time – electrical
  storms, as well as the periods of sunrise and sunset, can distort
  or reflect the signals from an NDB.

NDB Signal Accuracy

An ideal NDB signal received by an aircraft may be accurate to
±2°; however, various factors may reduce this accuracy
considerably. These factors include:

THUNDERSTORM EFFECT causes the ADF needle to be deflected
towards a nearby electrical storm (cumulonimbus cloud) and away
from the selected NDB.

NIGHT EFFECT when strong skywaves from the NDB returning to earth from the ionosphere cause interference with the surface waves from the NDB, possibly resulting in a fading signal and a wandering ADF needle (most pronounced at dawn and dusk).

INTERFERENCE from other NDBs transmitting on similar frequencies.

MOUNTAIN EFFECT due to reflections of the NDB signals from mountains.

COASTAL EFFECT caused by the NDB signal bending slightly towards the coastline when crossing it at an angle.

NDB Identification

Each NDB or locator is identifiable by a two- or three-letter Morse code identification signal which is transmitted together with its normal signal. This is known as its **ident.**

You must identify an NDB before using it for any navigational purpose within its promulgated range and, if using it for some length of time, periodically re-identify it.

If a test or incorrect ident is heard, the NDB must not be used.

The lack of an ident may indicate that the NDB is out of service, even though it may still be transmitting (say for maintenance or test purposes), and it must not be used for navigation. If an incorrect ident is heard, then those signals must not be used.

	L	L	
	'LUT' 345	'TD' 347.5	'NH' 371.5
Morse code	· — · · · · —	— — · ·	— ·

Monitor the ident frequently if an NDB is the only navaid you are using, as a signal failure will not be indicated on the ADF display.

To identify most NDBs, simply select AUDIO on the ADF, listen to the Morse code signal, and confirm that it is the correct one. (Morse code sheets are included on the legend of the ICAO 1:500,000 aeronautical chart series.)

Different NDBs have different ident characteristics which are associated with the type of transmission.

All NDBs in the UK can be identified with the ADF mode selector in the ADF position. In Continental Europe, however, there are some NDBs that require the pilot to select BFO (beat frequency oscillator) to enable identification. The BFO imposes a tone onto the NDB carrier wave to make it audible.

Some NDBs carry voice transmissions, such as the automatic terminal information service (ATIS) at some aerodromes. It is also possible, in a situation where the communications radio (VHF-COM) has failed, for ATC to send voice messages to the pilot on the NDB frequency. They can be received on the ADF if AUDIO is selected.

NOTE Broadcasting stations such as the BBC and commercial stations may also be received by an ADF, since they transmit in the LF/MF bands. But it is not good airmanship to use a broadcasting station as a navigational aid, since they are difficult to identify precisely. Even if an announcer says "This is BBC Radio 2", it is possible that the transmission is coming, not from the main transmitter, but from an alternative or emergency transmitter located elsewhere, or even a relay station many miles away from the main transmitter. To use information from a radio broadcasting station, you must be absolutely certain of its geographical position – something which is difficult to determine. It is not good airmanship to listen to a broadcasting station in flight, as it will distract you from operational tasks and responsibilities.

The ADF

The airborne partner of the NDB is the automatic direction finder, usually referred to as the ADF. It operates on the *radio compass* principle whereby the ADF needle indicates the direction from which the signals are coming.

The ADF is a receiver in the aircraft.

The automatic direction finder has three main components:

THE ADF RECEIVER, which the pilot tunes to the frequency of the desired NDB and verifies with the ident.

THE AERIAL SYSTEM, consisting of a **loop aerial** (or its modern equivalent), plus a **sense aerial,** which together determine the direction from which the signal is coming.

THE ADF COCKPIT DISPLAY, either a fixed–card or a rotatable compass card with a pointer or needle indicating the direction from which the signals are coming. The cockpit instrument is fitted into the instrument panel, usually to the right of the attitude flight instruments, with the top of the dial representing the nose of the aeroplane, and the bottom of the dial representing its tail. Ideally, the ADF needle will point continuously and automatically towards the NDB ground station.

ADF antenna mounted under fuselage

ADF control panel

ADF card and pointer

■ *Figure 22-10* **The airborne ADF equipment**

ADF Aerials

Improved reception on a portable radio is sometimes possible by rotating it to a particular position, because of the directional properties of its receiving antenna. The automatic direction finder works on the same principle.

The ADF Control Panel

ADF units vary from type to type, so you must become familiar with the set you will be using prior to flight.

■ *Figure 22-11* **Typical ADF control panel**

You must be able to select and identify positively the NDB that you want to use, and then verify that the ADF needle is indeed responding to the signals from that NDB. The correct procedure, any time a new NDB is to be used, is to confirm (verbally if so desired):

• **selected;**
• **identified;** and
• **ADFing** (and giving a sensible bearing).

The Mode Selector or Function Switch

The mode selector switches between ADF modes of operation:

OFF. Switches the ADF off.

The ADF mode selector is usually selected to ADF.

ADF. The normal position when you want bearing information to be displayed automatically by the needle. Most NDBs can be identified with the mode selector in this position (and the volume knob adjusted suitably).

ANT or REC. Abbreviations for **antenna** or **receiver.** In this position, only the signal from the sense antenna is used, with no satisfactory directional information being available to the ADF needle. The reason for this function position is that it gives the best audio reception to allow easier identification, and better understanding of any voice messages. Never leave the mode selector in this position if you are navigating using the ADF – the ADF needle will remain stationary with no obvious indication that it is not responding! It is possible, however, to identify most NDBs with the mode selector in the ADF position (which is a safer position), and for the ANT position to be avoided.

BFO or CW. Abbreviations for **beat frequency oscillator** or **carrier wave.** This position is selected when identifying the few NDBs that use A0/A1 or A1 transmissions, which are unmodulated carrier waves whose transmission is interrupted in the pattern of the NDB's Morse code identification. Since no audio message is carried on an unmodulated carrier wave, the BFO (as part of the airborne equipment) imposes a tone onto the carrier wave signal to make it audible to the pilot so that the NDB signal can be identified. Again, do not leave the mode selector switch in this position when navigating using the ADF.

TEST. Switching the mode selector to the TEST position will deflect the ADF needle from its current position. Placing the mode selector back to ADF should cause the needle to swing back and indicate the direction of the NDB. This function should be tested every time as part of the *selected, identified, ADFing* tuning procedure. Some ADF sets have a separate TEST button which only needs to be pressed to deflect the needle, and then released to check the return of the needle.

NOTE On some ADF equipment, the TEST function is achieved using the ANT/REC position, which drives the needle to the 090 position. Returning the mode selector to ADF should see the needle start 'ADFing' again.

VOL. The **volume** knob will probably be separate from the mode selector. With audio selected to the pilot's headset or to the cockpit speakers, the VOL should be adjusted so that the ident or any voice messages on the NDB may be heard. If signal reception is poor in ADF, then try ANT/REC; if there is no signal reception, try BFO/CW. But remember to return the mode selector to ADF!

Frequency Knobs

NDBs transmit on a frequency in the range 200–1,750 kHz, the most common band being 200–400 kHz. To allow easier and accurate selection of any particular frequency, most modern ADFs have knobs that allow digital selection, in 100, 10 and 1 kHz steps. Some older ADFs may have a band selector (200–400; 400–1,600 kHz), with either a tuning knob or digital selection for precise tuning.

ADF Cockpit Displays

The basic purpose of an automatic direction finder in an aeroplane is for its needle to point directly towards the selected NDB ground station.

The ADF cockpit display is a card or dial placed vertically in the instrument panel so that:
- if the ADF needle points up, the NDB is ahead;
- if the ADF needle points down, then the NDB is behind;
- if the ADF needle points to one side, then the NDB is located somewhere to that side of the fore–aft axis of the aeroplane.

To convey this information to the pilot, various presentations are used, three of which we will consider:

1. The fixed-card ADF, or relative bearing indicator (RBI);

2. The rotatable-card ADF (the poor man's RMI); and

3. The radio magnetic indicator (RMI).

The Relative Bearing Indicator (RBI)

A fixed-card display has an ADF needle that can rotate against the background of a fixed azimuth card of 360° with 000° (360°) at the top, 180° at the bottom, and so on. The fixed-card ADF is also known as the relative bearing indicator (RBI), and is common in many general aviation aircraft.

> *On the fixed-card ADF, the needle indicates the relative bearing of the NDB from the aeroplane.*

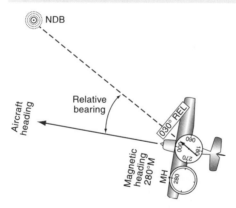

■ *Figure 22-12* **A fixed-card ADF is a relative bearing indicator (RBI)**

The **relative bearing** of the NDB from the aircraft is the angle between the aircraft's heading and the direction of the NDB. Usually relative bearings are described clockwise from 000° to 360°, but it is sometimes convenient to describe the bearing of the NDB relative to the nose or tail of the aeroplane.

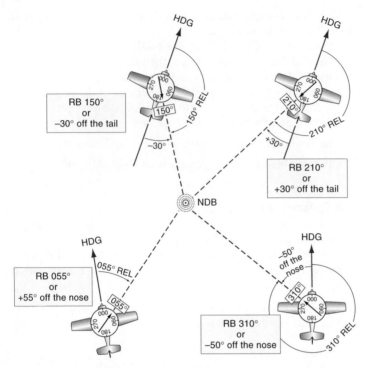

■ *Figure 22-13* **The RBI or fixed-card ADF shows relative bearings**

Each time the aeroplane changes its magnetic heading, it will carry the fixed card with it. Therefore:

With each change of magnetic heading, the ADF needle will indicate a different relative bearing (RB).

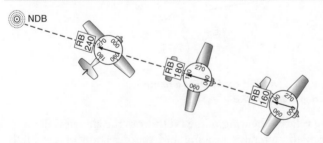

■ *Figure 22-14* **Each time heading is changed, the relative bearing also changes**

Orientation using the RBI

The aeroplane can be orientated with respect to the NDB if you know:

* the **magnetic heading** (MH) of the aeroplane (from the compass or direction indicator); plus
* the **relative bearing** (RB) of the NDB from the aeroplane.

In practice, magnetic heading is flown using the direction indicator, which should be realigned with the magnetic compass in steady flight every 10 minutes or so. Our illustrations will therefore display the DI instead of the magnetic compass.

In Figure 22-15, the aeroplane is heading 280°M, and the ADF indicates RB 030° to the Bristol locator, i.e. MH 280 and RB 030.

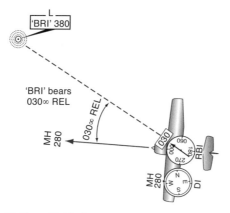

■ Figure 22-15 **Orientation (Where am I?) using an RBI**

MH 280	+	RB 030	=	310°M to NDB
Aircraft magnetic heading	**+**	**Relative bearing of NDB from aircraft**	**=**	**Magnetic bearing of NDB from aircraft**

Visualising Magnetic Bearing To the NDB (QDM)

The magnetic bearing of the NDB from the aeroplane is also known as QDM, and in this case is QDM 310.

A quick pictorial means of determining QDM using a relative bearing indicator and a direction indicator is to translate the ADF needle onto the DI, by paralleling a pencil or by using your imagination.

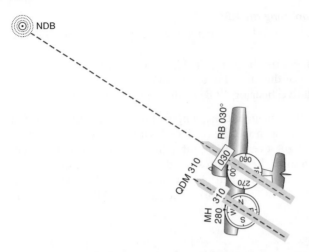

■ *Figure 22-16* **A pictorial (but clumsy) method of finding QDM**

Visualising Magnetic Bearing From the NDB (QDR)

The magnetic bearing of the aircraft from the NDB, i.e. the reciprocal to QDM, is known as the QDR, and in Figure 22-16 is QDR 130. QDR can be visualised as the tail of the pencil (or needle) when it is transferred from the RBI onto the DI.

NOTE An easier method of finding reciprocals than adding or subtracting 180°, is to either:

* add 200 and subtract 20; or
* subtract 200 and add 20.

EXAMPLE 2

QDM 310	QDM 270	QDM 085
−200	−200	+200
+20	+20	−20
QDR 130	QDR 090	QDR 265

The Rotatable-Card ADF

The rotatable-card ADF is an advance on the fixed-card ADF, because it allows you to rotate the card so that the ADF needle indicates, not relative bearing, but magnetic bearing to the NDB (also known as QDM). Do this by aligning the ADF card with the DI compass card each time the aeroplane's magnetic heading is changed.

To align a rotatable-card ADF:
- note magnetic heading on the direction indicator; then
- rotate the ADF card, setting magnetic heading under the index.

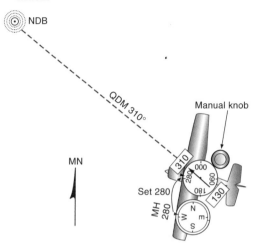

■ Figure 22-17 **Using a rotatable-card ADF**

When the ADF card is aligned with the DI, the ADF needle will indicate QDM, the magnetic bearing to the NDB. This eliminates any need for mental arithmetic. Note also that the tail of the needle, 180° removed from its head, indicates QDR, the magnetic bearing of the aeroplane from the NDB.

> Any time the aircraft changes magnetic heading, you must manually align the ADF card with the DI (ensuring, of course, that the DI is correctly aligned with the magnetic compass).

If desired, the rotatable card can still be used as a fixed card simply by aligning 000 with the nose of the aeroplane and not changing it.

The next step up from a rotatable card is one that remains aligned automatically, a radio magnetic indicator (RMI).

The Radio Magnetic Indicator (RMI)

The RMI display has the ADF needle superimposed on a card that is continuously and automatically aligned with magnetic north. It is, if you like, an automatic version of the rotatable-card ADF – an automatic combination of the direction indicator and RBI.

The RMI is the best ADF presentation, and the easiest to use, but unfortunately the most expensive and usually only encountered in more sophisticated aircraft.

> The RMI **needle** will always indicate QDM, the magnetic bearing
> **to** the NDB.
> The **tail** of the RMI needle will indicate QDR, the magnetic bearing
> **from** the NDB.

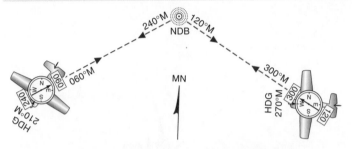

■ Figure 22-18 **The RMI compass card remains aligned with magnetic
north**

As an aeroplane turns and its magnetic heading alters, the RMI
card (which automatically remains aligned with magnetic north)
will appear to turn together with the ADF needle. In reality, of
course, it is the compass card and the RMI needle that remain
stationary, while the aeroplane turns about them. Before, during
and after the turn, the RMI's needle will constantly indicate the
current QDM.

Tracking

Tracking Inbound to an NDB using the Relative Bearing Indicator

The ADF/NDB combination is often used to provide guidance
for an aeroplane from a distant position to a position overhead the
NDB ground position. This is known as **tracking.** Just how you
achieve this depends to a certain extent on the wind direction and
speed, since an aeroplane initially pointing directly at the NDB
will be blown off course by a crosswind.

Tracking Towards an NDB, with No Crosswind Effect

With no crosswind, a direct track inbound can be achieved by
heading the aeroplane directly at the NDB. This is achieved with
a heading that maintains the ADF needle on the nose of the
aeroplane (RB 000).

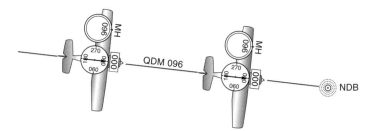

■ Figure 22-19 **Tracking inbound, with no crosswind**

If there is no crosswind to blow the aeroplane off track, then everything will remain constant as in Figure 22-19 – the magnetic heading 096, the relative bearing of 000, and the QDM 096 will all remain constant. This will be the situation in:
• nil-wind conditions;
• a direct headwind; or
• a direct tailwind.

Tracking Inbound with a Crosswind

WITH NO CORRECTION FOR DRIFT made by the pilot, and the aeroplane heading directly to the NDB so that the ADF needle indicates a relative bearing of 000, any crosswind will cause the aeroplane to be blown off track.

Time	0715		Time	0725
MH	096		MH	096
RB	000		RB	357 (i.e. –3)
QDM	096		QDM	093

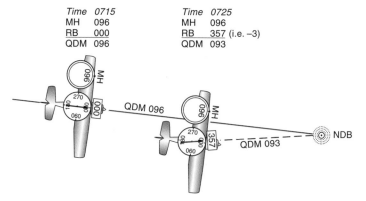

■ Figure 22-20 **Crosswind causes drift**

In Figure 22-20, the wind, with a northerly component, has blown the aeroplane to the right of track. This is indicated by the ADF needle starting to move down the left of the dial. To return to track, the aeroplane must be turned towards the left, i.e. towards the direction in which the head of the needle is moving.

If the pilot turns left to RB 000 to put the NDB on the nose again, then after a short while the aeroplane will again have been blown to the right of track, and the ADF needle will move to the left of the nose. A further turn to the left will be required – and the process will need to be repeated again and again.

In this way, the track made good (TMG) to the NDB will be curved, the aeroplane finally approaching the NDB heading roughly into-wind, and a longer distance will be travelled compared to the direct track from the original position. This rather inefficient means of arriving overhead the NDB is known as **homing** (keeping the NDB on the nose). It is not a very tidy procedure. Professional pilots rarely use it.

WITH CORRECT DRIFT CORRECTION made by the pilot – a far better procedure than homing is to **track direct to the NDB** by heading into wind and laying off a wind correction angle (WCA) to counteract drift. If 5° left is indeed the correct WCA, the aeroplane can achieve a track of 096°M direct to the NDB by the pilot steering MH 091.

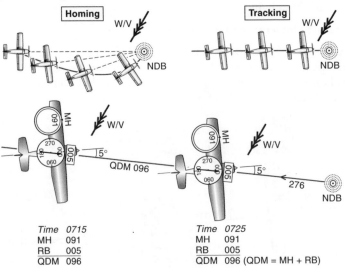

Time 0715
MH   091
RB   005
QDM   096

Time 0725
MH   091
RB   005
QDM   096 (QDM = MH + RB)

■ Figure 22-21 **Tracking direct to the NDB**

Different Winds Require Different Wind Correction Angles

An aeroplane is on track when the relative bearing is equal and opposite to the difference between the actual magnetic heading and the desired track. This is illustrated in Figure 22-22. In each situation, the aeroplane is on the desired track of 010°M, but using a different wind correction angle to counteract the drift under different wind conditions.

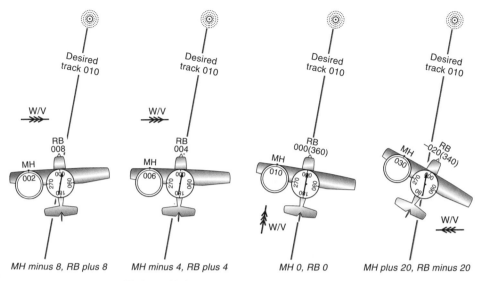

Figure 22-22 *Laying off drift to achieve the desired track*

If the precise wind effect is not known, then use a 'best guess' WCA estimated from the available information as an initial WCA. For the same crosswind, slower aeroplanes will need to allow a greater WCA than faster aeroplanes.

It is possible that the wind effect will change as you track towards an NDB, so regular adjustments to the heading may be required. This is often the case as an aeroplane descends using the NDB as the tracking aid, due to variations in wind velocity and true airspeed.

WITH INCORRECT DRIFT CORRECTION made by the pilot, the aeroplane will move off the desired track, i.e. the QDM (magnetic track to the NDB) will change. If a steady heading is being flown, this will become obvious through a gradually changing relative bearing, with the ADF needle moving left or right down the dial.

Suppose, for instance, the pilot steers a heading with a 5° wind correction angle to the left to counteract the effect of a wind from the left. If the wind effect turns out to be less than expected, then the aeroplane will gradually move to the left of the desired track to the NDB, and the QDM will gradually increase. Typical cockpit indications could be:

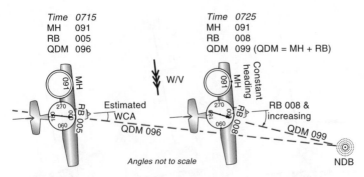

■ Figure 22-23 **An incorrect wind correction angle causes QDM to change**

The head of the ADF needle falling away to the right indicates that a turn right must be made to track to the NDB. Conversely, the head of the ADF needle falling away to the left indicates that a left turn must be made to track to the NDB. Just how great each correcting turn should be depends on the deviation from track.

NOTE Be careful of terminology. *Drift* is the angle between heading and the actual track made good, which may not be the desired track. The perfect *wind correction angle* will counteract any drift exactly, and the actual TMG will follow the desired track, which is usually the aim of tracking.

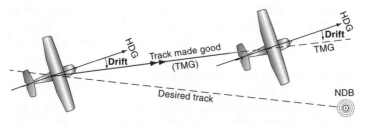

■ Figure 22-24 **Drift is the angle between heading and TMG**

Maintaining Track

Flying straight and level usually consists of many tiny climbs and descents as the pilot attempts to maintain the desired altitude perfectly. Similarly, it is almost impossible to maintain a perfect track, and so many small turns will usually have to be made by the pilot in an attempt to do so, by correcting any deviations from track.

Re-intercepting a track, having deviated from it, involves the same procedure as the initial intercept of a new track, except that the angles will be smaller provided that you are vigilant and do not allow large deviations to occur. Realising that the aeroplane is diverging from the direct track to the NDB, you have several options. You may either:

1. Track direct from the present position (along a new track); or

2. Regain the original track.

1. TO TRACK DIRECT TO THE NDB from the present position (even though it is not the originally desired track) turn slightly right (say 3° in this case), and track direct to the NDB from the present position. In most NDB tracking, this technique is used only when very close to the station (say 1 or 2 nm from the NDB), when there is insufficient distance remaining to regain track.

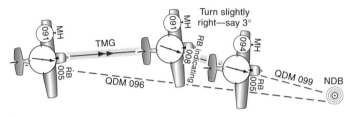

■ Figure 22-25 **Flying a new track to the NDB**

Needle head falling right; turn right.

2. TO REGAIN THE ORIGINAL TRACK, turn further right initially (say 5° onto MH 096), re-intercept the original track by allowing the wind to blow the aeroplane back onto it and, once the track is regained, turn left and steer a heading with a different wind correction angle (say WCA 3° left instead of 5° left), MH 093 instead of MH 091. This is a very moderate correction, something you would expect to see from an experienced instrument-trained pilot, who would have noticed any deviation from track fairly quickly.

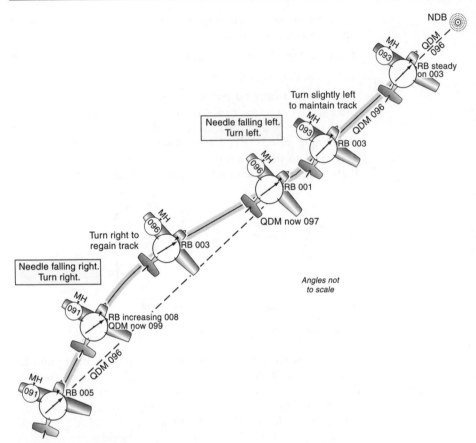

■ Figure 22-26 **Regain the desired track**

Attempting to maintain the desired track (or remain on the one QDM) is the normal navigational technique when at some distance from the NDB. If, when maintaining a steady magnetic heading, the ADF needle near the top of the dial indicates a constant relative bearing, then the aeroplane is tracking directly to the NDB, and no correction to heading is necessary.

If MH + RB = desired QDM constantly, then ADF tracking is good.

CORRECTING TURNS TO MAINTAIN TRACK. Just how great each correcting turn should be depends on the deviation from track. A simple method is to double the error. If the aeroplane has deviated 10° left indicated by the RBI moving 10° right, then alter heading by 20° to the right. (If you alter heading by only 10° to the right, the result will probably be a further deviation to the left, a further correction to the right, with this being repeated again and again, resulting in a curved *homing* to the NDB).

Having regained track, turn left by only half the correcting turn of 20°, i.e. turn left 10° to intercept and maintain track. This leaves you with a WCA different from the original one (remembering that the original WCA caused you to deviate from track). The new WCA should provide reasonable tracking. If not, make further minor corrections to heading!

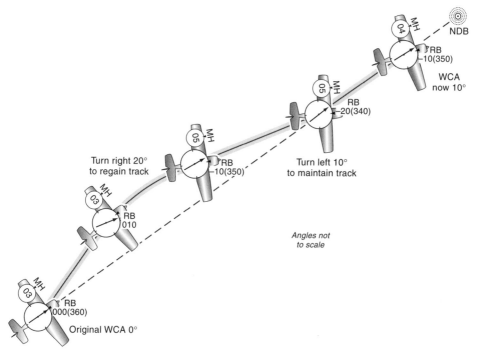

■ *Figure 22-27* **Regaining track by 'doubling the error', and maintaining track thereafter**

Bracketing Track

In practice, an absolutely perfect direct track is difficult to achieve. The actual track made good will probably consist of a number of minor corrections such as those just described, a technique known as **bracketing** the track, i.e. making regular corrections, left or right as required, to maintain or regain the desired track.

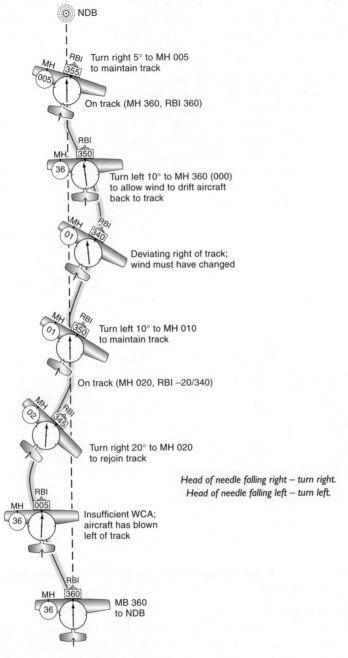

The aim of bracketing is to find the precise WCA needed to maintain track. If, for instance, a WCA of 10° right is found to be too great and the aeroplane diverges to the right of track, and a WCA of only 5° right is too little and the wind blows the aeroplane to the left of track, then try something in between, say WCA 8° right.

Monitor the tracking of the aeroplane on a regular basis, and make corrections earlier rather than later. The result will be a succession of small corrections rather than just one big correction. However, if a big correction is required as may be the case in strong winds, make it. Be positive in your actions!

Wind Effect

If the wind direction and strength is not obvious, then the best technique is initially to **steer track as heading** (make no allowance for drift). The effect of the wind will become obvious as the ADF needle moves to the left or right. Observe the results, and then make heading adjustments to bracket track.

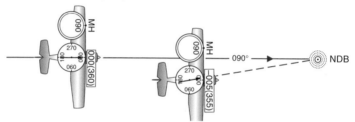

■ *Figure 22-29* **If uncertain of wind, initially steer track as heading**

Tracking Overhead an NDB

The ADF needle will become more and more sensitive as the NDB station is approached. Minor displacements left or right of track will cause larger and larger changes in relative bearing and QDM, and the ADF needle becomes 'agitated' as the NDB is approached. For a very precise track to be achieved, you must be prepared to increase your scan rate as the NDB is approached, and to make corrections more frequently.

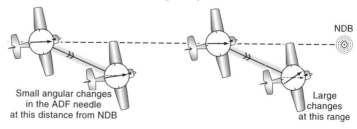

■ *Figure 22-30* **Approaching the NDB, the ADF needle becomes more sensitive**

Close to the station and just prior to passing overhead, however, the ADF needle becomes very sensitive. At this point, you can relax a little and steer a steady heading until the aeroplane passes overhead the NDB, indicated by the ADF needle moving towards the bottom of the dial and settling down.

Having passed overhead the NDB, tracking *from* the NDB should be checked and suitable adjustments made to heading. If the track outbound is different from that inbound, then a suitable heading change estimated to make good the new desired track could be made as soon as the ADF needle falls past the 090 or 270 position on its way to the bottom of the dial.

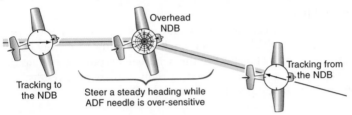

■ *Figure 22-31* **Do not overcorrect when close to the station**

The ADF needle becoming extremely active and then falling rapidly to the bottom of the dial indicates that the aeroplane has passed directly overhead the NDB.

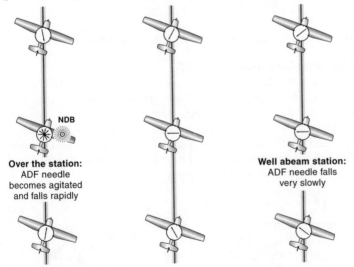

■ *Figure 22-32* **Good ADF tracking (left); reasonable and poor tracking**

The ADF needle moving gradually to one side and slowly falling to the bottom of the dial indicates that the aeroplane is passing to one side of the beacon – the rate at which the needle falls being an indication of the aeroplane's proximity to the NDB. If it falls very slowly, then perhaps your tracking could have been better. Time overhead (or abeam) the NDB can be taken as the needle falls through the approximate 090 or 270 position.

Tracking Away From an NDB

When tracking away from an NDB, the head of the ADF needle will lie towards the bottom of the dial.

Tracking Away From an NDB with No Crosswind Effect

If you track overhead the NDB and then steer track as heading, the aeroplane will track directly away from the NDB with the head of the ADF needle steady on 180, and the tail of the ADF needle steady at the top of the dial on 000.

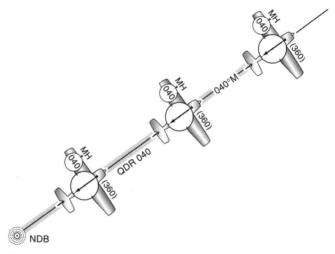

■ *Figure 22-33* **Tracking away from an NDB with no crosswind effect**

The aeroplane shown in Figure 22-33 has a QDR of 040 (magnetic track from the station to the aeroplane), and a QDM of 220 (magnetic track from the aeroplane to the station).

Tracking Away From an NDB with a Crosswind

Suppose that the desired track outbound from an NDB is 040°M, and you estimate that a WCA of 5° to the right is necessary to counteract a wind from the right. To achieve this, you steer MH 045, and hope to see the tail of the ADF needle stay on –005 (i.e. 355). The magnetic track away from the station (QDR) is found from:

QDR = MH ± deflection of the tail of the needle.

In this case, MH 045 – 005 tail = QDR 040, and the chosen WCA and magnetic heading to steer are correct.

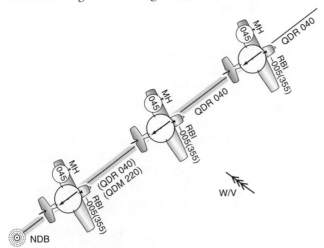

■ Figure 22-34 **Tracking away from an NDB, with a WCA of 5°**
into wind

If the estimated WCA is incorrect, then the track made good by the aeroplane will differ from that desired. If, in Figure 22-34, the wind is stronger than expected, the aeroplane's actual TMG may be 033°M, and to the left of the desired track of 040°M.

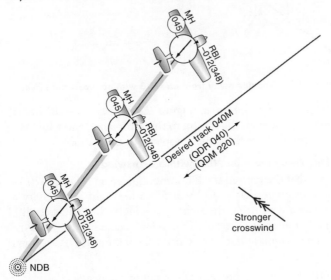

■ Figure 22-35 **Tracking away from an NDB with an incorrect**
wind correction angle

Whereas inaccurate tracking *to* an NDB is indicated by the ADF needle falling, incorrect tracking away *from* an NDB can occur with the ADF needle indicating a steady reading. Having passed overhead the NDB, an aeroplane can track away from it in any direction. You must always ensure that you are flying away from the NDB along the correct track, and the easiest way to do this is to calculate QDR or QDM using the DI and the RBI.

Regaining Track Away from an NDB in a Crosswind

If an incorrect wind correction angle is flown, the aeroplane will be blown off track. A vigilant pilot will see the incorrect TMG, probably by visualising QDR (from the NDB) or QDM (to the NDB) while a constant magnetic heading is flown.

EXAMPLE 3 In Figure 22-36, the pilot is flying track as heading, i.e. initially making no allowance for drift. If the head of the ADF needle moves right from 180 into the negative quadrant, then the aeroplane must be turned right to regain track.

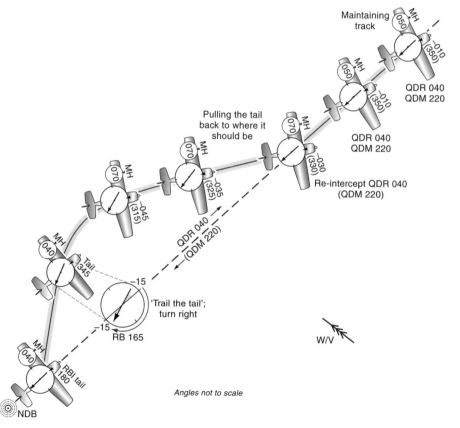

■ Figure 22-36 **Turning right to 'trail the tail' or 'pull the tail around'**

NOTE It is generally easier to work off the top of the dial, since that is where the aeroplane is going, rather than off the bottom of the dial. The right turn necessary to regain track, turning right towards the head of the needle and therefore away from the tail of the needle, can be thought of as *pulling the tail of the ADF needle around* or *trailing the tail*. Some instructors, however, prefer to say that if the head of the needle is moving left, then turn left (and vice versa), even though the head of the needle is at the bottom of the dial. Your instructor will recommend a method.

In Figure 22-36, the aeroplane has been blown to the left of track. The off-track QDR is given by:

MH 040 − 015 tail = QDR 025;
which is left of the desired QDR 040.

To regain track, the pilot has turned right by 30° (double the error) from MH 040 to MH 070, which causes a simultaneous change in the relative bearing of the NDB, the ADF needle tail moving from −015 (345) to −045 (315). (The head of the needle, indicating relative bearing, will move from 165 to 135, but this is not a calculation for the pilot to make, only an observation.)

The relative bearing will naturally change as the aeroplane is turned but, once the aeroplane is flown on its steady intercept heading of MH 070, the tail of the needle will be gradually pulled around.

The pilot will continue with the intercept heading until the aeroplane approaches the desired track, QDR 040. This is indicated to the pilot by MH 070 and the tail of the needle moving up towards −030 (since QDR 040 = MH 070 − 030 tail). For a 30° intercept of 040°M outbound, the pilot is steering + 30 (040 + 30 = MH 070), waiting for the tail of the needle to rise to −030.

Flying track plus 30, waiting for minus 30 on the needle.

As the desired outbound track is approached, the pilot turns left to maintain QDR 040. Estimating a WCA of 10° into wind to be sufficient, the pilot steers MH 050 and checks regularly that the needle tail stays on −010.

EXAMPLE 4 If, on the other hand, the head of the ADF needle moves left from 180 into the positive quadrant, then the aeroplane must be turned left to regain track. Looking at the top of the ADF dial and the tail of the needle, turn left and 'trail the tail'.

In Figure 22-37, the aeroplane has been blown to the right of track. The off-track QDR is given by:

MH 040 + 015 tail = 055;
which is right of the desired QDR 040.

To regain track, the pilot has turned left by 30° from MH 040 to MH 010, which causes a simultaneous change in the relative bearing of the NDB, the tail of the ADF needle moving from 015 to 045.

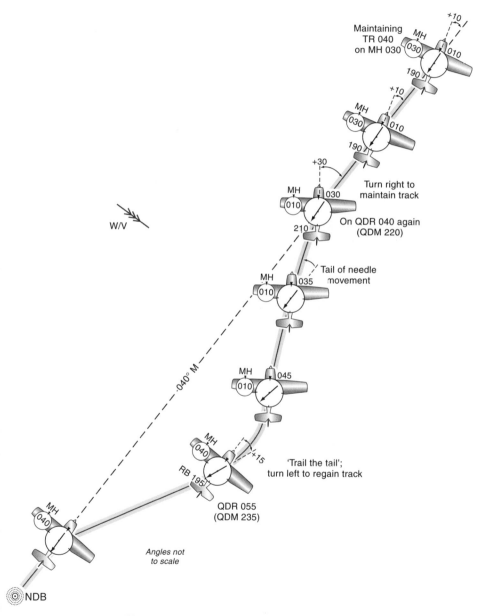

Maintaining TR 040 on MH 030

+10

MH (030) 010

190

+10

MH (030) 010

190

+30

MH (010) 030

Turn right to maintain track

210

On QDR 040 again (QDM 220)

Tail of needle movement

MH (010) 035

MH (010) 045

W/V

040° M

MH (040)

RB 195

+15

'Trail the tail'; turn left to regain track

QDR 055 (QDM 235)

MH (040)

Angles not to scale

NDB

■ Figure 22-37 **Turning left to 'trail the tail' or 'pull the tail around'**

The relative bearing will naturally change as the aeroplane is turned but, once the aeroplane is flown on its steady intercept heading of MH 010, the tail of the needle will be gradually pulled around. For a 30° intercept of 040°M outbound, the pilot is steering −30 (040 − 30 = MH 010), waiting for the tail of the needle to rise to + 030.

Flying track minus 30, waiting for plus 30 on the needle.

The pilot will continue with the intercept heading until the aeroplane approaches the desired track, QDR 040. This is indicated by MH 010 and the tail of the needle moving up towards 030 (since QDR 040 = MH 010 + 030 tail).

As the desired track outbound is approached, the pilot turns right to maintain QDR 040. Estimating a WCA of 10° into wind to be sufficient, the pilot steers MH 030 and checks regularly that the needle tail stays on +010.

NOTE This chapter explains the principle of tracking an NDB with the least sophisticated cockpit instrument. If an aircraft is fitted with a rotatable-card ADF, it is not necessary to perform the mental arithmetic processes to assure alignment between the ADF instrument and the DI. The radio magnetic indicator further reduces workload by automatically setting magnetic north. The same basic tracking principles apply to tracking with the rotatable-card ADF and RMI and will not be explained here. If you wish to consider this in more detail, please refer to *Air Pilot's Manual, Volume 5, Chapter 13* for a full account.

Now complete: **Practice Questions - NDB**

1. NDB operates in which frequency band?

   (a) *Microwave*

   (b) *VHF*

   (c) *UHF*

   (d) *LF/MF*

2. An aircraft is tracking away from an NDB maintaining a track of 040° with 9° left drift. What bearing should the relative bearing indicator (RBI) be reading?

   (a) *189°R*

   (b) *180°R*

   (c) *031°R*

   (d) *171°R*

3. A Non-Directional Beacon (NDB) is:

   (a) *An airborne system comprising of a loop antenna and a sense antenna.*

   (b) *A ground based station that radiates two signals out of phase.*

   (c) *An airborne system to measure the range and bearing from a ground station.*

   (d) *A ground based station that transmits omni-directionally.*

4. An aircraft is travelling away from an NDB on a track of 300° with 5° right drift. The relative bearing indicator (RBI) should indicate a bearing of:

   (a) *185° relative.*

   (b) *180° relative.*

   (c) *175° relative.*

   (d) *300° relative.*

5. An aircraft is heading 150°M, the head of the relative bearing indicator needle indicates 055°R. What is the QDM of the NDB?

   (a) *075°M*

   (b) *345°M*

   (c) *205°M*

   (d) *120°M*

6. An aircraft is heading 270° towards an NDB with 8° right drift. The relative bearing indicator (RBI) should indicate a bearing of:

(a) 352° relative.
(b) 008° relative.
(c) 260° relative.
(d) 172° relative.

7. Which of the following ADF instruments need not be used in conjunction with the aircraft's Direction Indicator?

(a) The Relative Bearing Indicator (RBI).
(b) The Rotatable Card ADF.
(c) The Radio Magnetic Indicator (RMI).
(d) The Omni Bearing Selector (OBS).

VHF Direction Finding (VDF)

General Principle

Some aerodromes are equipped with radio aerials that can sense the direction of VHF-COM signals (normal voice signals) received from an aeroplane.

This information is presented to the air traffic controller (usually the approach controller) as a radial line on a cathode ray tube similar to a radar screen or, with the most modern VDF equipment, as a very accurate digital readout of bearing.

The controller can then give the pilot the bearing of the aircraft relative to the aerodrome. This is known as **very high frequency direction finding,** and is often abbreviated to VDF or VHF D/F.

VDF enables a controller to determine the direction a VHF-COM signal is coming from.

An advantage of VDF is that no specific aircraft equipment is required other than a VHF-COM – normal VHF communications radio.

A typical VDF air–ground exchange would be a pilot requesting ATC to provide QDM (magnetic bearing to the ground station), followed by the controller advising it. For example:

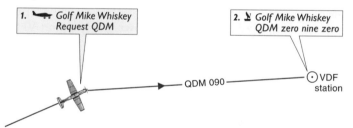

■ *Figure 23-1* **QDM is magnetic bearing to the VDF ground station**

By steering the QDM, the pilot is able to *home to,* or head towards, the ground station.

Whereas no special equipment is required in the aeroplane for VDF other than a VHF-COM radio, it does require a special installation at the ground station. Two typical designs for VDF aerials at aerodromes are the H–type aerial (a double-H dipole aerial in technical terms), or the Doppler-type VDF aerial.

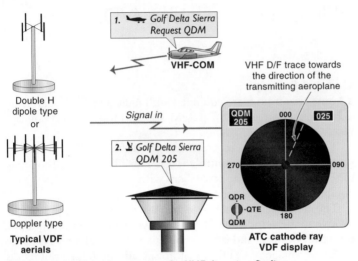

■ Figure 23-2 **Ground equipment for VHF direction finding**

VDF ground equipment from years ago was known as a **manual homer,** and used an ADF-type null-seeking aerial which the operator had to rotate manually to determine the direction of the aeroplane. It also required long transmissions from the aeroplane while the operator sought the null position.

Modern equipment is fully automatic. The direction of the aeroplane is displayed automatically following only a short VHF-COM transmission from the pilot.

Information Available from VDF

Bearings that a pilot may request from a VDF operator are:

VDF BEARINGS	
QDM	*magnetic bearing* **to** *the station*
QDR	*magnetic bearing* **from** *the station (the reciprocal of the QDM)*
QTE	*true bearing* **from** *the station*

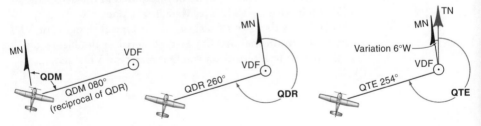

■ Figure 23-3 **QDM, QDR and QTE**

QDR

QDR, the magnetic bearing from the station, is useful for orientation (Where am I?). QDR is similar information to a VOR radial. QTE, the true bearing from the station, is useful if you want to plot a position line from the VDF ground station to the aeroplane on a map (against true north). However, it is QDM, the magnetic bearing to the station, that is the most commonly used and requested VDF bearing.

QDM

QDM is the most commonly requested bearing. It is the heading to steer direct to the VDF station provided that no crosswind exists. In a crosswind, however, a wind correction angle (WCA) into wind must be used to counteract the drift if a reasonably straight track is to be achieved, rather than a curved (and inefficient) homing.

At typical light aircraft speeds, it is reasonable for the pilot to request a QDM each half-minute or so to check tracking, and to modify heading if necessary.

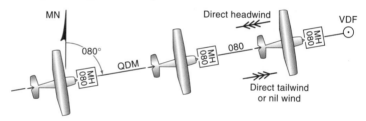

■ *Figure 23-4* **Steering QDM to a VDF ground station in nil-crosswind conditions is satisfactory**

If QDM is steered as heading in crosswind conditions, then the aeroplane will drift downwind, and its QDM will gradually change. The next QDM passed by the ground operator will be different from the first.

In Figure 23-5, an original QDM 080 has become QDM 075, and so the pilot would turn slightly left from a heading of 080°M to a heading of 075°M (the new QDM) to continue homing to the station.

There would be further changes to QDM advised by the operator as the aeroplane continued on, the end result being a curved path with the aeroplane arriving overhead the ground station heading roughly into wind – not a particularly professional arrival!

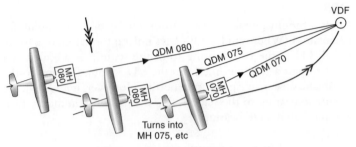

■ Figure 23-5 **An inefficient homing to a VDF ground station**

A more efficient arrival can be achieved by allowing for wind effect, i.e. tracking using a wind correction angle into wind to counteract drift, rather than homing to the station by flying a continually changing QDM as heading.

VDF Bearing Accuracy
The quality of the bearings obtained by VDF is classified by the VDF ground operator to the pilot as:

Class A	Accurate to within ±2°
Class B	Accurate to within ±5°
Class C	Accurate to within ±10°
Class D	Less accurate than Class C

Most modern equipment is generally accurate to ±1°, although accuracy may be decreased by:
- **VDF site errors** such as reflection from nearby uneven ground, buildings, aircraft or vehicles; and
- **VHF propagation errors** caused by irregular propagation over differing terrain, especially if the aeroplane is at long range from the VDF ground station.

VDF Tracking

Tracking Inbound using QDM
To achieve a desired track to a VDF ground station, the pilot should try to maintain a **datum QDM** which is the same as the **desired track**. For instance, to maintain a track of 080°M to the VDF ground station, the pilot should fly a heading so that QDM 080 is consistently maintained.

While VDF ground operators can advise QDM, they will not advise heading to steer to counter any crosswind effect. The pilot must determine this if a direct track to the VDF station is to be achieved. If the selected WCA is perfectly correct, then the ground operator will advise, on request for QDM, the same QDM as previously.

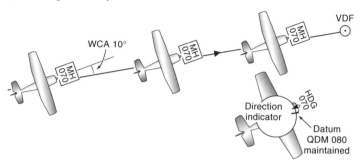

■ *Figure 23-6* **Perfect allowance for drift**

The supply of QDMs by ATC may be thought of as a 'talking RMI'. You can, by mentally placing the QDM onto the direction indicator, form the same picture as that given to you by an RMI.

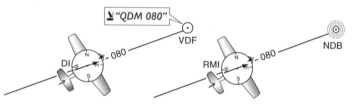

■ *Figure 23-7* **The stated QDM is like a talking RMI**

If the stated QDM moves to the right of the datum QDM, then the aeroplane has drifted to the left of the desired track, and should be turned right to re-intercept the desired track (to re-establish the datum QDM). This is exactly the same response as for the head of an RMI needle moving to the right of the datum QDM.

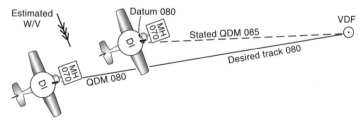

■ *Figure 23-8* **Tracking towards a VDF ground station; if QDM moves right of the datum, turn right**

In this case, while flying on a magnetic heading of 070, the actual QDM has moved to the right of the datum QDM 080, indicated by ATC stating QDM 085. To regain the desired track, the pilot should turn right and increase heading (to say MH 090), and then request QDMs until the desired QDM 080 is reached. At this time, a more suitable heading to maintain QDM 080 would be flown, say MH 075.

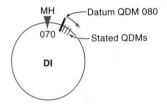

■ *Figure 23-9* **If QDM moves right of datum, turn right**

If the stated QDM moves to the left of the datum QDM, then the aeroplane has drifted to the right of the desired track, and should be turned left to re-intercept the desired track (to re-establish the datum QDM). This is exactly the same response as for the head of an RMI needle moving to the left of the datum QDM.

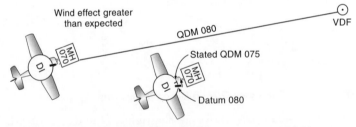

■ *Figure 23-10* **Tracking towards a VDF ground station; if QDM moves left of the datum, turn left**

In this case, the stated QDM has moved left of the datum QDM 080 to 075. The pilot should turn left and decrease heading (to say MH 060), and request QDMs until the desired QDM 080 is reached. At this time, a more suitable heading to maintain QDM 080 would be flown, say MH 065.

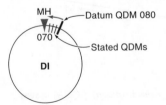

■ *Figure 23-11* **QDM moving left of datum, turn left**

IN KNOWN WIND CONDITIONS, use a 'best-guess WCA' as a starting point in estimating a magnetic heading to maintain the datum QDM, making modifications to heading if the actual or stated QDM gradually moves away from the datum QDM.

IN UNKNOWN WIND CONDITIONS, when unable to estimate a suitable wind correction angle to counter drift, a simple procedure is to steer the QDM as heading, and see what develops. Suitable corrections can then be made as changes in the QDM become apparent.

WHEN TRACKING TOWARDS THE VDF STATION:

• *turn right if actual QDM moves to the right of datum;*
• *turn left if actual QDM moves to the left of datum.*

The aim is to establish a wind correction angle that allows for drift and results in the desired track being maintained – indicated by the QDM remaining constant. The process of finding a suitable WCA by trial and error is known as **bracketing.** Typically, it will take a number of heading changes to establish the WCA required to maintain track.

Changes to heading will also be required if the wind effect changes, which is often the case. Like most instrument flying, VDF tracking will consist of a continuing series of small (and sometimes not so small) corrections.

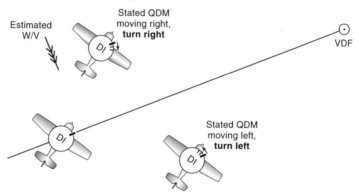

Estimated W/V

Stated QDM moving right, **turn right**

VDF

Stated QDM moving left, **turn left**

■ *Figure 23-12* **Tracking towards a VDF ground station**

Tracking Outbound

When tracking away from a VDF ground station, the datum QDM is the reciprocal of the outbound track. For instance, to maintain a track of 060°M away from the VDF ground station, the aeroplane should be flown so that datum QDM 240 is maintained.

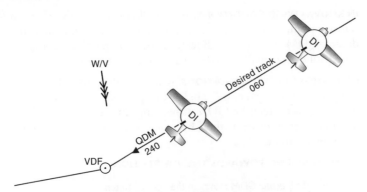

■ *Figure 23-13* **Tracking away from a VDF ground station**

If the stated QDM moves to the right of the datum QDM, the aeroplane has drifted to the left of the desired track, and should be turned right to re-intercept the desired track (to re-establish the datum QDM). This is exactly the same response as for the head of an RMI needle moving to the right of the datum QDM.

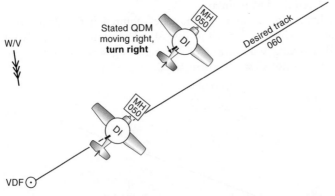

■ *Figure 23-14* **Tracking away from a VDF ground station; if QDM moves right of the datum, turn right**

In this case, the pilot would turn right and increase heading (to say MH 060), which would allow the wind to blow the aeroplane back onto track, and request QDMs until the desired QDM 240 is reached. At this time, a more suitable heading to maintain datum QDM 240 would be flown, say MH 055.

If the stated QDM moves to the left of the datum QDM, the aeroplane has drifted to the right of the desired track, and should be turned left to re-intercept the desired track (to re-establish the datum QDM). This is exactly the same response as for the head of an RMI needle moving to the left of the datum QDM.

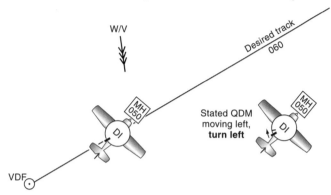

■ *Figure 23-15* **Tracking away from a VDF ground station; if QDM moves left of the datum, turn left**

In this case, since MH 050, allowing for an estimated 10° of drift, has taken the aeroplane to the right of track, the pilot should turn left and decrease heading (to say MH 040), and then request QDMs until the desired QDM 240 is reached. At this time, a more suitable heading to maintain QDM 240 should be flown, say MH 045, allowing a WCA of 15° into wind.

IN KNOWN WIND CONDITIONS, use a 'best-guess' WCA as a starting point in an attempt to maintain the datum QDM, making modifications to heading if the actual QDM changes from the datum.

IN UNKNOWN WIND CONDITIONS, when unable to estimate a suitable wind correction angle to counter drift, a simple procedure is to steer the reciprocal of the QDM as heading, and see what develops. Suitable corrections can then be made as changes in the QDM become apparent.

WHEN TRACKING AWAY FROM THE VDF STATION:

• *turn right if actual QDM moves to the right of datum;*
• *turn left if actual QDM moves to the left of datum.*

Note that these are exactly the same rules as for tracking towards the VDF ground station.

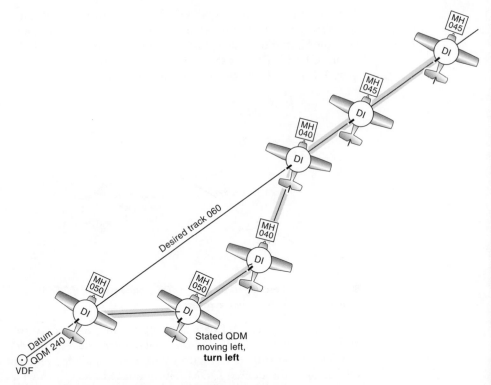

■ *Figure 23-16* **Tracking away from a VDF ground station**

VDF Tracking Rules

1. Determine datum QDM for the desired track;

  – inbound: datum QDM = desired track;
  – outbound: datum QDM = reciprocal of desired track.

2. Use best-guess WCA to establish an initial heading in an attempt to maintain datum QDM.

3. Both inbound and outbound from the VDF ground station:

  – if stated QDM moves left of datum, turn left;
  – if stated QDM moves right of datum, turn right; (treat the stated QDM on the DI as a command instrument).

Flying Overhead the VDF Ground Station

As the aeroplane passes overhead (or near to overhead) the VDF ground station, the ground operator will be unable to determine the direction from which VHF-COM signals are received, even though the actual voice communications will be received normally. He will report this to the pilot as "No bearing".

If the outbound track differs significantly from the inbound track, then the pilot will need to take up a suitable intercept heading until the datum QDM for the outbound track is established, at which time normal tracking to maintain it should occur.

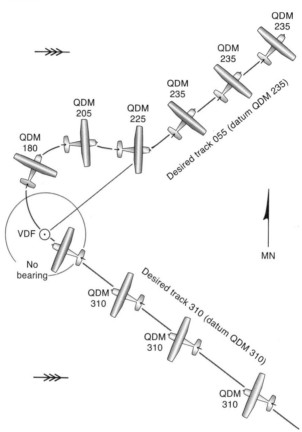

■ *Figure 23-17* **Flying overhead the VDF ground station, and intercepting an outbound track**

Requests for QDM by the pilot should be more frequent the closer the aeroplane is to the ground station so that suitable adjustments to heading can be made.

Other Uses for VDF

Bearings obtained by VDF can be used for a number of common navigational purposes. For instance, you may request a QDM from an abeam VDF station to verify that you are indeed flying abeam it.

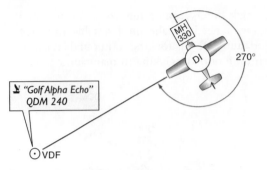

■ *Figure 23-18* **QDM abeam a ground station**

A position line given by a VDF bearing can be used together with another position line from say a VOR, NDB or even another VDF station to fix the position of the aeroplane.

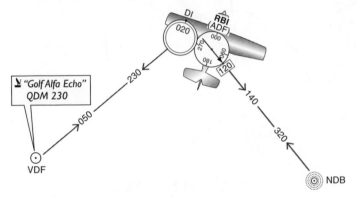

■ *Figure 23-19* **Fixing position with VDF**

Now complete: **Practice Questions - VDF**

1. When requesting a true bearing from a VDF station, the correct Q code phrase to use is:

(a) QDR

(b) QGH

(c) QDM

(d) QTE

2. The correct Q code for a magnetic bearing from a VDF station is:

(a) QDM

(b) QDR

(c) QUJ

(d) QTE

3. The correct Q code for a magnetic bearing to a VDF station is:

(a) QDM

(b) QDR

(c) QUJ

(d) QTE

4. A Class B VDF bearing is accurate to:

(a) ± 5°

(b) ± 2°

(c) ± 10°

(d) ± 8°

5. The accuracy of a VDF may be decreased by:

(a) *Thunderstorms effect.*

(b) *Site and propagation errors.*

(c) *Night effect.*

(d) *Coastal effect.*

6. VDF operates in which frequency band?

(a) *Microwave*

(b) *VHF*

(c) *UHF*

(d) *LF/MF*

Index